LEED v4 BD&C EXAM GUIDE

A Must-Have for the LEED AP BD+C Exam: Study Materials, Sample Questions, Green Building Design and Construction, LEED Certification, and Sustainability

Gang Chen

ArchiteG®, Inc.
Irvine, California

LEED v4 BD&C EXAM GUIDE:
A Must-Have for the LEED AP BD+C Exam: Study Materials, Sample Questions, Green Building Design and Construction, LEED Certification, and Sustainability

Edition 4.0.0

Copy Editor: Nick F. E.

ArchiteG®, Inc.
http://www.ArchiteG.com
http://www.GreenExamEducation.com

ISBN: 978-1-61265-017-3

PRINTED IN THE UNITED STATES OF AMERICA

What others are saying about *LEED BD&C Exam Guide* …

"Passed on first try, only used this guide
"This is the best study guide HANDS DOWN. If you're serious about passing the LEED AP BD&C exam on your first try, this is the one you've been looking for! I bought Mr. Chen's *LEED Green Associate Exam Guide*2 months ago and passed it on the first try as well. I purchased the USGBC reference guide and Mr. Chen's *LEED BD&C Exam Guide*. I never opened the USGBC reference guide, only studied from Mr. Chen's study guide. I followed Mr. Chen's instructions and studied the guide for 2 weeks (yes, I have a full-time job). I did ignore the mnemonics, not my learning style (makes it more confusing to me). The exam was not easy, but I prepared and stuck to this material. I am not a good test taker by no means. I reviewed the technical data of the guide about 6 times and ignored everything else I had read or heard about the exam. Here's a piece of advice that I picked up from this book, spend less time on practice tests and more time studying! I have a subscription to a web exam simulator (rated the best) and only did about 100 questions, until I realized that I was wasting my valuable time. Find a good book and stick to it. This is also a great reference guide to use on everyday projects. Review the material, try to understand it, then try to memorize it through repetition. I would like to shake your hand and say THANKS AGAIN MR. GANG CHEN !!! "
—LOBO

"Excellent Guide and Good Manual
"I passed the LEED AP BD+C and the LEED AP ID+C exams this year and Gang Chen's books were my primary study material! The books are easy to read and use. Gang Chen provides study hints and guidance as well as an outline format that makes it easy for the reader to grasp key points. He also provides an excellent review of the entire accreditation process which can save people time in personal research. The books are more than study guides; they are helpful as reference manuals because of the easy to follow format. Definitely a keeper in my bookshelf for future project reference."
—Karen M. Scott

"Great resource for studying for the LEED Exam!
"I have taken and passed the LEED AP BD+C exam and know what it takes. As this author says, it's not an easy exam and he is right. What is critical to passing is having great teaching tools and this book is one of them. He touches on every aspect of how to memorize data, how questions are formed, what to expect on tricky questions, the content the test writers are looking for and every little detail you need to know when preparing for this exam. I highly recommend this author's books if you are serious about passing any of the LEED exams, hopefully on the first try!"
—S. Jennifer Sakiewicz

"LEED BD & C Exam Study Guide
"Gang Chan's study guide is an excellent resource in preparing to take the LEED AP BD+C exam particularly if one follows the study recommendation made in the guide. It does not replace the LEED Reference manual as the definitive source for technical information but more importantly provides a structure for the study of the information that is easily understood and when followed should provide good assurance of success in passing the exam the 1st time. This is a 'keeper'!"
—Spock

"Good summary of information to memorize for the test
"Chen's exam guide is a good summary of the test relevant information in the LEED reference guide. He underlines specific information that is important to commit to memory for the test. It is a good way to understand which information needs to be strictly memorized if you are preparing for the test in a short

amount of time and have a good understanding of the LEED process through your professional experience. I passed the test with a very high score on my first try, and I did use this guide, one other, the LEED reference manual, online sources, a class, and many years of personally working on and completing online LEED submittals through my work. The week before taking the test I used it to commit point values and those kind of details to memory... "
—Denver

"Not a bulky ref guide
"*LEED BD&C Exam Guide* does a great job in highlighting and summarizing the key points and concepts in USGBC ref guide. If you only have limited amount of time for LEED AP BD+C exam preparation, definitely go for this book."
—Metcalf

"Very valuable guide!
"I am a lighting designer and am preparing to take the LEED BD+C exam...I got *LEED BD&C Exam Guide* to prepare for the LEED AP BD+C Exam and it was fairly well organized to help me refresh my memory on the background LEED knowledge I had. All the specifics that one needs to know about each credit such as the Purpose of the credit, Credit path, Submittals, Strategies and technologies etc, are clearly organized for every credit. In addition the author also employs the smart technique of Mnemonics which helps in memorizing the vast amount of information in a simplified manner."
—Visswapriya Prabakar

"Immensely valuable and utterly to the point, a true must have!
"This is an excellent publication by Gang Chen that outlines precisely all the key points one need for success. I personally appreciate the easy to adopt memorization technique offered by the author. Practice exams are very comprehensive yet summarized and not to mention highly effective learning tool as it is designed in this book. It is a very delightful experience for me to have this outstanding publication. In a word, this definitely worth the money and for me it turns out extraordinarily helpful."
—Shanaz, who passed LEED AP BD+C Exam on the first try

"Very Helpful!
"I found *LEED BD&C Exam Guide* to be very detailed and very helpful. I plan to take the exam soon, and I feel fully prepared for it."
— Yousuf Asadzoi

"Good book!
"I had appeared for GA and passed. I loved the content and the underlined highlights. I read your book; it gave me insight and knowledge on how credits are applied. Some questions in your book helped me answer ones on the test. Good book, I'll go through it once again when I appear for AP."
—Haresh Vibhakar, AIIA (India), AIA, LEED Green Associate, Architect

"A good outline
"The book is an excellent outline to learn the necessary items required to study for the exam. It is not a comprehensive study guide in and of itself. Practice exam is good indicator of test preparation."
—Paul Levine
"Solid LEED Study Guide
"This is the kind of book I wish was available when I did my original LEED AP exam. It teaches you how to study, which is so important when school is a distant memory. The bulk of the book helps you

review and memorize with mnemonics the concepts for each credit that you need to know for the exam. The questions are good representations of questions on the exam. I would recommend to anyone studying for their exam, that they:
- First read the chapters in this book on how to study;
- Second read the actual LEED BD+C guide to give you the background information on the credits and gain comprehension. Underline and review as the author indicates to get the most out of your study time.
- Finally read the rest of this exam guide to help you review and memorize for the exam."
—missfitz "missfitz"

"Very Helpful Guide
"Gang Chen's *LEED BD&C Exam Guide*s very helpful in consolidating information from USGBC and GBCI sources as well as providing the information that is necessary for the exam without excess irrelevant information. I highly recommend this book for preparation for the LEED BD+C exams."
—leedap

Leadership in Energy and Environmental Design (LEED)

LEED CERTIFIED
LEED SILVER
LEED GOLD
LEED PLATINUM

LEED GREEN ASSOCIATE

LEED AP BD+C LEED AP ID+C
LEED AP O+M
LEED AP HOMES LEED AP ND

LEED FELLOW

Dedication

To my parents, Zhuixian and Yugen,
my wife Xiaojie, and my daughters
Alice, Angela, Amy, and Athena.

Disclaimer

This book provides general information about the LEED AP BD+C Exam and green building LEED Certification. It is sold with the understanding that the publisher and author are not providing legal, accounting, or other professional services. If legal, accounting, and other professional services are required, seek the services of a competent professional firm.

It is not the purpose of this book to reprint the content of all other available texts on the subject. You are urged to read other available texts and tailor them to fit your needs.

Great effort has been made to make this book as complete and accurate as possible; however, nobody is perfect, and there may be typographical or other mistakes. You should use this book as a general guide and not as the ultimate source on this subject.

This book is intended to provide general, entertaining, informative, educational, and enlightening content. Neither the publisher nor the author shall be liable to anyone or any entity for any loss or damages, or alleged loss and damages, caused directly or indirectly by the content of this book.

USGBC and LEED are trademarks of the US Green Building Council. The US Green Building Council is not affiliated with the publication of this book.

If you do not wish to be bound by the above, you may return this book to the publisher for a full refund.

Legal Notice

LEED Exam Guides series by ArchiteG, Inc.

Time and effort is the most valuable asset of a candidate. How to cherish and effectively use your limited time and effort is the key of passing any exam. That is why we publish the LEED Exam Guides series to help you to study and pass the LEED exams in the shortest time possible. We have done the hard work so that you can save time and money. We do not want to make you work harder than you have to.

Do not force yourself to memorize a lot of numbers. Read through the numbers a few times, and you should have a very good impression of them.

You need to make the judgment call: If you miss a few numbers, you can still pass the exam, but if you spend too much time drilling these numbers, you may miss out on the big pictures and fail the exam.

There is no official GBCI sample questions or explanations. The USGBC has been separated from GBCI and should have no clue of how GBCI constructs the LEED exam questions. Otherwise, the LEED exams will NOT be legally defensible. The existing practice questions or exams by others are either way too easy or way over-killed. They do NOT match the real LEED exams at all.

We have done very comprehensive research on the official GBCI guides, many related websites, reference materials, and other available LEED exam prep materials. We match our mock exams questions as close as possible to the GBCI samples and the real LEED exams. Some other readers had failed an LEED exam two or three times before, and they eventually passed the exam with our help.

Some authors rewrite the same information in a generic format for LEED Green Associate Exam, but I prefer to follow the LEED rating systems format that used by the USGBC for both exams and the related exam reference guides and not reinvent the wheel.

This will save you time because you know exactly what you have already studied after you have prepared for LEED Green Associate Exam, which is the same as part I of the LEED AP BD+C exam. You just need to spend maybe 30% more time (instead of double) to study for part II of the LEED AP BD+C exam (specialty exam).

After studying this book, you will become very familiar the LEED rating systems and you will be able to quickly locate the information in the USGBC reference guide when you work on the actual LEED projects. In fact, many of my readers simply use my book 90% of the time, and just use the USGBC reference guide to look up some very detailed information.

Other books on LEED Exams will become almost useless instantly once you pass the exam because they are NOT designed as a reference book, while my book, *LEED v4 BD&C Exam Guide*, is an exam guide *and* a LEED reference book. It becomes even more valuable *after* the exam.

All our guide books include study guide, a set of sample questions matching the real LEED exams, including number of questions, format, type of questions, etc. We also include detailed answers and explanations to our questions.

There is some extra information on LEED overviews and exam-taking tips in Chapter One. This is based on GBCI *and* other valuable sources. This is a bonus feature we included in each book because we want our readers to be able to buy our LEED mock exam books together or individually. We want you to find all necessary LEED exam information and resources at one place and through our books.

All our books are available at
http://www.GreenExamEducation.com

Strategies for Preparing for the LEED AP BD+C Exam

There are several strategies for preparing for the LEED AP BD+C Exam:

1. Bare bones strategy:
This strategy is bold and risky but effective, low cost, and takes the least amount of time. You only need about two weeks to prepare for and pass the exam:

a. Download and read the latest candidate handbook for the LEED AP BD+C Exam
b. Study the FREE PDF files listed at the end of the latest candidate handbook for the LEED AP BD+C Exam (20% to 30% of the test content will come from these materials).
c. Study my books, *LEED v4 BD&C Exam Guide* and *LEED v4 BD&C Mock Exam* (Covers the fundamental and most important information of the remaining 70% to 80% of test content).
d. Do NOT buy or read the USGBC reference guide AT ALL.

Pros:
a. Save time and money and still have a good chance of passing. In fact, a number of my readers did pass the exam using this approach.
b. You can prepare and pass the exam in about **two weeks**.

Cons:
a. Your score may not be as high as you want since you COMPLETELY skip the USGBC reference guide (it may range from 170 to 180).
b. You may feel nervous during the real exam. You may swear that you will fail in the exam, but end up passing anyway. You may have no clue why you pass, but it is because my books cover the fundamental and most important information on the exam and set up a solid foundation for your LEED knowledge.

2. Middle of the road strategy:
This strategy is exactly the same as the **bare bone strategy** except that you do the following extra things:

a. Buy or read portion of the USGBC reference guide to supplement my two books:
Only refer to or read the USGBC reference guide for items you have questions about or for detailed information not covered by my books, such as the "Behind the Intent" and "Step-by-Step Guidance" sections and calculations. I skip these sections in *LEED v4 BD&C Exam Guide* because it takes too much time for you to read the information, and I think you should be able to handle most of the tasks covered in these sections if you MASTER the other sections.
b. Do a few extra mock exams.

Pros:
a. Save time and money and still have an excellent chance of passing.
b. You can prepare for and pass the exam in about **two to four weeks**.

Cons:
a. Your score may not be as high as you want (it may range from 170 to 185).
b. You may still feel nervous during the real exam.

3. Comprehensive strategy:
This strategy is exactly the same as **bare bone strategy**, except that you do the following extra things:

a. Buy or read the USGBC reference guide from cover to cover several times.
b. Write your own notes or create your own spreadsheets based on the USGBC reference guide.
c. Do every mock exam that you can find.

Pros:
a. You have an excellent chance of passing if you can REALLY read the reference guide.

Cons:
a. Your score may be either very high or very low (it may range from 180 to 200, OR fail).
b. You need to spend two months or more to prepare for and pass the exam.
c. You drag the exam prep process on too long and become tired of reading the USGBC reference guide OR you can NOT find enough time to read the reference guide, and you end up failing the exam.

If you can pass the specialty exam, you should be able to pass the LEED Green Associate Exam. Make sure you download the PDF files listed in the candidate's handbook and peruse them. See FREE slides at our website on the exam prep at:
http://www.GreenExamEducation.com

How to Use This Book

We suggest you read *LEED v4 BD&C Exam Guide* at least three times:

Read once and cover Chapters One and Two, the Appendixes, the related FREE PDF files, and other resources. Highlight the information you are not familiar with.

Read twice focusing on the highlighted information to memorize. You can repeat this process as many times as you want until you master the content of the book.

After reviewing these materials, you can take the sample questions, and then check your answers against the answers and explanations in the back, including explanations for the questions you answer correctly. You may have answered some questions correctly for the wrong reason. Highlight the information you are not familiar with.

Like the real exam, the sample questions include three question types: Select the correct answer, check all that apply, and fill in the blank.

Review your highlighted information, and take the sample questions again. Try to answer 100% of the questions correctly this time. Repeat the process until you can answer all the questions correctly.

LEED AP BD+C is one of the most difficult LEED exams because many questions require calculations or test you very detailed LEED information. This book includes most if not all the information you need to do the calculations, as well as step-by-step explanations. After reading this book, you will greatly improve your ability to deal with the real LEED AP BD+C calculations, and have a great chance of passing the exam on the first try.

Take the sample questions and the mock exam in my other book, "LEED BD&C Mock Exam," at least two weeks before the real exam. You should definitely NOT wait until the night before the real exam to take the sample questions. If you do not do well, you will go into panic mode and NOT have enough time to review your weaknesses.

Read for the final time the night before the real exam. Review ONLY the information you highlighted, especially the questions you did not answer correctly when you took the sample questions for the first time.

The Table of Contents is very detailed so you can locate information quickly. If you are on a tight schedule you can forgo reading the book linearly and jump around to the sections you need.

All our books, including "ARE Mock Exams Series" and "LEED Exam Guides Series," are available at **GreenExamEducation.com**

Check out FREE tips and info at **GeeForums.com**, you can post your questions or vignettes for other users' review and responses.

Contents

Preface

The USGBC released LEED v4 in GreenBuild International Conference and Expo in November, 2013. The GBCI started to include the new LEED v4 content for all LEED exams in late Spring 2014. We have incorporated the new LEED v4 content in this book.

Starting on December 1, 2011, GBCI began to draw LEED AP BD+C Exam questions from the second edition of *Green Building and LEED Core Concepts Guide*. We have incorporated this information in our books. See Appendix 5 for Important Items Covered by the Second Edition of *Green Building and LEED Core Concepts Guide*.

There are two main purposes for this book: to help you pass the LEED AP BD+C (Building Design and Construction) Exam and to assist you with understanding the process of getting a building LEED certified.

The LEED AP BD+C Exam has two parts (or sections):

Part One is EXACTLY the same as the LEED Green Associate Exam. It has 100 multiple choice questions and must be finished within two hours (The total exam time for BOTH parts of the exam is four hours). In this book, "LEED AP BD+C Exam Part One," "LEED AP BD+C Exam Section One," and "LEED Green Associate Exam" are used interchangeably since they are EXACTLY the same.

Part Two is the LEED AP BD+C specialty exam. It focuses on information and knowledge related directly to green building design and construction (BD+C). It also contains 100 multiple choice questions and must be finished within two hours.

You can take the LEED Green Associate Exam first. After you pass it, you can then take the Part Two (2 hours) of the LEED AP BD+C later.

OR
you can take both sections (Part One and Part Two) of the LEED AP BD+C Exam back-to-back in the same sitting. When a test taker fails one of the two parts, he can retake only the failed section of the exam at a later date.

The raw exam score is converted to a scaled score ranging from 125 to 200. The passing score is 170 or higher. You need to answer <u>about</u> 60 questions correctly for each section to pass. There is an optional 10-minute tutorial for computer testing before the exam and an optional 10-minute exit survey.

The LEED Green Associate Exam is the most important LEED exam for two reasons:

1. You have to pass it in order to get the title of LEED Green Associate.

2. It is also the required <u>Part One</u> (2 hours) of <u>ALL</u> LEED AP+ exams. You have to pass it plus

Part Two (2 hours) of the specific LEED AP BD+C exam of your choice to get any LEED AP+ title unless you have passed the old LEED AP exam before June 30, 2009.

There are a few ways to prepare for the LEED AP BD+C Exam:

1. You can take USGBC courses or workshops. You should take USGBC classes at both the 100 (Awareness) and 200 (LEED Core Concepts and Strategies) level to successfully prepare for Part One of the exam. USGBC classes at 300 level (Green Building Design & Construction: The LEED Implementation Process) can be taken to prepare for Part Two of the exam. A one-day course normally costs $445 (as of publication) with an early registration discount, otherwise it is $495. You will also have to wait until the USGBC workshops or courses are offered in a city near you.

OR

2. Take USGBC online courses. Refer to the USGBC or GBCI websites for information. The USGBC online courses are less personal and still expensive.

OR

3. Read related books. Instead of USGBC, GBCI is now handling the LEED exams. Unfortunately, there are no official GBCI books on the LEED AP BD+C Exam (v4). *LEED v4 BD&C Exam Guide* is one of the first books covering the current version of the exam for this subject and will fill in this blank to assist you with passing the exam.

To stay at the forefront of the LEED and green building movement and make my books more valuable to their readers, I sign up for USGBC courses and workshops myself. I review the USGBC and GBCI websites and many other sources to get as much information as possible on LEED. *LEED v4 BD&C Exam Guide* is a result of this very comprehensive research. I have done the hard work so that you can save time preparing for the exam by reading this book.

Strategy 101 for the LEED AP BD+C Exam is that you must recognize that you have only a limited amount of time to prepare for the exam. So, you must concentrate your time and effort on the most important content of the LEED AP BD+C Exam. To assist you with achieving this goal, the book is broken into two major sections: (1) the study materials and (2) the sample questions and mock exam.

Chapter One covers LEED Exam Preparation Strategies, Methods, Tips, Suggestions, Mnemonics, and Exam Tactics to Improve Your Exam Performance.

Chapters Two and Three cover general information. I use the question and answer format to try to give you the most comprehensive coverage on the subject of the LEED AP exam. I have given you only the correct answers and information to save you time, i.e., you do not need to waste your time reading and remembering the wrong information. As long as you understand and remember the correct information, you can pass the test, no matter how the USGBC changes the format of the exam.

Chapter Four contains the LEED AP BD+C Exam Technical Review, including Overall Purpose, Mnemonics, Core Concepts, Recognition, Regulation and Incentives, Overall Strategies and Technologies, and **Specific Technical Information**.

Specific Technical Information for **each credit** includes Purpose, Credit Path, Submittals, Synergies, Possible Strategies and Technologies, Extra Credit (Exemplary Performance), Project Phase, LEED

Submittal Phase, Related Code or Standard, and Responsible Party.

The final section contains sample questions. These are intended to match the latest real LEED AP BD+C Exam as closely as possible and assist you in becoming familiar with the format of the exam.

Most people already have some knowledge of LEED. I suggest that you use a highlighter when you read this book; you can highlight the content that you are not familiar with when you read the book for the first time. Try covering the answer and then read the question. If you come up with the correct answer before you read the book, you do not need to highlight the question and answer. If you cannot come up with the correct answer before you read the book, then highlight that question. This way, when you do your review later and read the book for the second time, you can focus on the portions that you are not familiar with and save yourself a lot of time. You can repeat this process with different colored highlighters until you are very familiar with the content of this book. Then, you will be ready to take the LEED AP BD+C Exam.

The key to passing the LEED AP BD+C Exam, or any other exam, is to know the scope of the exam, and not to read too many books. Select one or two really good books and focus on them. Actually *understand* the content and *memorize* it. For your convenience, I have underlined the fundamental information that I think is very important. You definitely need to memorize all the information that I have underlined. You should try to understand the content first, and then memorize the content of the book by reading it multiple times. This is a much better way than "mechanical" memory without understanding.

There is a part of the LEED AP BD+C Exam that you can control by reading study materials: the section regarding the number of points and credit process for the LEED building rating system. Become very familiar with every major credit category and try to answer all questions related to this part correctly.

There is also a part of the exam that you may not be able to control. You may not have done actual LEED building certification, so there will be some questions that may require you to guess. This is the hardest part of the exam, but these questions should be only a small percentage of the test if you are well prepared. Eliminate the obvious wrong answers and then attempt an educated guess. There is no penalty for guessing. If you have no idea what the correct answer is and cannot eliminate any obvious wrong answer, then do not waste too much time on the question, just pick a guess answer. The key is to use the same guess answer for all of the questions that you are completely unsure of. For example, if you choose "a" as the guess answer, then be consistent and use "a" as the guess answer for all the questions that are completely unsure of. That way, you likely have a better chance of guessing more correct answers.

This is not an easy exam, but you should be able to pass it if you prepare well. If you set your goal for a high score and study hard, you will have a better chance of passing. If you set your goal for the minimum passing score of 170, you will probably end up scoring 169 and fail, and you will have to retake the exam again. That will be the last thing you want. Give yourself plenty of time and do not wait until the last minute to begin preparing for the exam. I have met people who have spent 40 hours preparing and passed the exam, but I suggest that you give yourself at least two to three weeks of preparation time. On the night before the exam, look through the questions on the mock exam that you did not answer correctly and remember what the correct answers are. Read this book carefully, prepare well, relax and put yourself in the best physical, mental and psychological state on the day of the exam, and you will pass.

Chapter 1

LEED Exam Preparation Strategies, Methods, Tips, Suggestions, Mnemonics, and Exam Tactics to Improve Your Exam Performance

1. **The nature of LEED exams and exam strategies**

LEED Exams are standardized tests. They should be consistent and legally defensible tests.
The earliest standardized tests were the Imperial Examinations in China that started in 587. In Europe, traditional school exams were oral exams, and the first European written exams were held at Cambridge University, England in 1792.

Most exams test knowledge, skills, and aptitude. There are several main categories of exams:
1) Math exams testing your abilities to do various calculations
2) Analytical exams testing skills in separating a whole (intellectual or substantial) into its elemental parts or basic principles
3) Knowledge exams testing your expertise, skills and understanding of a subject
4) Creativity exams testing your skills to generate new ideas or concepts
5) Performance exams such as driving tests or singing competitions

LEED exams test your knowledge of LEED as well as some very basic analytical and calculation skills (on average about 10% to 15% of the exam questions require calculations). The LEED AP BD+C Exam is like a history or political science test, and requires the memorization of a lot of LEED information and knowledge.

All LEED exams test candidates' abilities at three hierarchical cognitive levels:
Recognition: ability to recall facts
Application: ability to use familiar principles or procedures to solve a new problem
Analysis: abilities to break the problem down into its parts, to evaluate their interactions or relationship, and to create a solution

LEED AP BD+C exam has 200 multiple-choice questions. You need to pick one, two, three, or even four correct answers (some questions have five choices), depending on the specific question.

The exam writers usually use errors that people are likely to make to create the incorrect choices (or **distracters**) to confuse exam takers, so you **HAVE to read the question very carefully**, pay special attention to words like may, might, could, etc. Creating effective distracters is a key to creating a good exam. This means that the more confusing a question is, the easier it is for the GBCI to separate candidates with strong LEED knowledge from the ones with weak LEED knowledge.

Since most LEED exam questions have four choices, the **distracters** in a strong LEED exam should be able to attract at least 25% of the weakest candidates to reduce the effectiveness of guessing.

For exam takers, it is to your advantage to guess for questions that you do not know, or are not sure about, because the exam writers expect you to guess. They are trying to mislead you with the questions to make your guessing less effective. If you do not guess and do not answer the questions, you will be at a disadvantage when compared with other candidates. Eliminate the obvious wrong answers and then try an educated guess. It is better to guess with the same letter answer for all the questions that you do not know, unless it is an obvious wrong answer and has been eliminated.

2. **LEED exam preparation requires short-term memory**
   Now that you know the nature of the LEED exam, you should understand that LEED exam preparation requires **Short-Term Memory**. Schedule your time accordingly: in the early stages of your LEED exam preparation, focus on understanding and an **initial** review of the material; in the late stages of your exam preparation, focus on memorizing the material as a **final** review.

3. **LEED exam preparation strategies and scheduling**
   Spend about 60% of your effort on the most important and fundamental LEED material, about 30% of your effort on sample exams, and the remaining 10% on improving your weakest areas, i.e., reading and reviewing the questions that you answered incorrectly, reinforcing the portions that you have a hard time memorizing, etc.

   Do NOT spend too much time looking for obscure LEED information because the GBCI will HAVE to test you on the most **common** LEED information. At least 80% to 90% of the LEED exam content will have to be the most common, important and fundamental LEED information. The exam writers can word their questions to be tricky or confusing, but they have to limit themselves to the important content; otherwise, their tests will NOT be legally defensible. At most, 10% of the test content can be obscure information. You only need to answer about 60% of all the questions correctly. So, if you master the common LEED knowledge (applicable to 90% of the questions) and use the guess technique for the remaining 10% of the questions on the obscure LEED content, you will do well and pass the exam.

   On the other hand, if you focus on the obscure LEED knowledge, you may answer the entire 10% obscure portion of the exam correctly, but only answer half of the remaining 90% of the common LEED knowledge questions correctly, and you will fail the exam. That is why we have seen many smart people who can answer very difficult LEED questions correctly because they are able to look them up and do quality research. However, they often end up failing the LEED exam because they cannot memorize the common LEED knowledge needed on the day of the exam. The LEED exam is NOT an open-book exam, and you cannot look up information during the exam.

   The **process of memorization** is like **filling a cup with a hole at the bottom**: You need to fill it faster than the water leaks out at the bottom, and you need to constantly fill it; otherwise, it will quickly be empty.

   Once you memorize something, your brain has already started the process of forgetting it. It is natural. That is how we have enough space left in our brain to remember the really important things.

   It is tough to fight against your brain's natural tendency to forget things. Acknowledging this truth and the fact that you cannot memorize everything you read, you need to focus your limited time, energy and brain power on the most important issues.

The biggest danger for most people is that they memorize the information in the early stages of their LEED exam preparation, but forget it before or on the day of the exam. The danger is that they still THINK they remember the information.

Most people fail the exam NOT because they cannot answer the few "advanced" questions on the exam, but because they have read the information but can NOT recall it on the day of the exam. They spend too much time preparing for the exam, drag the preparation process on too long, seek too much information, go to too many websites, do too many practice questions and too many mock exams (one or two sets of mock exams can be good for you), and **spread themselves too thin**. They end up **missing out on the most important information** of the LEED exam, and they fail.

The LEED Exam Guide Series along with the tips and methodology in each of the books will help you MEMORIZE the most important aspects of the test to pass the exam ON THE FIRST TRY.

So, if you have a lot of time to prepare for the LEED exam, you should plan your effort accordingly. You want your LEED knowledge to peak at the time of the exam, not before or after.

For example, if you have two months to prepare for the exam, you may want to spend the first month focused on reading and understanding all of the study materials you can find as your **initial** review. Also during this first month, you can start memorizing after you understand the materials as long as you know you HAVE to review the materials again later to retain them. If you have memorized something once, it is easier to memorize it again later.

Next, you can spend two weeks focused on memorizing the material. You need to review the material at least three times. You can then spend one week on mock exams. The last week before the exam, focus on retaining your knowledge and reinforcing your weakest areas. Read the mistakes that you have made and think about how to avoid them during the real exam. Set aside a mock exam that you have not taken and take it seven days before test day. This will alert you to your weaknesses and provide direction for the remainder of your studies.

If you have one week to prepare for the exam, you can spend two days reading and understanding the study material, two days repeating and memorizing the material, two days on mock exams, and one day retaining the knowledge and enforcing your weakest areas.

The last one to two weeks before the LEED exam is absolutely critical. You need to have the "do or die" mentality and be ready to study hard to pass the exam on your first try. That is how some people are able to pass the LEED exam with only one week of preparation.

4. **Timing of review: the 3016 rule; memorization methods, tips, suggestions, and mnemonics**
Another important strategy is to review the material in a timely manner. Some people say that the best time to review material is between 30 minutes and 16 hours (the **3016** rule) after you read it for the first time. So, if you review the material right after you read it for the first time, the review may not be helpful.

I have personally found this method extremely beneficial. The best way for me to memorize study materials is to review what I learn during the day again in the evening. This, of course, happens to fall within the timing range mentioned above.

Now that you know the **3016** rule, you may want to schedule your review accordingly. For example, you may want to read new study materials in the morning and afternoon, then after dinner do an initial review of what you learned during the day.

OR

If you are working full time, you can read new study materials in the evening or at night, and then get up early the next morning to spend one or two hours on an initial review of what you learned the night before.

The initial review and memorization will make your final review and memorization much easier.

Mnemonics is a very good way for you to memorize facts and data that are otherwise very hard to memorize. It is often arbitrary or illogical but it works.

A good mnemonic can help you remember something for a long time or even a lifetime after reading it just once. Without the mnemonics, you may read the same thing many times and still not be able to memorize it.

There are a few common mnemonics:

1) **Visual** Mnemonics: Link what you want to memorize to a visual image.
2) **Spatial** Mnemonics: Link what you want to memorize to a space, and the order of things in it.
3) **Group** Mnemonics**:** Break up a difficult piece into several smaller and more manageable groups or sets, and memorize the sets and their order. One example is the grouping of the 10 digit phone number into three groups in the U.S. This makes the number much easier to memorize.
4) **Architectural** Mnemonics: A combination of Visual Mnemonics and Spatial Mnemonics and Group Mnemonics.

   Imagine you are walking through a building several times, along the same path. You should be able to remember the order of each room you walk through. Then, if you want to remember some type of information, you could break up the information into several representative images and imagine you hanging these images on the walls of the various rooms you walk through as you move through the building. You should be able to easily recall each group in an orderly manner by imagining you are walking through the building again on the same path, and looking at the images hanging on walls of each room. When you look at the images on the wall, you can easily recall the related information.

   You can use your home, office, or another building that you are familiar with to build an Architectural Mnemonics to help you organize the things you need to memorize.
5) **Association** Mnemonics: You can associate what you want to memorize with a sentence, a similarly pronounced word, or a place you are familiar with, etc.
6) **Emotion** Mnemonics: Use emotion to fix an image in your memory.
7) **First Letter** Mnemonics: You can use the first letter of what you want to memorize to construct a sentence or acronym. For example, **"Roy G. Biv"** can be use to memorize the order of the 7 colors of the rainbow, it is composed of the first letter of each primary color.

For example, fixtures for Water Efficiency (WE) in LEED system, you can use **Association** Mnemonics and memorize them as all the plumbing fixtures for a typical home, PLUS Urinal.

OR
You can use "Water S K U L" (**First Letter** Mnemonics selected from website below) to memorize them:

Water Closet
Shower
Kitchen Sink
Urinal
Lavatory

Here is another example of **First Letter** Mnemonics:
Materials and Resources (MR) - Mandatory materials to be collected for recycling:

People Can Make Green Promises

Paper
Cardboard
Metal
Glass
Plastics

5. **The importance of good and effective study methods**
   There is a saying: "Give a man a fish and you feed him for a day. Teach a man to fish and you feed him for a lifetime." I think there is some truth to this. Similarly, it is better to teach someone HOW to study than just to give him good study materials. In this book, I give you good study materials to save you time, but more importantly, I want to teach you effective study methods so that you can not only study and pass LEED exams, but also so that you will benefit throughout the rest of your life for anything else you need to study or achieve. For example, I give you samples of mnemonics, but I also teach you the more important thing: HOW to make mnemonics.

   Often in the same class, all the students study almost the SAME materials, but there are some students that always manage to stay at the top of the class and get good grades on exams. Why? One very important factor is they have good study methods.

   Hard work is important, but it needs to be combined with effective study methods. I think people need to work hard AND work SMART to be successful at their work, career, or anything else they are pursuing.

6. **The importance of repetition: read this book at least three times**
   Repetition is one of the most important tips for learning. That is why I have listed it under a separate title. For example, you should treat this book as the core study materials for your LEED exam and you need to read this book at least three times to get all of its benefits:

   1) The first time you read it, it is new information. You should focus on understanding and digesting the materials, and also do an initial review with the **3016** rule.
   2) The second time you read it, focus on reading the parts I have already highlighted AND you have highlighted (the important parts and the weakest parts for you).

3) The third time, focus on memorizing the information.

Remember the analogy of the memorization process as **filling a cup with a hole on the bottom**?

Do NOT stop reading this book until you pass the real exam.

7. **When should you start to do sample questions and mock exams?**
After reading the study materials in this book at least three times, you can start to do mock exams.

8. **How much time do you need for LEED exam preparation?**
Do not give yourself too much time to prepare for the LEED exam. Two months is probably the maximum time you should allow for preparing for the LEED exam.

Do not give yourself too little time to prepare for LEED exam. You want to force yourself to focus on the LEED exam but you do NOT want to give yourself too little time and fail the exam. One week is probably the minimum time you should allow for preparing for the LEED exam.

9. **The importance of a routine**
A routine is very important for studying. You should try to set up a routine that works for you. First, look at how much time you have to prepare for the LEED exam, and then adjust your current routine to include LEED exam preparation. Once you set up the routine, stick with it.

For example, you can spend from 8:00 a.m. to 12:00 noon, and 1:00 p.m. to 5:00 p.m. studying new LEED exam study materials, and from 7:00 p.m. to 10:00 p.m. performing an initial review of what you learned during the daytime. Then, switch your study content to mock exams, memorization and retention when it gets close to the exam date. This way, you have eleven hours for LEED exam preparation everyday. You can probably pass the LEED exam in one week with this method. Just keep repeating it as a way to retain the LEED knowledge.

OR
You can spend from 7:00 p.m. to 10:00 p.m. studying new LEED exam study materials, and from 6:00 a.m. to 7:00 a.m. performing an initial review of what you learned the evening before. This way, you have four hours for LEED exam preparation everyday. You can probably pass LEED in five weeks with this LEED preparation schedule.

A routine can help you to memorize important information because it makes it easier for you to concentrate and work with your body clock.

Do NOT become panicked and change your routine as the exam date gets closer. It will not help to change your routine and pull all-nighters right before the exam. In fact, if you pull an all-nighter the night before the exam, you may do much worse than you would have done if you had kept your routine.

All-nighters or staying up late are not effective. For example, if you break your routine and stay up one-hour late, you will feel tired the next day. You may even have to sleep a few more hours the next day, adversely affecting your study regimen.

10. The importance of short, frequent breaks and physical exercise

Short, frequent breaks and physical exercise are VERY important, especially when you are spending a lot of time studying. They help relax your body and mind, making it much easier to concentrate when you study. They make you more efficient.

Take a five-minute break, such as a walk, at least once every one to two hours. Do at least 30 minutes of physical exercise everyday.

If you feel tired and cannot concentrate, stop, go outside, and take a five-minute walk. You will feel much better when you come back.

You need your body and brain to work well to be effective with your studying. Take good care of them. You need them to be well-maintained and in excellent condition. You need to be able to count on them when you need them.

If you do not feel like studying, maybe you can start a little bit on your studies. Just casually read a few pages. Very soon, your body and mind will warm up and you will get into study mode.

Find a room where you will NOT be disturbed when you study. A good study environment is essential for concentration.

11. A strong vision and a clear goal

You need to have a strong vision and a clear goal: to master the LEED system and become very familiar with the LEED certification process. This is your number one priority. You need to master the LEED information BEFORE you attempt any sample questions or mock exams. It will make the process much easier. Otherwise, there is nothing in your brain to be tested. Everything we discuss in this chapter is to achieve this goal.

As I have mentioned on many occasions, and I say it one more time here because it is so important:

It is how much LEED information you can understand, digest, memorize, and firmly retain that matters, not how many books you read or how many sample tests you have taken. The books and sample tests will NOT help you if you cannot understand, digest, memorize, and retain the important information for the LEED exam.

Cherish your limited time and effort and focus on the most important information.

Chapter 2
Overview

1. **What is LEED? What is the difference between LEED, LEED AP, LEED Green Associate, LEED AP+ and LEED Fellow?**
   Answer: LEED is a term for buildings. It stands for the Leadership in Energy and Environmental Design (LEED) Green Building Rating System™. It is a voluntary system set up by the U.S. Green Building Council (USGBC) to measure the sustainability and performance of a building.

   LEED AP, LEED Green Associate, LEED AP+, and LEED Fellow are terms for people.

   LEED AP stands for LEED Accredited Professional. A LEED AP is a person who has passed at least one of the three old versions of the LEED exam (LEED-NC, LEED-CI, and LEED-EB) before June 30, 2009. This person has the skills and knowledge to encourage and support integrated design, to take part in the design process, and to control the application and certification process for a LEED building.

   LEED APs have **three choices:**

   1) Do nothing and keep the title of LEED AP. It is also called LEED AP without specialty, or a legacy LEED AP.

   2) Starting June 2009, a LEED AP can choose to enroll in the new tiered system, accept the GBCI disciplinary policy, and **complete** the prescriptive Credentialing Maintenance Program **(CMP)** for the initial two-year reporting period. After opting in, a LEED AP can use one of the new specialty designations (Building Design and Construction ("BD+C"), Interior Design and Construction ("ID+C"), or Building Operation and Maintenance ("O+M")) after his name. The LEED AP must opt in before summer of 2011.

   3) Starting June 2009, a LEED AP can choose to opt in, accept the GBCI disciplinary policy, **agree** to CMP, and **pass** Part Two of one of the LEED AP+ specialty exams to become a LEED AP+. The LEED AP only needs to take Part Two of the LEED AP+ exam if he takes the exam by summer, 2011. After opting in, he can use one of the new specialty designations (BD+C, ID+C, or O+M) after his name.

   By choosing Paths 2 or 3 above, a LEED AP will become a LEED AP+ or a LEED AP with Specialty. See detailed information below:

   A LEED AP who passed the old LEED-NC exam will become a LEED AP BD+C, or a LEED AP BD&C.

A LEED AP who passed the old LEED-CI exam will become a LEED AP ID+C or a LEED AP ID&C.

A LEED AP who passed the old LEED-EB exam will become a LEED AP O+M or a LEED AP O&M.

Credential Maintenance Program (CMP): After completing one of these three choices, a LEED AP will be treated like any other LEED AP+ and will need to pay a $50 fee and take 30 hours of required class every two years to maintain the title of LEED AP+. Six of the hours must be LEED-specific. The $50 fee is waived for the first two years for a Legacy LEED AP who decides to opt in.

See detailed information on CMP at the following link:
http://www.gbci.org/cmp-wizard

LEED Green Associate, LEED AP+, and LEED Fellow are the three new tiers of professional credentials for LEED professionals. The GBCI started to use these new designations in 2009.

A **LEED Green Associate** is a green building professional with a basic level of LEED knowledge, i.e., a person who has passed the LEED Green Associate Exam and possesses the skills and knowledge to understand and support LEED projects and green building in the areas of design, construction, operation, and maintenance, AND has signed the paperwork to accept the GBCI disciplinary policy.

The LEED Green Associate Exam will NOT test the detailed information for each LEED credit. It will test you on the overall core concepts. You need to know the strategies for the overall categories of WE, EA, etc.

However, it IS much easier to understand, digest and organize LEED information, and it will be to your advantage to learn and memorize the LEED information for each specific LEED credit. You will be a much more desirable and useful support member for a LEED project team. You will definitely be able to answer generic LEED questions for the major LEED categories and pass the LEED Green Associate Exam.

You also need to know the codes and regulations related to each of the main LEED categories, i.e., WE, EA, etc. but NOT information for each credit within the category.

Exam Cost: The cost of LEED Green Associate Exam is $200 for USGBC members or full-time students and $250 for non-members per appointment.

Maintenance: A LEED Green Associate will need to pay a $50 fee and take 15 hours of required class every two years to maintain the title. Three of the hours must be LEED-specific.

LEED AP+ is a green building professional with an advanced level of LEED knowledge, i.e., a person who has passed the LEED Green Associate Exam (or Part One of the LEED AP+ exams) and Part Two of a LEED AP+ specialty exam based on one of the LEED rating systems or the equivalent, AND has signed paperwork to accept the GBCI disciplinary policy.

There are five different categories of LEED AP+ specialty exams (Part Two of LEED AP+ exams) and five categories of related LEED AP+ credentials, including:

LEED AP BD+C (Building Design and Construction)
LEED AP ID+C (Interior Design and Construction)
LEED AP O+M (Operation and Maintenance)
LEED AP ND (Neighborhood Development)
LEED AP Homes

For example, if you want to become a LEED AP BD+C, you need to pass the LEED Green Associate Exam (Part One of ALL LEED AP+ Exams) and the LEED AP BD+C Specialty Exam (Part Two of LEED AP+ exam specializing in LEED BD+C).

Both Part One and Part Two of the LEED AP+ exam have 100 multiple-choice questions, asking for one, two, three or even four correct answers (Some questions have five choices).

Exam Cost: The cost of the LEED AP+ exam is:

1) If you are taking the combined exam (both Part One and Part Two): $400 for USGBC members and $550 for non-members.
2) If you are taking only the Part Two specialty exam: $250 for USGBC members and $350 for non-members.

Maintenance: A LEED AP+ will need to pay a $50 fee and take 30 hours of required class every two years to maintain the title. Six of the hours must be LEED-specific.

A **LEED Fellow** is a green building professional with an extraordinary level of LEED knowledge, and has made major contributions to green building industry. The GBCI is still developing the criteria for becoming a LEED Fellow.

Note: These are current fees. They may be changed by the GBCI at a later point, please check the GBCI website for exact fees.

2. **Why did the GBCI create the new three-tier LEED credential system?**
   Answer: To pursue on-going improvement and excellence, to assure stakeholders of the LEED professionals' current competence and latest knowledge in green building practice, and to meet three prevailing market challenges: modernization, differentiation, and specialization.

3. **Do I need to have LEED project experience to take the LEED exams?**
   Answer: Anyone who is 18 years of age or older can take the LEED Green Associate Exam,

   You also need to agree to the GBCI credential maintenance requirements and the disciplinary policy. See LEED Green Associate Exam candidate handbook for detailed requirements.

   If you are taking the LEED AP+ exam, you must have documented experience on one or more LEED projects within three years of your exam application submittal date. See LEED AP+ exam candidate handbook for detailed requirements.

4. **How do I become a LEED AP+? Do I have to take the LEED Green Associate Exam first to become a LEED AP+?**
   Answer: There are four paths to become a LEED AP+. See below. Paths One and Two do NOT require taking the LEED Green Associate Exam first, while Paths Three and Four do.

Paths One and Two: If you are one of those lucky people who passed one of the three old LEED AP exams before June 30, 2009 and decided to opt into the new tiered system, you just need to opt in and accept the GBCI disciplinary policy and CMP requirements,

AND

1) **pass** Part Two of the LEED AP+ exam before summer of 2011 and **agree** to the CMP

   OR

2) **complete** the CMP before summer of 2011.

Path Three: If you have already passed the LEED Green Associate Exam, you only need to pass one of the specialty exams (Part Two of the LEED AP+ exams) to become a LEED AP with specialty.

Path Four: If you have not taken any LEED exams, you need take both parts of the LEED AP+ exam. You need to take both parts at the same time (back to back in the same sitting), UNLESS you have passed one of sections before. In this case, you can schedule to retake only the failed section at a different time for an additional fee.

5. **How many questions do you need to answer correctly to pass the LEED exams?**
   Answer: Many readers have asked me this question before. The short answer is about 60 correct questions or 60% of the 100 total questions for each exam section. The only official answer you can get is from the GBCI, but they do NOT give out an exact number. So, different people have different opinions. Here is my justification:

   1) The GBCI intends to use 60% of the correct questions as the benchmark for a passing score. Here is a simple calculation:

      LEED Exams
      Maximum Score: 200
      Minimum Score: 125
      Difference: 200-125 = 75 points (The score difference between someone who answers everything correctly and someone answers everything incorrectly.)

      75 × 60% = 45 (points)
      125 + 45 = 170 points = passing score

      Total questions: 100
      60% × 100 = 60 = correct answers needed to pass the LEED exams.

   2) The exact number may be different depending on the difficulty of the version of the exam that you are taking.

      Why?

      Because GBCI wants the LEED passing score to be legally defensible. So, it uses subject matter experts to set the minimum level of required LEED knowledge and professional psychometricians to analyze the performance of people taking the beta tests, and uses the **Angoff Method** to decide the final passing score.

The easier versions of the test will need a higher number of correct answers to pass, and the harder versions of the test will need a lower number of correct answers to pass. So, the end result is the correct number of the questions needed to pass the exam is about 60, but probably NOT exactly 60.

If you reach the required level of LEED knowledge, no matter which version of the test you take, you should pass.

6. **What are the key areas that the USGBC uses to measure the performance of a building's sustainability?**
   Answer: Integrated Process (IP), Location and Transportation (LT), Sustainable Site (SS), Water Efficiency (WE), Energy and Atmosphere (EA), Materials and Resource (MR), Indoor Environmental Quality (IEQ), Innovation (IN), and Regional Priority (RP).

   Mnemonics: Ian and Larry, Shall We Make It Italic and Red?

7. **How many LEED exams does the USGBC have?**
   Answer:
   1) Before 2009, there were three old versions of the LEED exams: LEED New Construction (LEED-NC) v2.2, LEED Commercial Interior (LEED-CI) v2.0, and LEED Existing Building (LEED-EB) v2.0. You just needed to pass one of the three exams to earn the old title of LEED AP.
   2) In 2009, GBCI started to introduce a new three-tier LEED credential system, and related new versions of LEED exams, including:
      a. The LEED Green Associate Exam. It is also Part One of ALL LEED AP+ exams.

      b. Part Two of LEED AP+ exams, including the following specialties (exam takers just need to choose one):
         LEED AP BD+C (Building Design and Construction)
         LEED AP ID+C (Interior Design and Construction)
         LEED AP O+M (Operation and Maintenance)
         LEED AP ND (Neighborhood Development)
         LEED AP Homes

8. **Are LEED Exams valid and reliable?**
   Answer: Yes. They are valid because they can measure what they intend to measure. They are reliable because they can accurately measure a candidate's skills.

9. **How many member organizations does the USGBC have?**
   Answer: More than 11,000 member organizations.

10. **How many regional chapters does the USGBC have?**
    Answer: 77.

11. **What is the main purpose of the USGBC?**
    Answer: To improve the way a building is designed, built, and used to achieve a healthy, profitable,

and environmentally responsible building and environment, and to improve the quality of life.

12. **What are the guiding principles of the USGBC?**
Answer: The USGBC emphasizes not only the decisions themselves but also *how* the decisions are made. Its guiding principles are: advocate the **triple bottom lines** (balance environmental, social and economic needs; some people summarize these as planet, people and profit); build leadership; strive to achieve the balance between humanity and nature; uphold integrity and restore, preserve and protect the environment, species and ecosystem; use democratic and interdisciplinary approaches to ensure inclusiveness to achieve a common goal; openness, honesty and transparency.

13. **How much energy and how many resources do buildings consume in the US?**
Answer: Per the USGBC and US Department of Energy, buildings consume about 39% of total energy, 74% of electricity, and 1/8 of the water in the US. Buildings also use valuable land that could otherwise provide ecological resources. In 2006, more than 1 billion metric tons of carbon dioxide was generated by the commercial building sector. That is over a 30% increase from 1990.

14. **What is the most important step to get your building certified?**
Answer: It is to register your building with USGBC online at usgbc.org.

15. **What are the benefits of green buildings and LEED certification?**
Answer: To enhance the building's and company's marketability and to provide branding opportunities, a positive impact on health and the environment. LEED certification may also increase occupants' productivity, reduce building operating costs, and help to create sustainable communities.

16. **Who develops the LEED green building rating systems?**
Answer: The USGBC committee and volunteers.

17. **What current reference guides and specific green building rating systems does the USGBC have?**
Answer: The USGBC has the following reference guides and green rating system portfolio:

    1) *The LEED Reference Guide for Building Design and Construction v4 (BD&C)*,which covers the following LEED rating systems:
        - LEED BD+C: New Construction
        - LEED BD+C: Core and Shell Development
        - LEED BD+C: Schools
        - LEED BD+C: Retails
        - LEED BD+C: Data Center
        - LEED BD+C: Warehouse and Distribution Center
        - LEED BD+C: Hospitality
        - LEED BD+C: Health Care
        - LEED BD+C: Homes
        - LEED BD+C: Multi-family Midrise

2) *The LEED Reference Guide for Interior Design and Construction v4 (ID&C)*,which covers the following LEED rating systems:
   - LEED ID+C: Commercial Interiors
   - LEED ID+C: Retails
   - LEED ID+C: Hospitality

3) *The LEED Reference Guide for Green Building Operations and Maintenance v4 (O&M)*,which covers the following LEED rating systems:
   - LEED O+M: Existing Buildings
   - LEED O+M: Retails
   - LEED O+M: Schools
   - LEED O+M: Hospitality
   - LEED O+M: Data Center
   - LEED O+M: Warehouse and Distribution Center

Note: These LEED-EB rating systems are the only systems that cover building operation. All other LEED systems cover building design and construction, but NOT operation.

4) *The LEED for Neighborhood Development Reference Guide v4 (LEED-ND).*
   - LEED ND: Plan
   - LEED ND: Built Project

5) **Application Guide for Multiple Buildings and On-Campus Building Projects (AGMBC)**, 2010 Edition. See link below:
   http://www.usgbc.org/campusguidance

The complete sample LEED v4forms are available at credit library future at link below:
http://www.usgbc.org/credits

Refer to the following link for various LEED rating systems:

After May 31, 2014, ALL LEED exams have been upgraded to LEED v4.
After May 31, 2015, ALL buildings have to be registered under LEED v4.

18. How does LEED fit into the green building market?

Answer: LEED fits into the green building market by providing voluntary, market-driven, and consensus-based rating systems. It is based on accepted environmental and energy principles, and maintains a balance between emerging concepts and established practices. Green buildings developed under the LEED rating systems can reduce operating costs and create branding and marketing opportunities for buildings and organizations. They are good for the environment and public health, increase occupant productivity and create sustainable communities.

19. What are the benefits of LEED certification for your building?
Answer:

a. The building is qualified for various government initiatives.
b. The building can obtain USGBC (third party) validation of your achievement.
c. You can be recognized for your commitment to environment issues.
d. Branding opportunities and market exposure through media, GreenBuild conference, USGBC, cases studies, etc.

20. What is the procedure of LEED certification for your building?
Answer:

a. Go to www.gbci.org to register your building, the earlier the better. This is the most important step.
b. You must document that your building meets prerequisites and a minimum number of points to be certified.

Refer to the LEED project checklist for the points needed for various levels of LEED certification.

21. How much is the building registration fee and how much is the building LEED certification fee?
Answer: The building registration fee is $900 for USGBC members and $1,200 for non-members.

The building certification fee varies, but it starts at $2,250 for USGBC members and $2,750 for non-members.

22. What are LEED's system goals?
Answer: LEED's system goals or LEED's **"Impact Categories"** are:

- Global **Climate Change**
- Social Equity, Environmental Justice, and **Community** Quality of Life
- Individual **Human Health** and well-being
- **Greener Economy**
- **Biodiversity** and Ecosystem
- **Water Resources**
- Sustainable and Regenerative **Material Resources** Cycles

These also answers the question: "What should a LEED project accomplish?"

23. How are LEED credits allocated and weighted?
Answer: Credits that can contribute to LEED's **"Impact Categories"** are given more points. These impact categories are weighted through a consensus driven process:

- Global **Climate Change** (35%)
- Social Equity, Environmental Justice, and **Community** Quality of Life (5%)
- Individual **Human Health** and well-being (20%)
- **Greener Economy** (5%)
- **Biodiversity** and Ecosystem (10%)
- **Water Resources** (15%)
- Sustainable and Regenerative **Material Resources** Cycles (10%)

The USGBC uses three **association factors** to measure and scale credit outcome to a given Impact Category component:

- **Relative Efficacy:** It measures whether a credit outcome has a positive or negative association with a given Impact Category component, and how strong that association is.
  - No association
  - Low association
  - Medium association
  - High association
  - Negative association

- **Benefit Duration:** How long will the benefits or consequences of the credit outcome last?
  - 1-3 Years
  - 4-10 Years
  - 11-30 Years
  - 30+ Years (Building/Community Lifetime)

- **Controllability of Effect:** It indicates which individual is most directly responsible for achieving the expected credit outcome. The more a credit outcome depends on active human effort, the less likely it will be achieved with certainty, and the credit will have fewer pints, vice versa.

The USGBC simplifies the weighting process of points into a score **card**:

- **100 base points** for the base LEED Rating System
- **1 point minimum** for each credit
- **Whole points** and no fractions for LEED points.

See detailed discussions at the FREE PDF file entitled "LEED v4 Impact Category and Point Allocation Development Process" at the following link:
http://www.usgbc.org/sites/default/files/LEED%20v4%20Impact%20Category%20and%20Point%20Allocation%20Process_Overview_0.pdf

24. Are there LEED certified products?

Answer: ALLLEED systems certify buildings or projects, NOT products. Products can contribute to a LEED project, and sometimes a product's data is required as part of a LEED submittal package.

Chapter 3

Introduction to the LEED AP BD+C Exam

1. **What is new for LEED v4?**
   Answer: LEED v4 is a major revision and has two new credit categories: Integrative Process as well as Location and Transportation. Many existing credits have different points. Some criteria for obtaining credits have also changed.

   The numbering system for the credit has been omitted. For example, "SSc5.1: Site Development: Protect or Restore Habitat" is now simplified as "SS: Site Development: Protect or Restore Habitat." SS stands for sustainable site development.

   In addition to the rating system for New Construction, Core and Shell, and Schools, the LEED BD+C reference guide has added information for these rating systems: Retail, Data Center, Warehouse and Distribution Center, Hospitality, and Healthcare.

   LEED APs without specialties (Legacy LEED AP) can no longer earn a point for innovation credit. Only a LEED AP with a specialty appropriate to the project and work as a principal participant of the project team can earn one point for innovation credit.

2. **What is the scope of the LEED Green Associate Exam?**

Answer: Per the USGBC, the content of the LEED Green Associate Exam is limited to:

a. **Understanding the fundamental credit intents, strategies, requirements, technologies, and submittals for the eight major credit categories:** integrative process (IP), location and transportation (LT),sustainable site development (SS), water savings/efficiency (WE), energy and atmosphere (EA), materials and resource (MR), indoor environmental quality (IEQ), innovation (IN), and Regional Priority (RP), as well as innovation in upgrades, maintenance, and operations.

b. **Process of LEED application and opportunities for synergy**
   Synergy means the combined effects of two or more agents or forces greater than the sum of their individual.
   The LEED Green Associate Exam may test the following aspects:
   - Site, budget, schedule, program, and other requirements
   - Hard, soft, and life-cycle costs
   - Environmental Building News, **USGBC**, **NRDC**(Natural Resources Defense Council), and other green resources
   - **Green Seal**, **SMACNA** (Sheet Metal and Air Conditioning Contractors National Association Guidelines), **ASHRAE** (American Society of Heating, Refrigeration, and Air-conditioning Engineers), and other standards for LEED credit
   - Waste management, IEQ and energy, and other interaction between LEED Credits
   - **CIR** (Credit Interpretation Requests/Rulings) and previous samples leading to extra points

- Project registration and **LEED Online**
- Score Card for LEED
- Supplementary documentation, project calculations, and other Letter Templates
- LEED credit **strategies**
- Property, project, and LEED boundaries
- Minimum LEED certification program requirements and/or **prerequisites**
- Certification goal and preliminary rating
- Opportunities for the same building to get multiple certifications, i.e., commercial interior as well as core and shell
- Certified building in LEED neighborhood development
- Operations and maintenance for certified new building construction
- Requirements for occupancy (e.g., an existing building must be fully occupied for 12 continuous months as described in minimum program requirements)
- Logo usage, trademark usage, and other USGBC policies
- Requirements for receiving LEED AP credit

c. Site factors of a project:

1) **Connectivity** for Communities
   a) Carts, shuttles, car-sharing membership (e.g. Zipcar™), bike storage, public transportation, fuel efficient vehicle parking, parking capacity, carpool parking, and other means to improve **transportation**
   b) Ramps, crosswalks, trails, and other means to improve **pedestrian access** and circulation

2) **Zoning requirements** (calculations of site area, floor to area ratio, and other density components, building footprint, open space, development footprint, construction limits, and specific landscaping restrictions)

3) **Development**
   Heat Islands including albedo, emissivity, non-roof/roof heat island effect; green roofs, Solar Reflectance Index (SRI), etc.

d. Management of water:

1) Understand quality and types of water, i.e., blackwater, graywater, storm water, and potable water

2) Understand water management, i.e., use low-flush fixtures such as water closets, urinals, sinks, lavatory faucets, and showers to reduce water use; calculations of FTE (Full Time Equivalent); baseline water demand; irrigation; rainwater harvesting

e. Project system and related energy impact:

1) Ozone depletion, chlorofluorocarbon (CFC) reduction, no refrigerant option, fire suppressions without halons or CFC's, phase-out plan, Hydrochlorofluorocarbons (HCFC), and other Environmental Concerns
2) Green-e providers, off-site generated, renewable energy certificates, and other Green Power

f. Project materials acquisition, installation and management:

1) Commingled, pre-consumer, post-consumer, collection, and other requirements regarding recycled materials

2) Locally/regionally manufactured and harvested materials
3) Accounted by weight or volume, written plan, polychlorinated biphenyl (PCB) removal and asbestos-containing materials (ACM) management, reduction strategies, and other requirements regarding construction waste management

g. **Project team coordination, stakeholder involvement in innovation and regional design:**
1) Civil engineer, landscape architect, architect, heating-ventilation-air-conditioning (HVAC) engineer, contractor, facility manager, and related integrated project team criteria
2) Building reuse, material lifecycle, and other durability, planning, and management
3) Appropriate and established requirements, regional green design and construction, and other innovative and regional design measures

h. **Codes and regulations, public outreach and project surroundings:** building, electrical, mechanical, plumbing, fire protection codes, etc.

i. **Ability to support the coordination of team and project and assist** with the process of gathering the necessary requirements and information for the **LEED process** and coordinating the different job functions for **LEED certification**

j. **Ability to support the process of LEED implementation**

k. **Ability to support technical analyses for LEED credits**

3. **What is the scope of the LEED AP BD+C Exam?**
Answer: Part One is exactly the same as the LEED Green Associate Exam. Part Two tests information specific to LEED green building and construction. For more information, refer to the detailed discussion of the exam scope in the LEED AP BD+C exam candidate handbook at
http://www.gbci.org/main-nav/professional-credentials/resources/candidate-handbooks.aspx

4. **What is the latest version of LEED and when was it published?**

a. **When was LEED v1.0 released?**
Answer: It was first launched in August 1998, but officially released in 1999.

b. **When was LEED-NC v2.0 released?**
Answer: It was first published in 1999, but officially released in March 2000.

c. **When was LEED-NC v2.1 released?**
Answer: November 2002.

d. **When was LEED-NC v2.2 published?**
Answer: It was first published in 2003, but officially released in 2005.

e. **When was LEED v3.0 launched?**
Answer: On 4/27/2009,the USGBC launched **LEED v3.0**, which includes: a new building certification model, a new LEED Online, and LEED 2009 (Improvement to the LEED rating systems). LEED v3.0 is a part of the continuous evolution of the LEED building rating system. For LEED v3.0, the USGBC is trying to synchronize the prerequisites and credits across each version of the LEED system, and to create a predictable LEED development cycle (similar to other building codes, likely every three years), a transparent environmental/human impact credit

weighting (redistributing the available points in LEED), as well as regionalization (regional bonus credits). Refer to the Appendixes of this book for links and more information on LEED v3.0.

f. **When was LEED v4 released?**
Answer: The USGBC released LEED v4 in GreenBuild International Conference and Expo in November, 2013.

5. **How many possible points does LEED v4 have?**
Answer: Starting with LEED v3.0 or LEED 2009, **ALL** updated rating systems have or will have **110** possible points, including **100** possible base points and **10** bonus points. LEED v4 maintains the same number of total points, but changes how many points a credit can get.

See latest scorecards for various LEED rating system at the following link:
http://www.usgbc.org/credits

For example, for LEED v4 for **LEED BD+C: New Construction**, there is 1 point for Integrative Process (IP), there are 16 points for Location and Transportation (LT), 10 points for Sustainable Sites (SS), 11 points for Water Efficiency (WE), 33 points for Energy and Atmosphere (EA), 13 points for Materials and Resource (MR), 16 points for Indoor Environmental Quality (IEQ), 6 bonus points for Innovation (IN), and 4 bonus points for Regional Priority (RP).

For LEED v4 for **LEED BD+C: Core and Shell**, there is 1 point for Integrative Process (IP), there are 20 points for Location and Transportation (LT),11 points for Sustainable Sites (SS), 11 points for Water Efficiency (WE), 33 points for Energy and Atmosphere (EA), 14 points for Materials and Resource (MR), 10 points for Indoor Environmental Quality (IEQ), 6 bonus points for Innovation (IN), and 4 bonus points for Regional Priority (RP).

For LEED v4 for **LEED BD+C: Schools**, there is 1 point for Integrative Process (IP), there are 15 points for Location and Transportation (LT), 12 points for Sustainable Sites (SS), 12 points for Water Efficiency (WE), 31 points for Energy and Atmosphere (EA), 13 points for Materials and Resource (MR), 16 points for Indoor Environmental Quality (IEQ), 6 bonus points for Innovation (IN), and 4 bonus points for Regional Priority (RP).

For LEED v4 for **LEED ID+C: Commercial Interiors (CI)**, there are 2 points for Integrative Process (IP), 18 points for Location and Transportation (LT), 12 points for Water Efficiency (WE), 38 points for Energy and Atmosphere (EA), 13 points for Materials and Resource (MR), 17 points for Indoor Environmental Quality (IEQ), 6 bonus points for Innovation (IN), and 4 bonus points for Regional Priority (RP).

For LEED v4 for **LEED for Existing Building Operation and Maintenance**, there are 15 points for Location and Transportation (LT), 10 points for Sustainable Sites (SS), 12 points for Water Efficiency (WE), 38 points for Energy and Atmosphere (EA), 8points for Materials and Resource (MR), 17 points for Indoor Environmental Quality (IEQ), 6 bonus points for Innovation (IN), and 4 bonus points for Regional Priority (RP).

6. **How many different levels of building certification does USGBC have?**
Answer: Four: Certified, Silver, Gold, and Platinum. They are based on the points that a building earns under the LEED green building rating system. For example, based on the scorecards or checklists provided by the USGBC:

No matter which **LEED v4.0** rating system you choose, each LEED v4.0 rating system has **100**base points; a maximum of **6** possible extra points for Innovation (IN), and a maximum of **4** possible extra points for Regional Priority (RP) for each project. There are 6 possible RP points, but you can only pick and choose a maximum of 4 points for each project.

Certified	**40**–49	points
Silver	**50**–59	points
Gold	**60**–79	points
Platinum	**80**	points and above

Refer to the following link for the **Regional Priority Credits (RPC)** for all 50 States. With this spreadsheet, you can locate the RPC for your area by zip code:
http://www.usgbc.org/rpc

A LEED Project team does not have to do anything special, since LEED v4Online will automatically decide which RPC your project will get once you enter the project zip code and other information. If you have more than 4 RPCs, then you need to decide which 4 RPCs you want to use for your project.

The USGBC has been working on developing similar RPC incentives for international projects. RPC is available for many countries.

7. **What is the process for LEED certification? What are the basic steps for LEED certification?**
Answer: The USGBC suggests 10 basic steps for LEED certification:
   1) **Initiate discovery phase:** gathering information, doing research and analysis, and a goal-setting workshop.
   2) **Select LEED rating system:** see *Rating System Selection Guidance*, as well as *Further Explanation* under each credit.
   3) **Check minimum program requirements (MPRs):** check MPRs for the selected rating system, available in the related reference guide and the USGBC website.
   4) **Establish project goals:** set up a goal-setting workshop (see Integrative Process Credit) for the project team members and the owner, which should include representatives from the design and construction disciplines.
   5) **Define LEED project scope:** consider shared facilities or off-site or campus amenities that may be used by project occupants; map the LEED project boundary; investigate special certification programs such as the **Volume Program** or the **Campus Program**.
   6) **Develop LEED scorecard:** focus on those credits with the highest value in a long term; seek synergistic benefits; set the target LEED certification level (Certified, Silver, Gold, or Platinum); be sure to meet **prerequisites**; include several extra points as a buffer.
   7) **Continue discovery phase:** Do additional research and analysis; reassemble occasionally to coordinate.
   8) **Continue iterative process:** continue the research and analysis as well as workshops until the solution satisfy the team and the owner.
   9) **Assign roles and responsibilities:** select a leader for the LEED application and documentation process; assign primary and supporting roles to appropriate team members for each credit;

Establish regular meeting dates and clear communication channels.

10) **Perform quality assurance review and submit for certification:** perform a thorough quality control check; numeric values (e.g., site area) must be consistent across credits.

The USGBC publishes three guides for LEED v4 certification. You should read these guides at least *three* times. They will not only help you pass a LEED exam on the first try, but also benefit your real LEED project. See the following:

- ***Guide to LEED v4 Certification: Commercial***

It includes four main steps:

a. **Register** the project: completing key forms and submitting payment.
b. **Apply** for LEED certification: submitting application via LEED Online and paying a certification review fee.
c. **Review**: reviewed by GBCI.
d. **Certify**: Receive the certification decision: "Denied" or "Achieved"

See the following link:
http://www.usgbc.org/cert-guide/commercial

Note: Registration *is an important step. The project administrator has access to the CIR database and LEED Online after registration.*

As part of the registration, the LEED project team will *have to* agree to report *post-occupancy water and energy use*. This is to allow the USGBC to have a better understanding of the relationship between building performance and LEED credits. There are several ways to achieve the reporting requirements, including signing up for LEED O&M, OR signing a waiver to allow the USGBC to acquire the data applicable directly from the utility company.

- ***Guide to LEED v4 Certification: Homes***

See the following link:
http://www.usgbc.org/cert-guide/homes

It includes four main steps (Please note the differences from Commercial Projects):

a. **Register** the project: *selecting your team*, completing key forms and submitting payment.
b. **Verify** your project: milestones and achievements via the on-site verification process. A mid-construction verification site visit, sometimes called the "pre-drywall" visit by the Green Rater and Energy Rater is mandatory. Final construction verification visit is required after construction including landscape is complete, and the **energy rater** also conducts the required performance testing at this visit.
c. **Review.** Submit the necessary information, calculations and documentation to your **Green Rater**. The Green Rater then submits the appropriate documentation to the **LEED for Homes Provider** for their *quality assurance* review. The LEED for Homes Provider review and then submit the documentation to GBCI for *certification* review.
d. **Certify**: Receive the certification decision: "Denied" or "Achieved"

For LEED for Homes, you need to deal with a LEED for Homes Provider, a Green Rater and an Energy Rater.

A LEED for Homes Provider is the referee when it comes to who is able to be a **Green Rater** for a LEED for Homes project. The Provider is responsible for hiring, training, and overseeing the Green Raters. The USGBC requires that each Provider have a quality assurance protocol for its Green Raters. Homebuilders who intend to achieve LEED for Homes certification **must contact a LEED for Homes Provider** organization. Refer to the following link for a complete list of LEED for Homes Provider organizations in the US:
http://www.usgbc.org/organizations/members/homes-providers

A Green Rater is a professional who has shown qualifications for energy rating certification, and demonstrates the ability to deal with a home's energy systems and performance. Certification can be obtained from accreditation bodies such as ENERGY STAR, RESNET, BPI, etc. Green Raters provide the required *on-site* verification.

Energy rater: a *performance* test by a qualified energy rater is mandatory for the LEED for Homes rating system. The largest body of energy raters is called **Home Energy Raters (HERS Raters).** The **Residential Energy Services Network (RES NET)** administers HERS Raters credentials.

- ***Guide to LEED v4 Certification: Volume supplement***

  See the following link:
  http://www.usgbc.org/cert-guide/volume

The LEED Volume Program is available for the following LEED rating systems:
- LEED for New Construction (LEED NC)
- LEED for Commercial Interiors (LEED CI)
- LEED for Retail: New Construction (LEED RN)
- LEED for Retail: Commercial Interiors (LEED RI)
- LEED for Existing Buildings: Operations and Maintenance (LEED EB: O+M)
- Including projects undergoing recertification

Participants in the **LEED Volume Program** finish precertification of a prototype, and then the projects based on this prototype can easily earn a common set of credits. This can save a lot of time and money for an organization.

All Volume Program participants are organizations that own, lease or manage real estate, but architects, consultants, and contractors are not eligible.

There are two forms of CIRs under the Volume Program (See detailed discussions on CIR on the following pages):
- A **prototype CIR** is applicable to all buildings in the participant's portfolio for the prototype.
- A **volume project CIR** is applicable only to the specific volume project for which it was submitted.

See the following links for more information on LEED certification, including and LEED certification fees:

  http://www.usgbc.org/cert-guide/fees
  http://www.usgbc.org/cert-guide

http://www.usgbc.org/leed/certification
http://www.gbci.org/main-nav/building-certification/certification-guide.aspx

USGBC offers the following resources and tools to assist LEED certification:

- **Credit Library:**
  http://www.usgbc.org/credits
- **Addenda database:**
  http://www.usgbc.org/leed-interpretations
- **Pilot Credit library:**
  http://www.usgbc.org/pilotcredits
- **Regional Priority Credit lookup:**
  http://www.usgbc.org/rpc

8. **What does the registration form include?**
   Answer: The registration form includes account login information, project contact information, project details (type, title, address, owner, gross square footage, budget, site condition, current project phase, scope, occupancy, etc.), and the confidentiality status of the project.

9. **What is precertification?**
   Answer: Precertification is mainly for the Core and Shell program. It is a formal recognition of a project where the owner intends to seek Core and Shell certification, and gives the owner/developer a marketing tool to attract financers and tenants. A project needs to meet a scorecard requirement for precertification. Precertification is granted after an early design review by the USGBC, and the review usually takes less than one month. Precertification costs $2,500 for USGBC members and $3,500 for non-members. It does NOT cover the fee for certification, and it does NOT guarantee the final certification of the project.

10. **What is a CIR?**
    Answer: CIR stands for a **Credit Interpretation Request** or **Credit Interpretation Ruling**, depending upon the context. Most of the time CIRs mean Credit Interpretation Rulings**.** CIRs are *not* precedent setting

    LEED Interpretation is similar to CIRs, but they *are* precedent-setting.

11. **When do you submit a CIR?**
    Answer: When there are conflicts between two credit categories or the USGBC Reference Guide does *not* give you enough information. The building registration fee used to cover two free CIRs, but after 11/15/05, it costs $200 to submit each CIR.

12. **What are the steps for submitting a CIR?**
    Answer:
    1) Check your projects against each LEED credit or prerequisite.
    2) Check the USGBC Reference Guide.
    3) Review the GBCI and USGBC websites for previous CIRs and LEED Interpretation.
    4) If you cannot find a similar CIR, then submit a new CIR to GBCI online.
    5) Do *not* mention the contact information, name of the credit, or confidential information.
    6) Submit only the essential and required information, and do not submit it in a letter format.
    7) Submit one CIR for each prerequisite or credit.
    8) Do not include any attachments.

9) Include details and background information, 600 words max (4,000 characters including spaces).

13. Will submitting a CIR guarantee a credit?
Answer: No, a CIR only provides feedback, and it will *not* guarantee a credit. Also, no credit will be awarded in the CIR process.

14. Which tasks are handled by the GBCI and what tasks are handled by the USGBC?
Answer: In 2008, the Green Building Certification Institute (GBCI) spun off from the USGBC.

The USGBC still handles the online tool, LEED rating system development, and related educational offerings, etc.

The GBCI took over some responsibilities from the USGBC and handles building LEED certification and LEED professional credentialing.

For building LEED certification, the GBCI oversees 10 organizations including Lloyd's Register Quality Assurance and Underwriters Laboratories, which manage the project review process.

This separation of the tasks for the USGBC and the GBCI will meet the protocols of the American National Standard Institute (ANSI) and International Organization for Standardization (ISO), and will make the building certification a true third-party process.

15. What are MPRs?
Answer: MPRs are LEED's **Minimum Program Requirements**. A project must meet MPRs to qualify for LEED certification.

MPRs serve three goals:
1) Clear guidance for customers
2) Maintain LEED program integrity
3) Make the LEED certification process easier

MPRs include some very basic requirements, including:
1) A LEED project must be must be in a permanent location on existing land
2) A LEED project must have a *reasonable* site boundary, and the building' **gross floor area** to **gross land area** within the LEED project boundary must be 2% or higher.
3) The building must comply with project size requirements. For example, it must be 1,000 s.f. minimum for LEED BD+C and LEED O+M rating systems, and 250 s.f. minimum for LEED ID+C rating system. For LEED for Neighborhood Development Rating Systems, the LEED project should be no larger than 1500 acres and contain a minimum of two habitable buildings.

Refer to the link below for detailed information:
http://www.usgbc.org/credits/homes/v4/minimum-program-requirements

16. Which LEED rating system should I choose?
Answer: The USGBC has published *LEED v4 User Guide* to assist you to choose the right rating system for your project.

For example, **LEED BD+C** rating systems should be used for new construction or major renovation with least 60% of the project's gross floor area that must be completed by the time of certification (except for LEED BD+C: Core and Shell).

A **major renovation** means major building envelope changes, significant HVAC renovation and interior rehabilitation.

LEED for Interior Design and Construction should be used for interior spaces that are a *complete interior fit-out* with at least 60% of the project's gross floor area must be complete by the time of certification.

LEED for Building Operations and Maintenance should be used for existing buildings undergoing improvement work or little to no construction.

LEED for Neighborhood Development should be used for new land development projects or redevelopment projects containing residential uses, nonresidential uses, or a mix. The USGBC recommends that a minimum of 50% of total building floor area should be new construction or major renovation.

Each of the aforementioned major rating systems includes more detailed and specific rating systems, such as LEED BD+C: New Construction and Major Renovations, LEED BD+C: Core and Shell Development, and LEED BD+C: Schools, etc.

The USGBC uses a **40/60 rule** to assist you when several rating systems seem to be acceptable for a project:

- Do not use a rating system if it is appropriate for less than 40% of the gross floor area of a LEED project building or space.
- Use a rating system if it is appropriate for more than 60% of the gross floor area of a LEED project building or space.
- A project team can decide which system to use if an appropriate rating system falls between 40% and 60% of the gross floor area.

See *LEED v4 User Guide* at the following link:
http://www.usgbc.org/sites/default/files/LEED%20v4%20User%20Guide_Final_0.pdf

Chapter 4

LEED AP BD+C Exam
Overall Technical Review

In this chapter, we introduce the LEED certification process, key components of the LEED rating system, as wells as the purpose, core concepts, strategies, incentives, recognitions, and regulations for each LEED credit category.

1. **What do green buildings address?**
   Green buildings mitigate degradation of ecosystems/habitat and resource depletion, reduce costs of operating and owning living and work spaces, improve occupant productivity and comfort, indoor environmental quality, and reduce water consumption.
   Mnemonics: DR. COIN C. See underlined letters in the sentences above.

   Note: *Some people like to use mnemonics and think they are very helpful, while some other don't. We provide them as an option for you. If you do not like to use mnemonics, just ignore them and read the information a few times and become familiar with it, and it should be fine.*

2. **Key stake holders and an integrative approach**
   Green buildings employ an **integrative approach** and encourage the participation of **key stake holders**, including the:

   1) **Client:** Facilities Management Staff, Facilities O&M Staff, Community Members, Owner, and Planning Staff. **Mnemonics**: MOM COP

   2) **Design team:** Civil Engineer, Landscape Architect, Architect, Mechanical and Plumbing Engineer, Electrical Engineer, Structural Engineer, Commissioning Authority, and Energy and Daylighting Modeler.
   Mnemonics: CLAMPES CAM

   3) **Builder:** General Contractors, EMP Subcontractors, Cost Estimator, Construction Manager, and Product Manufacturer.
   Mnemonics: G EMP EMP

   There are many **benefits** of an **integrative approach**, including better indoor air quality, improved occupant performance, reduced operating and maintenance costs, durable facilities, reduced environmental impact, potentially no increase in construction cost, optimized return on investment, and opportunity of learning.
   Mnemonics: bird in pool

3. The Mission of the USGBC

The **mission** of the USGBC is:

1) To improve the quality of life
2) To change the way we design, build and operate communities and buildings
3) To create a healthy, prosperous, socially, and environmentally responsible environment

4. The structure of LEED rating system

In addition to the main credit categories of IP, LT, SS, WE, EA, MR, IEQ, ID, and RP, the following factors are very important to the LEED rating systems: awareness and education, green buildings and infrastructure, neighborhood design and pattern.

The structure of the LEED rating system includes three tiers:

1) The main credit categories of IP, LT, SS, WE, EA, MR, IEQ, ID, and RP
2) Each main credit category include prerequisites and credits
3) Each prerequisite or credit includes intents and requirements (or paths to achieve LEED points)

5. LEED certification tools

LEED certification tools include (See discussions on LEED certification process in Chapter Three also):

1) USGBC Reference Guides
2) LEED Rating systems
3) LEED Online
4) LEED Scorecard
5) LEED letter template
6) CIRs (Credit Interpretation Rulings)
7) LEED Case Studies
8) USGBC and GBCI websites:
   www.USGBC.org
   www.GBCI.org

The GBCI requires that the project team submit an overall narrative and complete the LEED Online documentation for the LEED certification application. The general documentation includes project timeline and scope, site conditions, project team identification, usage data and occupant, etc.

The project's overall narrative includes the team, building, site, and applicant's organization.

LEED Online includes the project's detailed information and template/complete documentation requirements for completing prerequisites and credits: my Action Items, potential LEED ratings, attempted credit summary (not awarded, anticipated, denied, and total attempted), appealed credit summary, and credit scorecard, etc. It also includes embed tables and calculators to assure accuracy and completeness of the submittal package.

LEED Online also includes definition for **declarant**, Licensed Professional Exemption Form and related information. A **declarant** is the team member(s) who signs off on the documents and indicates who is responsible for each credit or prerequisite.

A licensed professional exemption form is the form for a team member who is a licensed/registered landscape architect, architect, or engineer to use as a tool to request waiver for eligible submittal requirements. Licensed professional exemptions are shown in the related LEED credit section of LEED Online.

With LEED Online, project teams can upload support files, submit applications for reviews and CIRs, receive feedback from the reviewer, contact customer service, generate specific reports for the project, and obtain project LEED certification, as well as gain access to additional LEED resources like tutorials, FAQs, sample documentation, offline calculators.

If you have multiple projects, you can access all of them via LEED Online.

The GBCI also issues LEED certificates for successful projects via LEED Online.

The credit scorecard includes the project name, address and a list of all points in various credit categories. With LEED Online, you can chose to collapse all credit categories or view a printer friendly scorecard.

The LEED letter template includes your name, your company name, specific and credit-related project information like project site area (s.f.), gross building area (s.f.), and the credit path you choose for each credit.

As a LEED professional, you also need to know the **Synergies** between main credit categories of IP, LT, SS, WE, EA, MR, IEQ, ID, and RP. Almost every LEED exam will have a large percentage of test questions related to **Synergies.**

Chapter 5

Integrative Process (IP)

IP Outline:

IP Prerequisite or Credit Name	Extra Credit	Responsible Party
*IP Prerequisite (IPP): Integrative Project Planning and Design (Required for Healthcare)	0	The owner or owner's representative, plus at least four professionals from the integrated project team
IP Credit (IPC): Integrative Process	0	The owner or owner's representative, plus at least four professionals from the integrated project team

Note: * indicates prerequisite or credit NOT applicable to all LEED rating systems. Refer to the specific prerequisite or credit for more information.

*IP Prerequisite (IPP): **Integrative Project Planning and Design (Required for Healthcare)**

Note: *We add an * for special information that is not common to ALL LEED BD+C systems.*

Purpose:

Maximize chances for cost-effective, integrated adoption of green design and construction strategies, use human health as a fundamental criterion for building operational strategies as well as design and construction. Use innovative techniques and approaches.

Prerequisite:

Starting at the programming and pre-design phase, use cross-discipline decision making and design. At least ensure the following:

1) **Owner's Project Requirements (OPR) Document**

   Prepare an OPR document, including a health mission statement addressing the following:
   - **"triple bottom line"** values—economic, environmental and social.
   - *Goals and strategies* to protect the global environment, the local community, and the health of building occupants.
   - Creating a *high-performance healing environment* for the building's patients, caregivers and staff.

2) **Preliminary Rating Goals**

   Conduct a preliminary LEED meeting with the owner or owner's representative and at least four key project team members as soon as possible (ASAP) preferably before schematic design. Create a LEED action plan to determine the following:
   - The LEED certification level to pursue (certified, silver, gold, or platinum);
   - The LEED credits to pursue
   - The responsible parties for each prerequisite and selected credit.

3) **Integrated Project Team**

   In addition to the owner or owner's representative, assemble an integrated project team with as many of the following as possible (at least four):
   - Owner's capital budget manager
   - Architect or building designer
   - Mechanical engineer
   - Structural engineer
   - Energy modeler
   - Equipment planner
   - Acoustical consultant
   - Telecommunications designer
   - Controls designer
   - Food Service Consultant
   - Infection Control Staff
   - Building science or performance testing agents
   - Green building or sustainable design consultant
   - Facility green teams
   - Physician and nursing teams

- Facility managers
- Environmental services staff
- Functional and space programmers
- Commissioning agent
- Community representatives
- Civil engineer
- Landscape architect
- Ecologist
- Land planner
- Construction manager or general contractor
- Life cycle cost analyst; construction cost estimator
- Lighting Designer
- Other disciplines appropriate to the specific project type

4) Design Charrette

Conduct a minimum *four-hour*, integrated design charrette with the project team to draw on the expertise of all participants ASAP, before schematic design. Optimize the integration of green strategies across all aspects and disciplines.

Submittals:

- Narrative explaining how health mission statement addresses credit requirements
- Action plan from preliminary rating goals

Synergies:

- IPC: Integrative Process Credit

Possible Strategies and Technologies:

1) OPR
2) Preliminary Rating Goals
3) Integrated Project Team
4) Design Charrette

Extra Credit (Exemplary Performance):

None

Project Phase:

Pre-design (**Note:** We separate a project into the following phases: Pre-Design, Schematic Design, Design Development, Construction Documents, Construction Administration, and Occupation/Operation.)

LEED Submittal Phase:

Design (**Reminder:** Some LEED credits or prerequisites may be submitted during the Design Submittal phase while others can *only* be submitted during the Construction Submittals phase.)

Related Code or Standard:

ANSI Consensus National Standard Guide 2.0 for Design and Construction of Sustainable Buildings and Communities (February 2, 2012): ansi.org

Responsible Party:

The owner or owner's representative, *plus* at least four professionals from the previous list of integrated project team

IP Credit (IPC): **Integrative Process**

Applicable to:

New Construction (1 point)
Core and Shell (1 point)
Schools (1 point)
Retail (1 point)
Data Centers (1 point)
Warehouses and Distribution Centers (1 point)
Hospitality (1–5 points)
Healthcare (1–5 points)

Purpose:

Use an early analysis of the interrelationships among systems to support cost-effective, high-performance project outcomes

Credit Path:

Identify and use opportunities to achieve *synergies* across building systems and disciplines in pre-design and continuing throughout the design phases. Use the following analyses to inform the OPR, basis of design (BOD), design and construction documents.

1) Energy-Related Systems

a) Discovery

Before the completion of schematic design, questioning default assumptions, complete a preliminary "simple box" energy modeling analysis to explore how to reduce energy loads in the building and achieve related sustainability goals. Evaluate at least two potential strategies related to the following:

- **Site conditions.** Evaluate adjacent site conditions, exterior lighting, shading, hardscape, and landscaping.
- **Massing and orientation.** Evaluate how massing and orientation affect energy consumption, HVAC sizing, lighting, and renewable energy opportunities.
- **Basic envelope attributes.** Evaluate window-to-wall ratios, window operability, glazing characteristics, insulation values, and shading.
- **Lighting levels.** Evaluate interior lighting levels and surface reflectance values in occupied spaces.
- **Thermal comfort ranges.** Evaluate thermal comfort range options.
- **Plug and process load needs.** Evaluate reducing plug and process loads through programmatic solutions (e.g., equipment and purchasing policies, layout options).

b) Implementation

Document how the design and building form decisions in the project's OPR and BOD and how the eventual design of the project is affected by the above analysis, including the following, as applicable:

- Site and building **program;**
- Building **form and geometry;**
- Building **envelope and façade treatments** on different orientations;
- Eliminating and/or significantly downsizing **building systems** (e.g., HVAC, lighting, controls, exterior materials, interior finishes, and functional program elements); and
- Other systems.

AND

2) **Water-Related Systems**

a) **Discovery**

Before the completion of schematic design, complete a preliminary water budget analysis on how to achieve related sustainability goals by reducing potable water loads in the building. Evaluate and estimate the project's water demand volumes and potential nonpotable water supply sources, including the following:

- **Indoor water demand**. Based on WEP: Indoor Water-Use Reduction, calculate flow and flush fixture design case demand volumes.
- **Outdoor water demand**. Based on WEC: Outdoor Water-Use Reduction, calculate landscape irrigation demand volume.
- **Process water demand**. Calculate cooling tower, laundry, kitchen, and other equipment demand volumes, as applicable.
- **Supply sources**. Calculate all potential nonpotable water supply source volumes, such as municipally supplied nonpotable water, on-site graywater and rainwater, and HVAC equipment condensate.

b) **Implementation**

Document how the site and building design decisions in the project's OPR and BOD are affected by the above analysis. Show how a minimum of *one* on-site nonpotable water supply source is used to reduce the demand on wastewater treatment systems or municipal supply by contributing to at least *two* of the water demand components listed above.

Show how the design of the project is affected by the analysis, including the following, as applicable:

- plumbing systems;
- on-site treatment systems and/or sewage conveyance;
- rainwater quality and quantity management systems;
- site elements, landscaping, irrigation;
- building form and geometry and/or roofing systems; and
- other systems.

Submittals:

- Integrative Process worksheet (energy and water analysis tabs)

Synergies:

- LT Credit (LTC): Quality Transit
- LTC: Reduced Parking Footprint
- SS Credit (SSC): Site Assessment
- SSC: Open Space
- SSC: Rainwater Management
- SSC: Heat Island Reduction
- SSC: Light Pollution Reduction
- WE Prerequisite and Credit (WEP & WEC):Outdoor Water Use Reduction
- WEP & WEC: Indoor Water Use Reduction
- WEC: Cooling Tower Water Use
- EA Prerequisite (EAP): Fundamental Commissioning and Verification
- EAP: Minimum Energy Performance and EA Credit Optimize Energy Performance

- EQ Prerequisite (EQP): Minimum Indoor Air Quality Performance
- EQ Credit (EQC): Enhanced Indoor Air Quality Strategies
- EQC: Thermal Comfort
- EQC: Daylight
- EQC: Quality Views

Extra Credit (Exemplary Performance):

None

Project Phase:

Pre-design

LEED Submittal Phase:

Design

Related Code or Standard:

ANSI Consensus National Standard Guide 2.0 for Design and Construction of Sustainable Buildings and Communities (February 2, 2012): ansi.org

Responsible Party:

The owner or owner's representative, *plus* at least four professionals from the previous list of integrated project team

Chapter 6

Location and Transportation (LT)

Overall purpose:

The LT category is an offshoot of the Sustainable Sites category. The current SS category focuses on on-site ecosystem services, while the LT category emphasizes the existing features of the surrounding community and their impact on occupants' behavior and environmental performance.

Well-located buildings utilize existing utilities and infrastructure, reduce ecological and material costs, encourage alternatives to private automobile use, such as biking, walking, public transit, and vehicle shares. LT strategies can enhance health by encouraging daily physical activity and reduce greenhouse gas emissions from transportation.

Consistent Documentation

Walking and Bicycling Distance

Walking and bicycling distances are measurements of distance from a point of origin to a destination, such as the nearest train station. They must be measured along a *safe* path, NOT a straight-line radius from the origin that does not follow the path.

Safe walking paths include sidewalks, crosswalks, all-weather-surface footpaths, or equivalent pedestrian facilities.

Safe bicycling paths include streets with low target vehicle speed, on-street bicycle lanes, and off-street bicycle paths or trails.

Total Vehicle Parking Capacity

It includes all the off-street spaces that the project building's users can use, both inside and *outside* the project boundary.

The following parking spaces should *not* be included:

- Bicycle or motorbike spaces
- On-street (parallel or pull-in) parking spaces
- Parking spaces for inventory and fleet vehicles, unless these vehicles are regularly used by employees for commuting as well as business purposes

Preferred Parking

Preferred parking spaces are closest to the main entrance of the project, exclusive of handicap spaces. For a multiple-level parking facility, locate preferred spaces on the level closest to the main entrance to the building.

LT Outline:

LT Prerequisite or Credit Name	Extra Credit	Responsible Party
LT Credit (LTC): LEED for Neighborhood Development Location	0	Owner
LTC: Sensitive Land Protection	0	Architect
LTC: High-Priority Site	Pursue **Choice 2 or 3** in addition to **Choice 1** to gain 1, 2 or 3 extra points.	Owner and Architect
LTC: Surrounding Density and Diverse Uses	0	Owner and Architect
LTC: Access to Quality Transit	Double the highest transit service point threshold (except for School projects using Choice 2)	Architect
LTC: Bicycle Facilities	0	Architect
LTC: Reduced Parking Footprint	Path 1): Realize a 60% parking reduction from the base ratios. Path 2): Realize an 80% parking reduction from the base ratios.	Architect
LTC: Green Vehicles	0	Architect

LT Credit (LTC): **LEED for Neighborhood Development Location**

Applicable to:

New Construction (8-16 points)
Core and Shell (8-20 points)
Schools (8-15 points)
Retail (8-16 points)
Data Centers (8-16 points)
Warehouses and Distribution Centers (8-16 points)
Hospitality (8-16 points)
Healthcare (5-9 points)

Purpose:

Use an early analysis of the interrelationships among systems to support cost-effective, high-performance project outcomes

Credit Path:

Locate the project within the boundary of certified (NOT just registered or submitted) LEED ND development. For the Pilot or 2009 rating systems, use Stage 2, or use Stage 3 for LEED v4: Certified Plan or Certified Projects.

Projects applying for this credit are not eligible to earn points under other LT credits.

Table 1 Points for LEED ND location

Certification Level	BD+C	BD+C (CS)	BD+C (Schools)	BD+C (Healthcare)
Certified	8	8	8	5
Silver	10	12	10	6
Gold	12	16	12	7
Platinum	16	20	15	9

1) **Identify a LEED ND–certified neighborhood or certified plan area for potential development**
   - Check the USGBC website for the latest lists of LEED ND projects.
   - Check with Local USGBC chapters in the United States or other green building councils in other countries.

2) **Confirm eligibility of a LEED ND project**
   - Rating system and rating system version
   - Certification designation (see Table 2; note differing terminology)
   - Certification date and certification level

Table 2 Eligibility by LEED ND certification designation

Version	Eligible	Ineligible
LEED ND Pilot	Stage 2 LEED ND Certified Plan Stage 3 LEED ND Certified Project	Stage 1 LEED ND Pre-reviewed Plan
LEED 2009	Stage 2 Pre-certified LEED ND Plan Stage 3 LEED ND Certified Neighborhood Development	Stage 1 Conditional Approval of LEED ND Plan
LEED v4	LEED ND Certified Plan LEED ND Certified Built Project	LEED ND Conditional Approval

Group Approach
The entire group boundary must be within the LEED ND project boundary. You can document all buildings in the group as one.

Campus Approach
The entire campus boundary must be within the LEED ND project boundary.

Submittals:
- LEED ND project information (name, ID number, rating system and version, certification level, and certification date)
- Vicinity base map with LEED project boundary and LEED ND certified neighborhood or plan boundary

Synergies:
- Projects applying for this credit are not eligible to earn points under other LT credits

Extra Credit (Exemplary Performance):
None

Project Phase:
Pre-design

LEED Submittal Phase:
Design

Related Code or Standard:
None

Responsible Party:
Owner

LTC: **Sensitive Land Protection**

Applicable to:

New Construction (1 point)
Core and Shell (2 points)
Schools (1 point)
Retail (1 point)
Data Centers (1 point)
Warehouses and Distribution Centers (1 point)
Hospitality (1 point)
Healthcare (1 point)

Purpose:

To reduce a building's environmental impact and avoid the development of environmentally sensitive lands.

Credit Path:

1) **Locate the development footprint on previously developed land.**

OR

2) **Do not locate the development footprint on the following sensitive land:**
   - **Prime farmland**, unique farmland, or farmland of statewide or local importance per the definition of the US Department of Agriculture (USDA) in the *US Code of Federal Regulations* (CFR) and identified in a state *Natural Resources Conservation Service* (NRCS) soil survey (or local equivalent for projects outside the U.S.). Visit the NRCS website for more information.

   - **Floodplains.** A flood hazard area shown on a legally designated map by the local jurisdiction or the state, or a legally adopted flood hazard map. For projects in places without flood hazard maps, locate on a site outside of any floodplain subject to a 1% or higher chance of flooding in any given year.

   - **Habitats** for the following:
     - ❖ species listed as threatened or endangered under the *U.S. Endangered Species Act* or the state's endangered species act, or
     - ❖ species or ecological communities classified by *NatureServe* as GH (possibly extinct), G1 (critically imperiled), or G2 (imperiled), or
     - ❖ species listed as threatened or endangered under local equivalent standards (for projects outside the U.S.) that are not covered by *NatureServe* data.

     Work with the state *Natural Heritage Program* and/or state *fish and wildlife agencies* (or a local equivalent outside the U.S.) to obtain more information. For international projects, check the *International Union for Conservation of Nature Red List (iucnredlist.org)*.

   - **Water bodies.** Areas on or within 100 feet (30 meters) of a water body, except for minor improvements.
   - **Wetlands.** Areas on or within 50 feet (15 meters) of a wetland, except for minor improvements.

The following exemptions are allowed for minor improvements within the wetland and water body buffers that are open to all building users:

- Grade changes necessary for public access;
- Activities to restore or maintain natural hydrology and/or native natural communities;

- Bicycle and pedestrian pathways 12 feet wide (3.5 meters) or less, including 8 feet (2.5 meters) or less that are impervious;
- Clearings that are 500 square feet (45 square meters) or less, limited to one per 300 linear feet (90 linear meters) on average;
- One single-story structure that is 500 square feet (45 square meters) or less, per 300 linear feet (90 linear meters) on average;
- Removal of the following tree types:
  - ❖ Hazardous trees, up to 75% of dead trees
  - ❖ Trees less than 6 inches (150 millimeters) in diameter at chest height
  - ❖ Up to 20% of trees more than 6 inches (150 millimeters) in diameter at chest height with a condition rating of 40% or higher.
  - ❖ Trees under 40% condition rating
- The condition rating must be based on an assessment by an arborist certified by the *International Society of Arboriculture (ISA)* using ISA standard measures, or local equivalent for projects outside the U.S.
- Brownfield remediation activities.

Group Approach
You can document all buildings in the group as one.

Campus Approach
Ineligible. Each LEED project can pursue the credit individually.

Submittals:

Submittals	Credit Path 1)	Credit Path 2)
Site map(s) showing project boundary, development footprint, any previous development, any sensitive areas, and any minor improvements in required buffers	X	X
Explanation of the previous development on the site	X	
Description of how the project team verified prime farmland and sensitive habit criteria		X

Synergies:

- LTC: High-Priority Site
- LTC: Surrounding Density and Diverse Uses
- LTC: Reduced Parking Footprint
- SSC: Site Assessment
- SSC: Rainwater Management
- SSC: Site Development—Protect or Restore Habitat

Extra Credit (Exemplary Performance):
None

Project Phase:
Schematic design

LEED Submittal Phase:
Design

Related Code or Standard:

- The US Department of Agriculture (USDA) in the *US Code of Federal Regulations (CFR)*
- *Natural Resources Conservation Service (NRCS)* soil survey
- The *U.S. Endangered Species Act* or the state's endangered species act
- *NatureServe*
- *Natural Heritage Program* and/or state *fish and wildlife agencies*
- *International Union for Conservation of Nature Red List (iucnredlist.org)*.
- *International Society of Arboriculture (ISA)*
- Local equivalent for projects outside the U.S.

Responsible Party:

Architect

LTC: **High-Priority Site**

Applicable to:

New Construction (1-2 points)
Core and Shell (3 points)
Schools (1-2 points)
Retail (1-2 points)
Data Centers (1-2 points)
Warehouses and Distribution Centers (1-2 points)
Hospitality (1-2 points)
Healthcare (1-2 points)

Purpose:

To encourage locating projects in places with development constraints and support the health of the adjacent areas.

Credit Path:

Choice 1. Historic District (1 point BD+C except CS, 2 points CS)
Locate the project on a historic district infill location. Excluding streets and rights-of-way within 1/2 mile (800 meters) of the project boundary, if 75% or more of the total land area is previously developed, then the location is considered an infill site.

OR

Choice 2. Priority Designation (1 point BD+C except CS, 2 points CS)
Locate the project on one of the following:

- a site listed by the EPA National Priorities List;
- a Federal Enterprise Community site;
- a Federal Renewal Community site;
- a Federal Empowerment Zone site;
- a Department of the Treasury Community Development Financial Institutions Fund Qualified Low-Income Community (a subset of the New Markets Tax Credit Program);
- a site in a U.S. Department of Housing and Urban Development's Difficult Development Area (DDA) or Qualified Census Tract (QCT); or
- a local equivalent program administered at the national level for projects outside the U.S.

OR

Choice 3. Brownfield Remediation (2 points BD+C except CS, 3 points CS)
Perform remediation of soil or groundwater contamination to the satisfaction of governing agencies. For this credit, asbestos and other contaminants in debris or inside buildings (whether demolished or remaining) do not count as contamination.

Group Approach
You can document all buildings in the group as one.

Campus Approach
Eligible.

Submittals:

Submittals	Credit Path 1)	Credit Path 2)	Credit Path 3)
Vicinity map indicating previously developed land within ½ mile (800 meters) of project boundary	x		
Document from historic preservation entity confirming location in historic district	x		
Vicinity map or other documentation confirming priority site designation		x	
Documentation from authority having jurisdiction declaring existence of specific contamination and confirming that remediation has been or will be completed to its satisfaction			x

Synergies:
- MRC: Building Life-Cycle Impact Reduction
- SSP: Environmental Site Assessment
- LT credit category (all credits)

Extra Credit (Exemplary Performance):
- Pursue Choice 2 or 3 in addition to Choice 1 to gain 1, 2 or 3 extra points.

Project Phase:
Pre-design

LEED Submittal Phase:
Design

Related Code or Standard:
- U.S. Environmental Protection Agency, National Priority List: epa.gov/superfund/sites/npl
- U.S. Housing and Urban Development, Federal Empowerment Zone, Federal Enterprise Community, and Federal Renewal Community: portal.hud.gov/hudportal/HUD?src=/program_offices/comm_planning/economicdevelopment/programs/rc
- U.S. Department of Treasury, Community Development Financial Institutions Fund: cdfifund.gov
- U.S. Department of Housing and Urban Development, Qualified Census Tracts and Difficult Development Areas: qct.huduser.org/index.html

Responsible Party:
Owner and Architect

LTC: **Surrounding Density and Diverse Uses**

Applicable to:

New Construction (1-5 points)
Core and Shell (1-6 points)
Schools (1-5 points)
Retail (1-5 points)
Data Centers (1-5 points)
Warehouses and Distribution Centers (1-5 points)
Hospitality (1-5 points)
Healthcare (1 point)

Purpose:

To protect wildlife habitat and farmland by encouraging development in areas with existing infrastructure and to conserve land. To reduce vehicle distance traveled and promote walkability, and transportation efficiency. To encourage daily physical activity and improve public health.

Credit Path:

***For New Construction, Core and Shell, Schools, Retail, Data Centers, Hospitality:**

Choice1. Surrounding Density (2–3 points BD+C except CS, 2-4 points CS)

Place the project on a site where surrounding existing density within a 1/4 mile (400-meter) radius of the project boundary meets the criteria of Tables 1 and 2. Use either the "combined density" or the "separate residential and nonresidential densities" values. ***Note:*** *DU = dwelling units*

Table 1 Points for average density within 1/4 mile of project (imperial units)

Combined Density	Separate Residential and Nonresidential Densities		Points BD+C (except CS)	Points BD+C (CS)
Square feet per acre of buildable land	Residential Density (DU/acre)	Nonresidential Density (FAR)		
22,000	7	0.5	2	2
35,000	12	0.8	3	4

Table 2 Points for average density within 400 meters of project (metric units)

Combined Density	Separate Residential and Nonresidential Densities		Points BD+C (except CS)	Points BD+C (CS)
Square meters per hectare of buildable land	Residential Density (DU/hectare)	Nonresidential Density (FAR)		
5050	17.5	0.5	2	2
8035	30	0.8	3	4

Schools only

Exclude physical education spaces from the development density calculations. These spaces are part of the project site, such as playgrounds with play equipment and playing fields and associated buildings used during sporting events only (e.g., concession stands).

AND/OR

Choice 2. Diverse Uses (1–2 points)

Renovate or construct a building or a space within a building so that the building's main entrance is within a 1/2-mile (800-meter) *walking* distance of the main entrance of eight or more (2 points) or four to seven (1 point) existing and publicly available diverse uses (listed in Appendix 1).

The following criteria apply:

- A use counts as only one type (e.g., a retail store may be counted only once even if it sells products in many categories).
- A maximum of two uses in each use type can be counted (e.g., if five restaurants are within walking distance, only two may be counted).
- The counted uses must include a minimum of three of the five categories, exclusive of the building's primary use.

***For Warehouses and Distribution Centers:**

Choice1. Development and Adjacency (2–3 points)

Renovate or construct the project on a previously developed *commercial or industrial* site (2 points).

OR

Renovate or construct the project on a site that is both a previously developed site and an adjacent site. The adjacent sites must be used for commercial or industrial purposes currently (3 points).

AND/OR

Choice 2. Transportation Resources (1–2 points)

Renovate or construct the project on a site with two or three (1 point) or four (2 points) of the following:

- within a 10-mile (16 kilometer) driving distance of a main logistics hub, defined as a seaport, airport, freight village with intermodal transportation, or intermodal facility.
- within a 1-mile (1 600-meter) driving distance of an on-off ramp to a highway.
- within a 1-mile (1 600-meter) driving distance of an access point to an active freight rail line.
- served by an active freight rail spur.

In all cases, a planned transportation resource must be funded, sited, and under construction by the date of the certificate of occupancy (C of O) and complete within 24 months of that date.

***For Healthcare**

Choice1. Surrounding Density (1 point)

Locate on a site that meets the following criteria:

With surrounding existing density within a 1/4-mile (400-meter) radius of the project boundary that is:

1. A minimum of 22,000 square feet per acre (5 050 square meters per hectare) of buildable land, or
2. A minimum of 7 dwelling units per acre (17.5 DU per hectare) with a 0.5 floor-area ratio. The counted density must be *existing* density, not zoned density.

Achieve a development density of at least 30,000 square feet per acre (6 890 square meters per hectare) for previously developed existing *rural* healthcare campus sites.

AND/OR

Choice 2. Diverse Uses (1 point)

Renovate or construct a building on a site so that the building's main entrance is within a 1/2-mile (800-meter) walking distance of the main entrance of a minimum of seven publicly accessible and operational uses per Appendix 1.

Subject to the following restrictions:

- A use counts as only one type (e.g., a retail store may be counted only once even if it sells products in many categories).
- A maximum of two uses in each use type can be counted (e.g. if five restaurants are within walking distance, only two may be counted).
- The counted uses must include a minimum of three of the five categories, exclusive of the building's primary use.

Group Approach
You can document all buildings in the group as one.

Campus Approach
Ineligible. Each LEED project can pursue the credit individually

Submittals:

All BD+C except Warehouses and Distribution Centers	Credit Path 1)	Credit Path 2)
Map or area plan showing project site and location of existing non-residential and residential buildings within ¼-mile (400-meter) radius of project site	X	
Description of the previous development on the site	X	
Map or area plan showing project site, location and type of each use, and walking routes		X
Warehouses and Distribution Centers	**Credit Path 1)**	**Credit Path 2)**
Map or area plan showing project site, its previous development, and (if any) commercial or industrial properties adjacent to project site	X	
Map or area plan showing project site, location and type of transportation resources, and driving distance to each		X
If planned transportation resources are counted, verification that they will be funded, sited, and under construction by the date of the C of O and complete within 24 months of that date		X

Synergies:

- LTC: High-Priority Site
- LTC: Access to Quality Transit

Extra Credit (Exemplary Performance):
None

Project Phase:
Schematic design

LEED Submittal Phase:
Design

Related Code or Standard:
None

Responsible Party:
Owner and Architect

LTC: **Access to Quality Transit**

Applicable to:

New Construction (1-5 points)
Core and Shell (1-6 points)
Schools (1-4 points)
Retail (1-5 points)
Data Centers (1-5 points)
Warehouses and Distribution Centers (1-5 points)
Hospitality (1-5 points)
Healthcare (1-2 points)

Purpose:

To reduce motor vehicle use and related greenhouse gas emissions, air pollution, and other public health and environmental harms by encouraging development in locations with multimodal transportation choices

Credit Path:

***For New Construction, Core and Shell, Data Centers, Warehouses and Distribution Centers, Hospitality:**

Place any functional entrance of the project within a 1/4-mile (400-meter) walking distance of existing or planned streetcar, bus, or rideshare stops or within a 1/2-mile (800-meter) walking distance of existing or planned light or heavy rail stations, commuter rail stations, bus rapid transit stops, or commuter ferry terminals.

The total number of trips provided by transit service at those stops and stations should meet the minimums listed in Tables 1 and 2. Planned stations and stops may count if they are funded, sited, and under construction by the date of the C of O and are complete within 24 months of that date.

The project must meet both weekend and weekday trip minimums.

- Qualifying transit routes must have service in both directions
- Only count trips in one direction towards the threshold for each qualifying transit route
- Only count trips from one stop towards the threshold if a qualifying transit route has multiple stops within the required walking distance

Table 1 Minimum daily transit service for projects with multiple transit types (bus, streetcar, rail, or ferry)

Weekday Trips	Weekend Trips	Points BD+C (except CS)	Points BD+C (CS)
72	40	1	1
144	108	3	3
360	216	5	6

Table 2 Minimum daily transit service for projects with commuter rail or ferry service only

Weekday Trips	Weekend Trips	Points (All Projects)
24	6	1
40	8	2
60	12	3

For projects served by at least two transit routes, if no one route provides more than 60% of the documented levels, the project can earn one additional point, up to the maximum number of points.

If temporarily rerouted outside the required distances for less than two years, the transit service may still be counted, as long as the local transit agency has committed to restoring the routes with service at or above the prior level.

***For Schools:**

Choice 1. Transit-Served Location (1–4 points)

Place any functional entrance of the project within a 1/4-mile (400-meter) walking distance of existing or planned streetcar, bus, or rideshare stops, or within a 1/2-mile (800-meter) walking distance of existing or planned light or heavy rail stations, commuter rail stations, bus rapid transit stops, or commuter ferry terminals.

The total number of trips provided by transit service at those stops and stations should meet the minimums listed in Tables 3 and 4. Planned stations and stops may count if they are funded, sited, and under construction by the date of the C of O and are complete within 24 months of that date.

The project must meet the trip minimums.

- Qualifying transit routes must have service in both directions
- Only count trips in one direction towards the threshold for each qualifying transit route
- Only count trips from one stop towards the threshold if a qualifying transit route has multiple stops within the required walking distance

Table 3 Minimum daily transit service for projects with multiple transit types (bus, streetcar, rail, or ferry)

Weekday Trips	Points
72	1
144	2
360	4

Table 4 Minimum daily transit service for projects with commuter rail or ferry service only

Weekday Trips	Points
24	1
40	2
60	4

For projects served by at least two transit routes, if no one route provides more than 60% of the documented levels, the project can earn one additional point, up to the maximum number of points.

If temporarily rerouted outside the required distances for less than two years, the transit service may still be counted, as long as the local transit agency has committed to restoring the routes with service at or above the prior level.

OR

Choice 2. Pedestrian Access (1–4 points)

Demonstrate that the project has an attendance boundary so that the required percentages of students live within a maximum of a 1 1/2-mile (2400-meter) walking distance for grades 9 and above or ages 15 and above and 3/4-mile (1200-meter) walking distance for grades 8 and below or ages 14 and below of a functional entrance of a school building. Points are awarded based on Table 5.

Table 5 Points for student population within walking distance

Percentage of Students	Points
50%	1
60%	2
70% or more	4

In addition, place the project on a site that allows all students pedestrian access to the site from their residential neighborhoods.

***For Healthcare:**

Place any functional entrance of the project within a 1/4-mile (400-meter) walking distance of existing or planned streetcar, bus, or rideshare stops, or within a 1/2-mile (800-meter) walking distance of existing or planned light or heavy rail stations, commuter rail stations, bus rapid transit stops, or commuter ferry terminals.

The total number of trips provided by transit service at those stops and stations should meet the minimums listed in Tables 6 and 7. Planned stations and stops may count if they are funded, sited, and under construction by the date of the C of O and are complete within 24 months of that date.

The project must meet the trip minimums.

- Qualifying transit routes must have service in both directions
- Only count trips in one direction towards the threshold for each qualifying transit route
- Only count trips from one stop towards the threshold if a qualifying transit route has multiple stops within the required walking distance

Table 6 Minimum daily transit service for projects with multiple transit types (bus, streetcar, rail, or ferry)

Weekday Trips	Weekend Trips	Points
72	40	1
144	108	2

Table 7 Minimum daily transit service for projects with commuter rail or ferry service only

Weekday Trips	Weekend Trips	Points
24	6	1
40	8	2

For projects served by at least two transit routes, if no one route provides more than 60% of the documented levels, the project can earn one additional point, up to the maximum number of points.

If temporarily rerouted outside the required distances for less than two years, the transit service may still be counted, as long as the local transit agency has committed to restoring the routes with service at or above the prior level.

The project team can use on-site mass transit to document credit compliance for military or other government projects with security restrictions.

Group Approach

You can document all buildings in the group as one.

Campus Approach
Ineligible. Each LEED project can pursue the credit respectively.

Submittals:

Submittals	All Projects	Schools Option 1	Schools Option 2
Map showing project, transit stop locations, project boundary, and walking routes and distances to those stops	x	x	
Timetables or other service-level documentation	x	x	
If applicable, documentation of restoration of temporarily rerouted service or planned transit	x	x	
Map showing walkshed boundary			x

Synergies:
- LTC: Bicycle Facilities

Extra Credit (Exemplary Performance):
- Double the highest transit service point threshold (except for Schools projects using Choice 2)

Project Phase:
Schematic design

LEED Submittal Phase:
Design

Related Code or Standard:
None

Responsible Party:
Architect

LTC: **Bicycle Facilities**

Applicable to:

New Construction (1 point)
Core and Shell (1 point)
Schools (1 point)
Retail (1 point)
Data Centers (1 point)
Warehouses and Distribution Centers (1 point)
Hospitality (1 point)
Healthcare (1 point)

Purpose:

To reduce vehicle use and promote bicycling and transportation efficiency. To encourage recreational and utilitarian physical activity and improve public health.

Credit Path:
***For New Construction, Core and Shell, Data Centers, Warehouses and Distribution Centers, Hospitality:**

Bicycle Network

Place or design the project so that a bicycle storage or functional entrance is within a 200-yard (180-meter) walking distance or bicycling distance from a bicycle network that connects to a minimum of one of the following:

- a minimum of 10 diverse uses (see Appendix 1);
- an employment center or school, if the project total floor area is 50% or more residential; or
- a light or heavy rail station, commuter rail station, bus rapid transit stop, or ferry terminal.

All destinations must be within a 3-mile (4800-meter) bicycling distance of the project boundary. The project team can count planned bicycle trails or lanes that are fully funded by the date of the C of O and are scheduled to complete within one year of that date.

Bicycle Storage and Shower Rooms

Situation 1. Commercial or Institutional Projects

Provide short-term bicycle storage for a minimum of 2.5% of all *peak* visitors, and maintain a minimum of four storage spaces per building.

Provide long-term bicycle storage for a minimum of 5% of all *regular* building occupants, and maintain a minimum of four storage spaces per building in addition to the short-term bicycle storage spaces.

Provide a minimum of one on-site shower with changing facility for the first 100 *regular* building occupants and one additional shower for every 150 *regular* building occupants thereafter.

Situation 2. Residential Projects

Provide short-term bicycle storage for a minimum of 2.5% of all *peak* visitors, and maintain a minimum of four storage spaces per building.

Provide long-term bicycle storage for a minimum of 30% of all *regular* building occupants, but at least one storage space per residential unit.

Situation 3. Mixed-Use Projects

Satisfy the afore-mentioned Path 1) and Path 2) storage criteria for the nonresidential and residential portions of the project, separately.

For All Projects
Place short-term bicycle storage within 100 feet (30 meters) walking distance of any *main* entrance. Place long-term bicycle storage within 100 feet (30 meters) walking distance of any *functional* entry.

Do not double-count bicycle storage capacity; if a storage is fully allocated to the occupants of non-project facilities, then it cannot also serve project occupants.

Refer to Appendix 2, Default Occupancy Counts, for Core and Shell projects occupancy count requirements and guidance.

***For Schools:**

Bicycle Network
Place or design the project so that a bicycle storage or functional entrance is within a 200-yard (180-meter) walking distance or bicycling distance from a bicycle network that connects to a minimum of one of the following:

- a minimum of 10 diverse uses (see Appendix 1);
- a light or heavy rail station, commuter rail station, bus rapid transit stop, or ferry terminal.

All destinations must be within a 3-mile (4800-meter) bicycling distance of the project boundary.

Provide dedicated bicycle lanes that extend at least to the end of the school property with no fences or other barriers on school property.

The project team can count planned bicycle trails or lanes that are fully funded by the date of the C of O and are scheduled to complete within one year of that date.

Bicycle Storage and Shower Rooms
Provide long-term bicycle storage for a minimum of 5% of all *regular* building occupants (excluding 3rd grade students and younger), and maintain a minimum of four storage spaces per building.

Provide a minimum of one on-site shower with changing facility for the first 100 *regular* building occupants (except students) and one additional shower for every 150 regular building occupants (except students) thereafter.

Long-term storage spaces have to be within 100 feet (30 meters) walking distance of any main entrance and be easily accessible to occupants.

Do not double-count bicycle storage capacity: If a storage is fully allocated to the occupants of non-project facilities, then it cannot also serve project occupants.

***For Retail:**

Bicycle Network
Place or design the project so that a bicycle storage or functional entrance is within a 200-yard (180-meter) walking distance or bicycling distance from a bicycle network that connects to a minimum of one of the following:

- a minimum of 10 diverse uses (see Appendix 1);
- a light or heavy rail station, commuter rail station, bus rapid transit stop, or ferry terminal.

All destinations must be within a 3-mile (4800-meter) bicycling distance of the project boundary. The project team can count planned bicycle trails or lanes that are fully funded by the date of the C of O and are scheduled to complete within one year of that date.

Bicycle Storage and Shower Rooms
Provide a minimum two short-term bicycle storage spaces for every 5,000 square feet (465 square meters), and maintain a minimum of two storage spaces per building.

Provide long-term bicycle storage for a minimum of 5% of all *regular* building occupants, and maintain a minimum of two storage spaces per building in addition to the short-term bicycle storage spaces.

Provide a minimum of one on-site shower with changing facility for the first 100 *regular* building occupants and one additional shower for every 150 *regular* building occupants thereafter.

Long-term storage spaces have to be within 100 feet (30 meters) walking distance of any *functional* entrance and be easily accessible to occupants. Short-term bicycle storage must be within 100 feet (30 meters) walking distance of any *main* entrance.

Do not double-count bicycle storage capacity: If a storage is fully allocated to the occupants of non-project facilities, then it cannot also serve project occupants.

Provide a bicycle route assistance for customers and employees or bicycle maintenance program for employees. Provide route assistance in a manner easily accessible to both customers and employees.

For projects that are part of a multitenant complex only:
If bicycle storage spaces are provided in the complex in which the project is located, calculate the number of spaces attributed to the project by dividing the project's floor area by the total floor area of the development (buildings only) and multiplying the percentage result by the total number of spaces. If this number does not meet the credit criteria, provide additional bicycle storage.

***For Healthcare:**

Bicycle Network
Place or design the project so that a bicycle storage or functional entrance is within a 200-yard (180-meter) walking distance or bicycling distance from a bicycle network that connects to a minimum of one of the following:

- a minimum of 10 diverse uses (see Appendix 1);
- a light or heavy rail station, commuter rail station, bus rapid transit stop, or ferry terminal.

All destinations must be within a 3-mile (4800-meter) bicycling distance of the project boundary. The project team can count planned bicycle trails or lanes that are fully funded by the date of the C of O and are scheduled to complete within one year of that date.

Bicycle Storage and Shower Rooms
Situation 1. Commercial or Institutional Projects
Provide short-term bicycle storage for a minimum of 2.5% of all *peak* visitors, and maintain a minimum of four storage spaces per building.

Provide long-term bicycle storage for a minimum of 5% of all *regular* building occupants (except patients), and maintain a minimum of four storage spaces per building in addition to the short-term bicycle storage spaces.

Provide a minimum of one on-site shower with changing facility for the first 100 *regular* building occupants (except patients) and one additional shower for every 150 *regular* building occupants thereafter.

Situation 2. Residential Projects
Provide enclosed, secure bicycle storage for a minimum of 30% of all *regula*r building occupants (except patients), but at least one storage space per residential unit.

For All Projects
Place short-term bicycle storage within 100 feet (30 meters) walking distance of any *main* entrance. Place long-term bicycle storage within 100 feet (30 meters) walking distance of any *functional* entry.

Do not double-count bicycle storage capacity; if a storage is fully allocated to the occupants of non-project facilities, then it cannot also serve project occupants.

Group Approach
You can document all buildings in the group as one. Measure distances from the farthest building.

Campus Approach
Eligible.

Submittals:

Submittals	New Construction, Core and Shell, Data Centers, Warehouses and Distribution Centers, Hospitality, Healthcare	Schools	Retail
Vicinity map showing bicycle network and route and distances along networks to eligible destination(s)	X	X	X
Site plan showing bicycle storage locations	X		X
Site plan showing bicycle storage location with walking route to main entrance and bicycling route to school boundary		X	
Calculations for storage and shower facilities	X	X	X
Description of programs to support bicycle use			X

Synergies:

- LTC: Surrounding Density and Diverse Uses

Extra Credit (Exemplary Performance):
None

Project Phase:
Schematic design

LEED Submittal Phase:
Design

Related Code or Standard:
None

Responsible Party:
Architect

LTC: **Reduced Parking Footprint**

Applicable to:

New Construction (1 point)
Core and Shell (1 point)
Schools (1 point)
Retail (1 point)
Data Centers (1 point)
Warehouses and Distribution Centers (1 point)
Hospitality (1 point)
Healthcare (1 point)

Purpose:

Minimizes land consumption, automobile dependence, rainwater runoff and other environmental harms associated with parking facilities.

Credit Path:

Do not exceed the minimum number of parking spaces required by local codes.

Reduce parking spaces by a certain percentage below the base ratios recommended by the Parking Consultants Council, as shown in the Institute of Transportation Engineers' Transportation Planning Handbook, 3rd edition, Tables 18-2 through 18-4.

Situation 1. Baseline Location

Projects not earning points under LTC: Surrounding Density and Diverse Uses or LTC: Access to Quality Transit have to realize a 20% reduction from the base ratios.

Situation 2. Dense and/or Transit-Served Location

Projects earning at least 1 point under either LTC: Surrounding Density and Diverse Uses or LTC: Access to Quality Transit have to realize a 40% reduction from the base ratios.

For All Projects

For the credit calculations:

- Include all new *and* existing **off-street** parking spaces that are owned or leased by the project, including parking that is used by the project but is *outside* the project boundary.
- Do not include **on-street** parking in public rights-of-way.

For projects using pooled parking:

Use the project's share of the pooled parking in the credit calculations.

Offer preferred parking for 5% of the total parking spaces for carpools after reductions from the base ratios. If no off-street parking is provided, preferred parking is not required

Mixed-use projects should determine the percentage reduction by:

- Aggregating the parking amount of each use (as specified by the base ratios)
- Determining the percentage reduction from the aggregated parking amount.

Do not count parking spaces for inventory and fleet vehicles unless employees regularly use them for commuting as well as business purposes.

The USGBC reference guide has a **table of base ratios for parking spaces, by building type (use, size or condition)**. For example, Arena needs 0.33Parking Spaces/seat; Supermarket & convenience market needs 6.75/1,000 ft2 (7.3/100 m2).

If the LEED AP BD+C exam requires you to calculate the number of parking spaces needed, the ratio should be provided in the exam. If you are working on a real LEED project, you can look up the ratio from the table in the USGBC reference guide.

Transportation Demand Management Strategies:

- Access to quality transit
- Compressed workweek schedule
- Residential units rented or sold separately from parking
- Shared parking between uses
- Shuttles
- Telecommuting
- Transit subsidy

Project Type Variations

Military Installations

The proportion of preferred parking for carpools must be applied to each pool of parking, including separated ranking officials parking.

Separated Employee or Visitor Parking

The proportion of preferred parking for carpools must be applied to each pool of parking, including separate parking areas for visitors, employees, or students.

Campus

Group Approach

A project team can document all buildings in the group as one and have to include all the parking located within the LEED project boundary in the calculations. Submit a site plan to illustrate a reasonable distribution of preferred parking spaces for the spaces or buildings seeking LEED certification.

Campus Approach

Eligible. A project team has to include all the parking located within the LEED campus boundary in the calculations (including parking related to projects not pursuing LEED certification). Submit a site plan to illustrate a reasonable distribution of preferred parking spaces.

Submittals:

- Site plan showing parking areas and preferred parking spaces
- Calculations showing threshold achievement
- Photographs or drawings of pavement markings or signage indicating reserved status of preferred parking areas

Synergies:

- LTC: Surrounding Density and Diverse Uses
- LTC: Access to Quality Transit
- LTC: Green Vehicles

Extra Credit (Exemplary Performance):

- Path 1): Realize a 60% parking reduction from the base ratios.
- Path 2): Realize an 80% parking reduction from the base ratios.

Project Phase:

Pre-Design

LEED Submittal Phase:

Design

Related Code or Standard:

Institute of Transportation Engineers, Transportation Planning Handbook, 3rd edition, Tables 18-2 through 18-4: ite.org

Responsible Party:

Architect

LTC: **Green Vehicles**

Applicable to

New Construction (1 point)
Core and Shell (1 point)
Schools (1 point)
Retail (1 point)
Data Centers (1 point)
Warehouses and Distribution Centers (1 point)
Hospitality (1 point)
Healthcare (1 point)

Purpose

Promotes other alternatives to fossil fueled automobiles and reduces pollution.

Credit Path:

A. **New Construction, Core and Shell, Data Centers, Hospitality, Retail, Healthcare:**
Assign 5% of all parking spaces as preferred parking for green vehicles. Clearly label and enforce for exclusive use by green vehicles. Allocate preferred parking spaces proportionally among different parking sections (e.g., between long-term and short-term spaces).

Note: *Green vehicles have to reach at least a green score of 45 on the* ***American Council for an Energy Efficient Economy (ACEEE)*** *annual vehicle rating guide (or local equivalent for international projects).*

A minimum of 20% discounted parking rate for green vehicles is an acceptable alternative for preferred parking spaces. The discounted rate has to be permanently offered to every qualifying vehicle and publicly posted at the parking area entrance.

The project must meet one of the following two additional requirements:

Choice 1. Electric Vehicle Charging

In addition to preferred parking spaces for green vehicles, install electrical vehicle supply equipment (EVSE) in 2% of all parking spaces. Reserve and clearly label these spaces for the exclusive use by plug-in electric vehicles.

The EVSE must:

- Have a Level 2 charging capacity (208 – 240 volts) or greater.
- Meet the related regional or local standard for electrical connectors, such as SAE Electric Vehicle Conductive Charge Coupler, SAE Surface Vehicle Recommended Practice J1772 or IEC 62196 of the International Electrotechnical Commission for projects outside the U.S.
- Be internet addressable or networked and be able to participate in a time-of-use pricing or demand-response program to encourage off-peak charging.

Choice 2. Liquid, Gas, or Battery Facilities

Install a battery switching station or gas or liquid alternative fuel fueling facilities that can refuel a number of vehicles per day equal to at least 2% of all parking spaces.

B. **Schools**

Choice 1. Green passenger vehicles

Same as Credit Path A.

Choice 2. Green Buses and School-owned Vehicles
Within seven years of the building **certificate of occupancy**, create and instigate a plan for each bus serving the school to meet the following emissions criteria:

- nitrogen oxide (NOx) emissions of not more than 0.50 grams per brake horsepower-hour; and
- particulate matter emissions of not more than 0.01 grams per brake horsepower-hour.

Each bus (not an average of the entire fleet serving the school) must meet the emission standards.

Create and instigate a plan for 100% of all other non-bus vehicles owned or leased to serve the school to be green vehicles.

Note: *Green vehicles have to reach at least a green score of 45 on the* ***American Council for an Energy Efficient Economy (ACEEE)*** *annual vehicle rating guide (or local equivalent for international projects).*

C. **Warehouses and Distribution Centers**
Choice 1. Alternative-Fuel Vehicles (1 point)
Offer an on-site fleet with a minimum of one yard tractor powered by propane, electricity, or natural gas. Offer on-site refueling or charging stations for the vehicles. Liquid or gas refueling stations must be located outdoors or separately ventilated.

OR
Choice 2. Reduced Truck Idling (1 point)
To limit truck idling at the dock, offer an electrical connection for 50% or more of all dock door locations.

Submittals:

Submittals	New Construction, Core and Shell, Data Centers, Hospitality, Retail, Healthcare		Schools	
	Option 1	Option 2	Option 1	Option 2
Parking or site plan showing preferred parking spaces and alternative-fuel fueling stations, main building entrance; calculations based on total parking capacity	X	X	X	
Photographs of pavement marking or signage for preferred parking spaces	X	X	X	
Photographs of pavement marking or signage for electric vehicle charging spaces	X		X	
Photograph of signage or copy of communication to building occupants for discounted parking rate	X	X	X	

Manufacturers' product specifications indicating compliance with Internet addressability, relevant standard, and charge level for electrical connectors	x		x	
Manufacturers' product specifications indicating refueling rate and fuel type for liquid or gas fueling stations		x	x	
Phase-in plan for emissions-compliant bus fleet, including responsible parties, emissions evaluation of current fleet, timeline, and retrofit strategies				x
Phase-in plan for green non-bus vehicles, including responsible parties, types of vehicles, and timeline				x

Warehouses and Distribution Centers		
Submittals	**Option 1**	**Option 2**
Manufacturer's documentation of yard tractor model and fuel type	x	
Site plan showing electrical connector locations at loading dock doors		x
Manufacturer's documentation for electrical connectors indicating ability to power in-cab amenities		x

Synergies:

- LTC: Reduced Parking Footprint
- EAC: Demand Response
- EQP: Minimum Air Quality Performance

Extra Credit (Exemplary Performance):

None

Project Phase:

Schematic Design

LEED Submittal Phase:

Design

Related Code or Standard:

- *American Council for an Energy Efficient Economy (ACEEE) Green Book: greenercars.org*
- *Society of Automotive Engineers, SAE Surface Vehicle Recommended Practice J1772, SAE Electric Vehicle*
- *Conductive Charge Coupler: standards.sae.org/j1772_201001*
- *International Electrical Commission 62196: iec.ch*

Responsible Party:

Architect

Chapter 7

Sustainable Sites (SS)

Overall Purpose

The Sustainable Sites (SS) category focuses on the vital relationships among ecosystems, ecosystem services, and buildings. It emphasizes integrating the site with regional and local ecosystems, restoring project site elements, and preserving the biodiversity of natural systems.

Earth's systems depend on "natural capital" such as biologically diverse coral reefs, wetlands, forests, and other ecosystems. They provide regenerative services. Per a United Nations study, about 60% of the ecosystem services that have been accessed worldwide, are currently used unsustainably or are degraded. The results are soil erosion, deforestation, disappearing rivers, drops in water table levels, and extinction of species. Sprawl and exurban development threatens natural landscapes and encroaches on the remaining farmlands, replacing and fragmenting them with hardscape or nonnative vegetation. An area the size of Illinois, or about 34 million acres (13,759 hectares) of open space was lost to development—approximately 6,000 acres a day, or 4 acres per minute between 1982 and 2001 in the United States alone. Hardscape areas increase rainwater runoff, and overload the capacity of natural infiltration systems. Rainwater runoff carries sediment, oil, lawn fertilizers, chemicals, and other pollutants to rivers and streams; harms aquatic species and ecosystems; and contributes to **eutrophication**. For example, rainwater runoff from parking lots, roads, and other hardscape carries about 200,000 barrels of petroleum into the Puget Sound every year per a Washington State Department of Ecology study. That is more than half of what was spilled in the 1989 Exxon Valdez accident in Alaska.

The prerequisites and credits in the SS category require project teams to complete an early site assessment, plan the locations of hardscape areas and buildings to avoid harming open space, habitat, and water bodies, and protect sensitive ecosystems. Project teams should reduce light pollution and heat island effects, minimize construction pollution, use low-impact development methods, remediate areas on the project site already in decline, and manage rainwater runoff by mimicking natural water flow patterns.

In addition to traditional approaches, the current SS category uses several new strategies, including replicating natural site hydrology (Rainwater Management credit); targeting financial support for off-site habitat protection (Site Development—Protect or Restore Habitat credit) with the help of conservation organizations; using the backlight-uplight-glare (BUG) method (Light Pollution Reduction credit); and using SR values for nonroof hardscape (Heat Island Reduction credit) and three-year aged SRI values for roofs.

The following are some specific measures:

1) **Construction activity pollution prevention** stops soil erosion by wind or storm water runoff during construction; protects and stockpiles topsoil for reuse; avoids waterway sedimentation; and prevents airborne dust and particle matter from polluting the air.
2) **Site development that protects or restores habitat** will maximize open space and promote biodiversity via a high ratio of open space to development footprint.
3) **Storm water design with quality control and quantity control** manages storm water

runoff; increases on-site infiltration; reduces impervious cover; eliminates contaminants and storm water run-off pollution; limits disruption of natural water hydrology or natural water flows; captures and processes storm water runoff with the help of a storm water management plan and acceptable **BMPs**(best management practices).

4) **Heat island reduction for non-roof and roof** impacts the wildlife habitat, humans, and microclimate. Heat island refers to the extra thermal gradient in developed areas when compared with undeveloped areas.
5) **Light pollution reduction** lowers development impact on nocturnal environments; reduces glare and improves nighttime visibility, and reduces sky-glow and light trespass from site and building to increase night sky access.

Core Concepts

1) **Management and design of the site**
   a) Stewardship of the site
   b) Site development
   c) Light pollution reduction
   d) Pest management integration
2) **Management of storm water**
   a) Storm water quantity reduction and water quality protection
   b) Impervious surface impact

Recognition, Regulation and Incentives

Financial incentives for local, state, and federal government programs**,** encourage the reuse of "brownfield" sites or infill and promote water quality protection with the help of combining low impact development and smart growth.

Overall Strategies and Technologies

Note: Not all strategies and technologies have to be used simultaneously for your project.

1) Protect or restore habitat during site development.
2) Restore and/or protect open spaces. (Plan for protected areas on-site and plan for easements and protected areas off site.)
3) Manage and intercept storm water.
4) Apply cool roof technologies.
5) Reduce duration of lighting use and lighting density, and also use light fixtures that comply with dark sky requirements.

SS Outline:

SS Prerequisite or Credit Name	Extra Credit	Responsible Party
SS Prerequisite (SSP): Construction Activity Pollution Prevention	0	Builder or general contractor
*SSP: Environmental Site Assessment	0	Owner or his environmental site assessment consultant
SSC: Site Assessment	0	Civil engineer, landscape architect, and architect
SSC: Site Development—Protect or Restore Habitat	**Choice 1.** Double the 30% restoration requirement (restore at least 60%). **Choice 2.** Double the financial donation requirement (offer at least $0.80 per square foot or $8.00 per square meter).	Owner & landscape architect
SSC: Open Space	0	Landscape architect
SSC: Rainwater Management	Manage 100% of rainwater that falls within the project boundary	Civil engineer
SSC: Heat Island Reduction	Achieve both Choices 1 and 2. Locate 100% of parking under cover.	Architect
SSC: Light Pollution Reduction	0	Architect
*SSC: Tenant Design and Construction Guidelines	0	Landlord
*SSC: Places of Respite	0	Architect
*SSC: Direct Exterior Access	0	Architect & landscape architect
*SSC: Joint Use of Facilities	0	Owner

Note: * indicates prerequisite or credit NOT applicable to all LEED rating systems. Refer to the specific prerequisite or credit for more information.

SS Prerequisite (SSP): **Construction Activity Pollution Prevention**

Mandatory for

New Construction (0 points)
Core and Shell (0 points)
Schools (0 points)
Retail (0 points)
Data Centers (0 points)
Warehouses and Distribution Centers (0 points)
Hospitality (0 points)
Healthcare (0 points)

Purpose

Controls airborne dust, soil erosion, and waterway sedimentation, and also reduces pollution from construction sites.

Prerequisite:

Develop and instigate an **erosion and sedimentation control (ESC)** plan for all construction activities related to the project. The plan has to comply with the erosion and sedimentation requirements of the 2012 U.S. Environmental Protection Agency (EPA) **Construction General Permit (CGP)** or local equivalent, whichever is more stringent.

Projects *must* conform to the CGP regardless of size. The plan must describe the measures instigated. Projects that use local codes derived from the CGP can often meet the criteria of the prerequisite.

Outside of the United States, project teams can use a local equivalent.

Note: *The* ***National Pollutant Discharge Elimination System (NPDES)*** *is a U.S. program that controls stormwater discharges from construction activities that disturb at least 1 acre (0.4 hectare); it also applies to smaller sites that are part of a larger sale or development. This LEED prerequisite applies to all sites, including the ones less than 1 acre (0.4 hectare).*

All project must meet **CGP Requirements:**

Section 2.1, erosion and sedimentation control

- Providing natural buffers
- Installing perimeter controls
- Minimizing sediment track-out
- Controlling discharges from stockpiled sediment or soil
- Minimizing dust
- Minimizing the disturbance of steep slopes
- Preserving topsoil
- Minimizing soil compaction
- Protecting storm drain inlets
- Maintaining control measures

Section 2.2, stabilization

- Deadlines for initiating and completing stabilization
- Criteria for stabilization

Section 2.3, pollution prevention

- Prohibited discharges

- General maintenance requirements
- Pollution prevention standards
- Emergency spill notification
- Fertilizer discharge restrictions

ESC Plan Description
Track execution of the ESC plan by maintaining date-stamped photographs or written records. A description of ESC plan execution should include the following:

- Scheduling of the execution of the plan
- Specific control measures applied on site
- Maintenance procedures used to ensure the proper function of control measures

Compliance in Late Design or Early Construction
Projects that intend to pursue LEED certification during the design phase may create or modify the ESC plan at that stage. Nevertheless, projects that intend to pursue LEED during early construction must have had a compliant ESC plan ready *before* construction began to meet the prerequisite requirements.

International Tips
If local code requirements are equally stringent or more stringent than the CGP and NPDES, a project team may follow them. Projects outside the U.S. do not have to comply with the permitting aspects of the CGP.

Construction pollution prevention priorities may be different for each region or locality.

Campus
Group Approach
A project team may document all buildings in the group as one.

Campus Approach
Unqualified. Each LEED project may pursue the credit individually.

Submittals:

Submittals	Projects Using 2012 EPA CGP	Projects Using Local Standards and Codes
Narrative of compliance with EPA CGP	x	
For projects with minimal or no exterior work and zero lot line projects: Narrative of compliance with any applicable ESC measures and special conditions	x	x
Comparison of EPA CGP with local standards and codes		x
Narrative of how project complies with local standards and codes		x
Drawings illustrating erosion and sedimentation control measures fulfilled		x
Written declaration from builder or general contractor who fulfilled plan OR Date-stamped photos OR A narrative of plan implementation.		x

Synergies

- SSC: Site Development—Protect or Restore Habitat
- SSC: Rainwater Management

Extra Credit (Exemplary Performance):
None

Project Phase:
Construction Documents or Construction Administration

LEED Submittal Phase:
Design (**Reminder:** Some LEED credits or prerequisites may be submitted during the Design Submittal phase while others can *only* be submitted during the Construction Submittals phase.)

Related Code or Standard:
Environmental Protection Agency (EPA) Construction General Permit (CGP): cfpub.epa.gov/npdes/stormwater/cgp.cfm

Responsible Party:
Builder or general contractor

*SSP: **Environmental Site Assessment**

Mandatory for

Schools (0 points) Healthcare (0 points)

Purpose

Makes sure the site is evaluated for environmental contamination, remediates the environmental contamination if the site is contaminated, and protects the health of vulnerable populations.

Prerequisite:

Project teams can use the American Society for Testing and Materials (ASTM) **environmental site assessment (ESA)** methodology for identifying and investigating a site's environmental contamination. This prerequisite encourages the use of an ESA (or local equivalent) and remediation of any confirmed site contamination to protect human health. Local assessment standards are acceptable if they are at least as stringent as ASTM Phase I and II ESA.

Perform a Phase I Environmental Site Assessment per ASTM E1527–05 (or a local equivalent) to determine whether environmental contamination exists at the site. If contamination is suspected, perform a Phase II Environmental Site Assessment as described in ASTM E1903–11 (or a local equivalent).

If a site is contaminated, remediate the site to meet the most stringent criteria of national, state, or local environmental protection agency region residential (unrestricted) standards.

Campus

Group Approach

All buildings in the group may be submitted as one.

Campus Approach

Eligible.

Submittals:

Submittals	No contamination, as confirmed by Phase I ESA (or local equivalent)	No contamination, as confirmed by Phase II ESA (or local equivalent)	Contamination, as confirmed by Phase III ESA (or local equivalent)
Phase I ESA or local equivalent assessment	X	X	X
Phase II or III ESA or local equivalent assessment		X	X
Narrative of contamination and remediation			XX
Confirmation that site has been remediated to residential use standards			

Synergies

- LTC: High-Priority Site

Extra Credit (Exemplary Performance):

None

Project Phase:

Pre-design

LEED Submittal Phase:

Design

Related Code or Standard:

- ASTM E1527—05 Standard Practice for Environmental Site Assessments: Phase I Environmental Site Assessment Process: astm.org
- ASTM E1903—11 Standard Practice for Environmental Site Assessments: Phase II Environmental Site Assessment Process: astm.org
- 40 CFR Part 312: Standards and Practice for All Appropriate Inquiries; Final Rule: epa.gov/brownfields/aai

Responsible Party:

Owner or his Environmental Site Assessment consultant.

SSC: Site Assessment

Applicable to

New Construction (1 point)
Core and Shell (1 point)
Schools (1 point)
Retail (1 point)
Data Centers (1 point)
Warehouses and Distribution Centers (1 point)
Hospitality (1 point)
Healthcare (1 point)

Purpose

Evaluates site conditions to assist related design decisions and assesses sustainable options before design.

Credit Path:

Finish and document a site assessment or survey including the following:

- **Climate:** Solar exposure, seasonal sun angles, heat island effect potential, monthly precipitation and temperature ranges, prevailing winds.
- **Human health effects:** Proximity to major sources of air pollution, adjacent physical activity opportunities, proximity of vulnerable populations.
- **Human use:** Construction materials with existing recycle or reuse potential, views, adjacent properties, adjacent transportation infrastructure.
- **Hydrology:** Flood hazard areas, rainwater collection and reuse opportunities, delineated lakes, streams, shorelines, wetlands, TR-55 initial water storage capacity of the site (or local equivalent for projects outside the U.S.).
- **Soils:** U.S. Department of Agriculture prime farmland, Natural Resources Conservation Service soils delineation, previous development, healthy soils, disturbed soils (local equivalent standards may be used for projects outside the U.S.).
- **Topography:** Contour mapping, slope stability risks, unique topographic features.
- **Vegetation:** Primary vegetation types, significant tree mapping, greenfield area, unique habitat, threatened or endangered species, invasive plant species.

Campus

Group Approach

All buildings in the group may be submitted as one.

Campus Approach

Eligible.

Submittals:

Submittals	All Projects
Site assessment plan or map or survey	x
Site assessment worksheet or equivalent description	x

Synergies

- IPC: Integrative Process
- LTC: Sensitive Land Protection
- LTC: Surrounding Density and Diverse Uses
- LTC: Access to Quality Transit
- LTC: Bicycle Facilities
- SSC: Site Development—Protect or Restore Habitat
- SSC: Open Space
- SSC: Rainwater Management
- SSC: Heat Island Reduction
- EAP: Minimum Energy Performance
- EAC: Optimize Energy Performance
- EAC: Renewable Energy Production
- EQC: Daylight
- EQC: Quality Views

Extra Credit (Exemplary Performance):
None

Project Phase:
Pre-design

LEED Submittal Phase:
Design

Related Code or Standard:

- Natural Resources Conservation Service, Soils: soils.usda.gov
- TR-55 initial water storage capacity: nrcs.usda.gov

Responsible Party:
Civil engineer, landscape architect, and architect

SSC: **Site Development—Protect or Restore Habitat**

Applicable to

New Construction (1-2 points)
Core and Shell (1-2 points)
Schools (1-2 points)
Retail (1-2 points)
Data Centers (1-2 points)
Warehouses and Distribution Centers (1-2 points)
Hospitality (1-2 points)
Healthcare (1 point)

Purpose

Restores damaged areas to promote biodiversity and provide habitat, and protects existing natural areas.

Credit Path:

Preserve and protect 40% of the greenfield area on the site (if available) from all construction and development activity.

AND

Choice 1. On-Site Restoration (2 points except Healthcare, 1 point Healthcare)

Using adapted or native vegetation, restore 30% (including the building footprint) of the previously developed site area. Projects that accomplish a density of 1.5 floor-area ratio (**FAR**) can include **vegetated roof** surfaces in this calculation if the plants are adapted or native, promote biodiversity, and provide habitat.

Restore all compacted or disturbed soils that will be revegetated within the project's development footprint to meet the following criteria:

- Soils (in situ and imported) should be reused for functions equivalent to their original function.
- Imported soil blends or topsoils designed to serve as topsoil may not include the following:
  - soils defined regionally as unique farmland, prime farmland, or farmland of statewide or local importance by the **Natural Resources Conservation Service** web soil survey (or local equivalent for projects outside the U.S.); or
  - soils from other greenfield sites, except those soils as a byproduct of a construction process.

- Restored soil must meet the criteria of reference soils in categories 1–3 and meet the criteria of either category 4 or 5:
  1. compaction;
  2. infiltration rates;
  3. organic matter;
  4. soil biological function; and
  5. soil chemical characteristics.

Vegetated landscape areas may be excluded from the vegetation and soil requirements if they are constructed to accommodate rainwater infiltration, as long as all such rainwater infiltration areas are treated consistently with SSC: Rainwater Management.

Schools Only

Dedicated athletic fields of exclusive athletic uses are exempted from the soil restoration criteria. These areas may not count toward the minimum required area.

OR

Choice 2. Financial Support (1 point)

Offer financial support of at least $0.40 per square foot (US $4 per square meter) for the total site area, including the building footprint.

Financial support has to be offered to a locally or nationally recognized land trust or conservation organization within the same EPA Level III ecoregion or the project's state (or within 100 miles of the project [160 kilometers] for projects outside the U.S.). For U.S. projects, the land trust must be accredited by the **Land Trust Alliance**.

Submittals:

Submittals	All Projects	Option 1	Option 2
Greenfield area calculations	x		
Narrative of greenfield area protection (if applicable)	x		
Adapted or native vegetation calculations		x	
Site plan indicating project boundary, previously developed area, preserved greenfield area(s) (if applicable), restored area, building footprint, adapted or native vegetation, plant species, other ecologically appropriate features, and any other relevant site conditions		x	
Narrative of compacted or disturbed soils to be revegetated		x	
Reference soil characteristics and soil test results		x	
Projects with vegetated roofs: provide the FAR		x	
Financial support calculations			x
Agreement with conservation organization or land trust			x
U.S. projects: verification that land trust is accredited by Land Trust Alliance			x
Projects outside U.S.: confirmation that the conservation organization is locally or nationally recognized; description of qualifications and mission of the conservation organization			x

Synergies

- LTC: High-Priority Site
- SSP: Construction Activity Pollution Prevention
- SSC: Site Assessment
- SSC: Open Space
- SSC: Rainwater Management
- SSC: Heat Island Reduction

Extra Credit (Exemplary Performance):

- Choice 1. Double the 30% restoration requirement (restore at least 60%).
- Choice 2. Double the financial donation requirement (offer at least $0.80 per square foot or $8.00 per square meter).

Project Phase:

Schematic design

LEED Submittal Phase:

Design

Related Code or Standard:

- U.S. EPA ecoregions: epa.gov
- Land Trust Alliance accreditation: landtrustalliance.org
- Natural Resources Conservation Service, web soil survey: websoilsurvey.nrcs.usda.gov
- Sustainable Sites Initiative (SITES™): sustainablesites.org

Responsible Party:

Owner& Landscape Architect

SSC: **Open Space**

Applicable to

New Construction (1 point)
Core and Shell (1 point)
Schools (1 point)
Retail (1 point)
Data Centers (1 point)
Warehouses and Distribution Centers (1 point)
Hospitality (1 point)
Healthcare (1 point)

Purpose

To create exterior open space that promotes interaction with the environment, passive recreation, social interaction, and physical activities.

Credit Path:

Provide outdoor space of at least 30% of the total site area (including building footprint). At least 25% of that outdoor space should be vegetated (turf grass does not count as vegetation) or have overhead vegetated canopy.

The outdoor space should be one or more of the following and be physically accessible:

- a garden space dedicated to urban food production or community gardens;
- a garden space with many vegetation types and species that provide year-round visual interest;
- a pedestrian-oriented turf or paving area with physical site elements that encourage outdoor social activities;
- a recreation-oriented turf or paving area with physical site elements that promote physical activity;
- preserved or created habitat that meets the criteria of SSC: Site Development—Protect or Restore Habitat and also includes elements of human interaction.

For projects with a density of 1.5 FAR and that are physically accessible, intensive or extensive vegetated roofs can be counted toward the minimum 25% vegetation criterion, and qualifying roof-based physically accessible paving areas can be counted toward credit compliance.

Naturally designed ponds or wetlands may count as open space if the side slopes are vegetated and average 1:4 (vertical: horizontal) or less.

For projects that are part of a multitenant complex only

Open space can be either next to the building or at another location in the site master plan. The open space can be at another master plan development site provided that it is protected from development. If the open space is not next to the building, supply documentation showing that the criteria have been met and the land has been returned to a natural state or is in a natural state and conserved for the life of the building.

Submittals:

Submittals	All Projects	Projects with Vegetated Roofs
Site plan that shows master plan boundary (if applicable) or project boundary and campus, highlighting size and location of any open spaces, wetlands or naturalistic man-made ponds (with side slopes noted), vegetated areas, plant species, and vegetated roofs	x	
Open space and vegetated area calculations	x	
Narrative of how open space is physically accessible and meets area type criteria	x	
FAR (floor-area ratio)		x

Synergies

- SSC: Site Development—Protect or Restore Habitat
- SSC: Rainwater Management
- SSC: Heat Island Reduction
- SSC: Site Assessment

Extra Credit (Exemplary Performance):

None

Project Phase:

Schematic design

LEED Submittal Phase:

Design

Related Code or Standard:

None

Responsible Party:

Landscape Architect

SSC: **Rainwater Management**

Applicable to

New Construction (2-3 points)
Core and Shell (2-3 points)
Schools (2-3 points)
Retail (2-3 points)
Data Centers (2-3 points)
Warehouses and Distribution Centers (2-3 points)
Hospitality (2-3 points)
Healthcare (1-2 points)

Purpose

Based on undeveloped ecosystems and historical conditions in the region, replicates the natural water balance and hydrology of the site to improve water quality and reduce runoff volume.

Credit Path:

Choice 1. Percentile of Rainfall Events

Path 1. 95th Percentile (2 points except Healthcare, 1 point Healthcare)

Use **low-impact development (LID)** and **green infrastructure (GI)** to manage on site the runoff from the developed site for the 95th percentile of local or regional rainfall events in a manner best replicating natural site hydrology processes.

Utilize daily rainfall data and the methodology in the U.S. EPA Technical Guidance on Implementing the Stormwater Runoff Requirements for Federal Projects under Section 438 of the Energy Independence and Security Act to establish the 95th percentile amount.

OR

Path 2. 98th Percentile (3 points except Healthcare, 2 points Healthcare)

Use **low-impact development (LID)** and green infrastructure to achieve Path 1 but for the 98th percentile of local or regional rainfall events.

OR

Path 3. Zero Lot Line projects only—85th Percentile (3 points except Healthcare, 2 points Healthcare)

The following criterion applies to zero lot line projects in urban areas with a minimum density of 1.5 FAR. Use **low-impact development (LID)** and green infrastructure to manage on site the runoff from the developed site for the 85th percentile of local or regional rainfall events in a manner best replicating natural site hydrology processes.

OR

Choice2. Natural Land Cover Conditions (3 points except Healthcare, 2 points Healthcare)

Manage on site the yearly growth in runoff volume resulting from changing the natural land cover condition to the post-developed condition.

Projects that are part of a multitenant complex only

The credit criteria can be met using a coordinated approach affecting the defined project site that is within the master plan boundary. Distributed techniques based on a watershed approach are then required.

Submittals:

Submittals	All Projects	Choice 1 Path 3	Choice 2
Rainfall data	x		
Rainfall event calculations or calculator for the chosen percentile storm	x		
Runoff volume calculations	x		
Plans, cross sections, or details depicting site conditions and GI or LID strategies, highlighting area of site that each facility addresses, topography, and direction of water flow.	x		
Description confirming measures qualified as GI or LID	x		
Calculations for volume of rainwater managed by GI or LID strategies	x		
Explanation for why 10 years of historic rainfall data are not available for the project location (if applicable)	x		
Narrative of conditions that make the project zero lot line		x	
FAR (floor area ratio)		x	
Documents illustrating natural land cover conditions			x
Multitenant complex projects only: summary of centralized approach and associated distributed techniques	x		

Synergies

- IPC: Integrative Process
- SSC: Site Development—Protect or Restore Habitat
- SSC: Open Space
- SSC: Site Assessment
- SSC: Site Master Plan
- SSC: Heat Island Reduction
- WEP and WEC: Outdoor Water Use Reduction
- WEP and WEC: Indoor Water Use Reduction

Extra Credit (Exemplary Performance):

- Manage 100% of rainwater that falls within the project boundary.

Project Phase:

Schematic Design, Design Development, & Construction Documents

LEED Submittal Phase:

Design

Related Code or Standard:

U.S. EPA Technical Guidance on Implementing the Rainwater Runoff Requirements for Federal Projects under Section 438 of the Energy Independence and Security Act: epa.gov

Responsible Party:

Civil Engineer

SSC: **Heat Island Reduction**

Applicable to

New Construction (1-2 points)
Core and Shell (1-2 points)
Schools (1-2 points)
Retail (1-2 points)
Data Centers (1-2 points)
Warehouses and Distribution Centers (1-2 points)
Hospitality (1-2 points)
Healthcare (1 point)

Purpose

Reduces heat islands and minimizes effects on human and wildlife habitats and microclimates.

Credit Path:

Choose one of the following:

Choice 1. Nonroof and Roof (2 points except Healthcare, 1 point Healthcare)

Meet the following:

$$\frac{\text{Area of Nonroof Measures}}{0.5} + \frac{\text{Area of High-Reflectance Roof}}{0.75} + \frac{\text{Area of Vegetated Roof}}{0.75} \geq \text{Total Site Paving Area} + \text{Total Roof Area}$$

Alternatively, an SRI and SR weighted average approach can be used.

Use any combination of the following:

Nonroof Measures

- Install plants that provide shade over paved areas (including playgrounds) on the site within 10 years of planting or use the existing plant material. Install vegetated planters. Plants cannot include artificial turf and must be in place at the time of occupancy permit.
- Offer shade with structures covered by photovoltaics, solar thermal collectors, and wind turbines or other energy generation systems.
- Offer shade with structures or architectural devices that have a three-year aged solar reflectance (SR) value of 0.28 or more or materials with an initial SR of 0.33 or more at installation.
- Offer shade with vegetated structures.
- Use paving materials with a three-year aged solar reflectance (SR) value of 0.28 or more or materials with an initial SR of 0.33 or more at installation.
- Use an open-grid pavement system (at least 50% unbound).

High-Reflectance Roof

Use roofing materials that have an SRI that is not less than the values in Table 1. Meet the three-year aged SRI value or use materials that meet the initial SRI value.

Table 1. Minimum solar reflectance index value, by roof slope			
	Slope	**Initial SRI**	**3-year aged SRI**
Low-sloped roof	≤ 2:12	82	64
Steep-sloped roof	> 2:12	39	32

OR

Choice 2. Parking under Cover (1 point)

Offer at least 75% of parking spaces under cover. Any roof used to shade or cover parking must (1) have a three-year aged SRI of 32 or more, or use materials with an initial SRI of 39 or more at installation, (2) be a vegetated roof, or (3) be covered by solar thermal collectors, photovoltaics, and wind turbines or other energy generation systems.

Submittals:

Submittals	Choice 1	Choice 2
Nonroof and roof area calculations	x	
Site plan(s) with measurements and elements, including building footprint, roof and hardscape area, LEED project boundary, and area of each roof and nonroof measure	x	
Manufacturer's documentation of SRI, SR, and paving permeability	x	
Parking space calculations		x

Synergies

- SSC: Site Development—Protect or Restore Habitat
- SSC: Open Space
- SSC: Rainwater Management
- EAP: Minimum Energy Performance
- EAC: Optimize Energy Performance

Extra Credit (Exemplary Performance):

- Achieve both Choices 1 and 2. Locate 100% of parking under cover.

Project Phase:

Pre-design

LEED Submittal Phase:

Design

Related Code or Standard:

ASTM Standards E903 and E892: astm.org

Cool Roof Rating Council Standard (CRRC-1): coolroofs.org

Responsible Party:

Architect

SSC: **Light Pollution Reduction**

Applicable to

New Construction (1 point)
Core and Shell (1 point)
Schools (1 point)
Retail (1 point)
Data Centers (1 point)
Warehouses and Distribution Centers (1 point)
Hospitality (1 point)
Healthcare (1 point)

Purpose

Reduces the consequences of development for people and wildlife, improves nighttime visibility, and increases night sky access.

Credit Path:

Satisfy uplight and light trespass criteria with either the **backlight-uplight-glare (BUG)** method (Choice 1) or the calculation method (Choice 2). Projects may use different options for light trespass and uplight.

Satisfy the criteria for all exterior **luminaires** (light fixtures) located inside the project boundary (except those listed under "Exemptions"), based on:

- the photometric features of each luminaire when tilt as specified in the project design and mounted in the same orientation; and
- the lighting zone of the project property (at the beginning of construction). Classify the project under one lighting zone using the lighting zones definitions provided in the **Illuminating Engineering Society and International Dark Sky Association (IES/IDA) Model Lighting Ordinance (MLO)** User Guide.

In addition, meet the internally illuminated signage criteria.

Table 1. Simple definitions of Lighting Zone (LZ) per Model Lighting Ordinance (MLO)

MLO lighting zone	Simple definitions
LZ0	Typically includes undeveloped areas of open space where protection of dark environment is critical.
LZ1	Typically includes single- and two-family residential communities, business parks, rural town centers, and other industrial, commercial, or storage areas with limited nighttime activity. May also include developed areas in parks and other natural settings.
LZ2	Typically includes multifamily residential uses, institutional residential uses, churches, schools, hospitals, motels, hotels, and commercial or businesses areas with evening activities in predominately residential areas. Also includes neighborhood playing and recreational fields and mixed-use development with predominance of residential uses.
LZ3	Typically includes commercial corridors, mixed-use areas, high-intensity town centers, suburban commercial areas, industrial uses and shipping and rail yards with high nighttime activity. Also includes high-use recreational and playing fields, regional shopping malls, car dealerships, gas stations, and other nighttime active exterior retail areas.
LZ4	Areas of very high ambient lighting levels, used only for special cases and not appropriate for most cities (currently only Times Square has this classification in the U.S.).

Uplight
Choice 1. BUG Rating Method
Do not surpass the following luminaire uplight ratings, based on the specific light source installed in the luminaire, as defined in IES TM-15-11, Addendum A.

Table 2. Maximum uplight ratings for luminaires

MLO lighting zone	Luminaire uplight rating
LZ0	U1
LZ1	U2
LZ2	U3
LZ3	U4
LZ4	U5

OR
Choice2. Calculation Method
Do not exceed the following percentages of total lumens emitted above horizontal.

Table 3. Maximum percentage of total lumens emitted above horizontal, by lighting zones

MLO lighting zone	Maximum allowed percentage of total luminaire lumens emitted above horizontal
LZ0	0%
LZ1	0%
LZ2	1.5%
LZ3	3%
LZ4	6%

AND
Light Trespass
Choice 1. BUG Rating Method
Do not surpass the following luminaire backlight and glare ratings (based on the specific light source installed in the luminaire), as defined in IES TM-15-11, Addendum A, based on the mounting location and distance from the lighting boundary.

Table 4. Maximum backlight and glare ratings

Luminaire mounting	MLO lighting zone				
	LZ0	LZ1	LZ2	LZ3	LZ4
	Allowed backlight ratings				
> 2 mounting heights from lighting boundary	B1	B3	B4	B5	B5
1 to 2 mounting heights from lighting boundary and properly oriented	B1	B2	B3	B4	B4
0.5 to 1 mounting height to lighting boundary and properly oriented	B0	B1	B2	B3	B3
< 0.5 mounting height to lighting boundary and properly oriented	B0	B0	B0	B1	B2
	Allowed glare ratings				
Building-mounted > 2 mounting heights from any lighting boundary	G0	G1	G2	G3	G4
Building-mounted 1 to 2 mounting heights from any lighting boundary	G0	G0	G1	G1	G2
Building-mounted 0.5 to 1 mounting heights from any lighting boundary	G0	G0	G0	G1	G1
Building-mounted < 0.5 mounting heights from any lighting boundary	G0	G0	G0	G0	G1
All other luminaires	G0	G1	G2	G3	G4

The lighting boundary is the same as the property lines of the property or properties of the LEED project.
The project team can modify the lighting boundary under the following conditions:

- When the property line is next to a public area that is a plaza, parking lot, walkway, or bikeway, the project team can move the lighting boundary to 5 feet (1.5 meters) beyond the property line.
- When the property line is next to a public alley, street, or transit corridor, the project team can move the lighting boundary to the center line of that alley, street, or corridor.
- When there are other properties owned by the same entity that are contiguous to the property, or properties, that the LEED project is within and have the same or higher MLO lighting zone designation as the LEED project, the project team can expand the lighting boundary to include those properties.

Adjust all luminaires less than two mounting heights from the lighting boundary such that the backlight points toward the nearest lighting boundary line. Building-mounted luminaires with the backlight oriented toward the building are exempt from the backlight rating requirement.

OR

Choice 2. Calculation Method

Do not surpass the following vertical illuminances at the lighting boundary (use the definition of lighting boundary in **Choice 1**). Calculation points must be 5 feet (1.5 meters) or less apart. Vertical illuminances must be calculated on vertical planes running parallel to the lighting boundary, with the normal to each plane oriented toward the property and perpendicular to the lighting boundary, extending from grade level to 33 feet (10 meters) above the height of the highest luminaire.

Table 5. Maximum vertical illuminance at lighting boundary, by lighting zone	
MLO lighting zone	**Vertical illuminance**
LZ0	0.05 fc (0.5 lux)
LZ1	0.05 fc (0.5 lux)
LZ2	0.10 fc (1 lux)
LZ3	0.20 fc (2 lux)
LZ4	0.60 fc (6 lux)

AND

Internally Illuminated Exterior Signage

Do not surpass a luminance of 200 cd/m2 (nits) during nighttime hours and 2000 cd/m2 (nits) during daytime hours.

Exemptions from Uplight and Light Trespass Requirements

The following exterior lighting is exempt from the requirements, provided it is controlled separately from lighting:

- government-mandated roadway lighting;
- hospital emergency departments, including associated helipads;
- internally illuminated signage;
- lighting for the national flag in MLO lighting zones 2, 3, or 4;
- lighting for theatrical purposes for stage, film, and video performances;
- lighting that is used solely for façade and landscape lighting in MLO lighting zones 3 and 4, and is automatically turned off from midnight until 6 a.m.; and
- specialized signal, directional, and marker lighting for transportation.

Submittals:

Submittals	All Projects	Choice 1, Uplight	Choice 1, Light Trespass	Choice 2, Uplight	Choice 2, Light Trespass
Site lighting plan with boundaries, location of fixtures, elements, and applicable measurements	x				
Projects with internally illuminated exterior signage only: provide maximum luminance data	x				
Luminaire schedule showing uplight ratings		x			
Luminaire schedule showing backlight and glare ratings and mounting heights			x		
Calculations for lumens per luminaire and lumens emitted above horizontal				x	
Greatest vertical illuminance value for each vertical calculation plane at lighting boundary; calculation grid for one vertical plane with greatest vertical illuminance (worst-case scenario), highlighting point of greatest illuminance					x

Synergies

- SSC: Site Assessment
- EAP: Minimum Energy Performance
- EAC: Optimize Energy Performance

Extra Credit (Exemplary Performance):

None

Project Phase:

Pre-design

LEED Submittal Phase:

Design

Related Code or Standard:

Illuminating Engineering Society and International Dark Sky Association (IES/IDA) Model Lighting Ordinance User Guide and IES TM-15-11, Addendum A: ies.org

Responsible Party:

Electrical Engineer

*SSC: Site Master Plan

Applicable to

Schools (1 point)

Purpose:

To make sure that the sustainable site benefits of the project continue, in spite of future changes in demographics or programs.

Credit Path:

The project should accomplish at least four of the following six credits via the associated calculation methods. The project team must then recalculate the accomplished credits using the data from the master plan.

- LTC: High Priority Site
- SSC: Site Development—Protect or Restore Habitat
- SSC: Open Space
- SSC: Rainwater Management
- SSC: Heat Island Reduction
- SSC: Light Pollution Reduction

The project team must develop a site master plan for the school in cooperation with school authorities and should consider previous sustainable site design measures in all master-planning efforts so that existing infrastructure is retained whenever feasible. The project team must include current construction activity plus future construction (within the building's lifespan) that affects the site in the master plan. The master plan development footprint have to also include paving, parking, and utilities.

Projects without planned future development are not eligible for this credit.

Campus

Group Approach

Separate submittal for each building.

Campus Approach

Qualified.

Submittals:

Submittals	All projects
Site plan with measurements and elements, including current and future phases of development	x
Documentation and credit forms for selected eligible credits, rewritten using data for site master plan	x
Narrative of documentation updates made for future development	x

Synergies:

- IPC: Integrative Process Credit
- SSC: Joint Use of Facilities

Extra Credit (Exemplary Performance):
None

Project Phase:
Schematic Design

LEED Submittal Phase:
Design

Related Code or Standard:
None

Responsible Party:
Architect

*SSC: **Tenant Design and Construction Guidelines**

Applicable to

Core and Shell (1 point)

Purpose:

To instruct tenants to apply sustainable design and construction elements in their tenant improvement build-outs.

Credit Path:

Publish for tenants an illustrated guideline with the following criteria, as applicable:

- a narrative of the sustainable design and construction elements incorporated in the core and shell project and the project's sustainability objectives and goals, including those for tenant spaces;
- suggestions, including examples, for sustainable services, strategies, products, and materials; and
- information that allows a tenant to coordinate space design and construction with the building systems when pursuing the following LEED v4 for Interior Design and Construction prerequisites and credits:
  - WEP: Indoor Water Use Reduction
  - WEC: Indoor Water Use Reduction
  - EAP: Minimum Energy Performance
  - EAP: Fundamental Refrigerant Management
  - EAC: Optimize Energy Performance
  - EAC: Advanced Energy Metering
  - EAC: Renewable Energy Production
  - EAC: Enhanced Refrigerant Management
  - MRP: Storage and Collection of Recyclables
  - EQP: Minimum Indoor Air Quality Performance
  - EQP: Environmental Tobacco Smoke Control
  - EQC: Enhanced Indoor Air Quality Strategies
  - EQC: Low-Emitting Materials
  - EQC: Construction Indoor Air Quality Management Plan
  - EQC: Air Quality Assessment
  - EQC: Thermal Comfort
  - EQC: Interior Lighting
  - EQC: Daylight
  - EQC: Quality Views
  - EQC: Acoustic Performance

Offer the guidelines to all tenants before signing the lease.

Campus

Group Approach

Separate submittal for each building.

Campus Approach

Not qualified. Each LEED project can pursue the credit separately.

Submittals:

- Tenant design and construction guidelines document

Synergies:

- All Core and Shell credits with performance thresholds
- LEED for Core and Shell credits

Extra Credit (Exemplary Performance):

None

Project Phase:

Pre-design

LEED Submittal Phase:

Design

Related Code or Standard:

None

Responsible Party:

Landlord

*SSC: Places of Respite

Applicable to

Healthcare (1 point)

Purpose:

To create outdoor places of respite on the healthcare campus to provide visitors, staff, and patients with the health benefits of the natural environment.

Credit Path:

Offer 5% of the net usable program area of the building as accessible places of respite to patients and visitors.

Provide 2% of the net usable program area of the building as additional dedicated places of respite for staff.

Places of respite should be outdoors or be located in interior solaria, greenhouses, atria, or conditioned spaces; if 90% of each qualifying interior space's gross floor area achieves a direct line of sight to unobstructed views of nature, such spaces can be used to meet up to 30% of the required area.

All areas must meet the following criteria:

- Locate the area within 200 feet (60 meters) of a building entrance or access point or accessible from within the building.
- Locate the area where no direct medical care or medical intervention is delivered.
- Provide options for indirect sun or shade with at least one seating space per 200 square feet (18.5 square meters) of each respite area, with one wheelchair space per five seating spaces.
- 50% or less of the required area can be specific clinical special-use gardens unavailable to all building occupants, such as horticulture therapy.
- If the trailhead is within 200 feet (60 meters) of a building entrance, universal-access natural trails that are available to visitors, staff, or patients can account for 30% or less of the required area.

In addition, outdoor areas must meet the following criteria:

- At least 25% of the total outdoor area has to have overhead vegetated canopy or be vegetated at the ground plane (not including turf grass).
- The area is open to the sky, fresh air, and the natural elements.
- Signage must meet the 2010 FGI Guidelines for Design and Construction of Health Care Facilities (Section 1.2-6.3 and Appendix A1.2-6.3: Wayfinding).
- Places of respite may not be within 25 feet (7.6 meters) of a smoking area (see EQP: Environmental Tobacco Smoke Control).

If they meet the credit criteria, existing places of respite on the hospital campus can qualify.

Campus

Group Approach

Separate submittal for each building.

Campus Approach
Not qualified. Each LEED project can pursue the credit separately.

Submittals:

Submittals	All Projects
Patient, visitor, staff, area, shading, and vegetation calculations	x
Site plan emphasizing qualifying outdoor and/or indoor places of respite, identified by user (patient and visitor versus staff), and specifying their access points and distances, planes of vegetation and vegetated canopy, proximity to smoking areas, and shaded seating spaces (showing shade pattern throughout day)	x
Drawings or photographs of wayfinding signage	x

Synergies:
- SSC: Direct Exterior Access
- SSC: Rainwater Management
- SSC: Site Development
- SSC: Open Space
- EQP: Environmental Tobacco Smoke Control

Extra Credit (Exemplary Performance):
None

Project Phase:
Schematic Design

LEED Submittal Phase:
Design

Related Code or Standard:
2010 FGI Guidelines for Design and Construction of Health Care Facilities: fgiguidelines.org

Responsible Party:
Architect

*SSC: **Direct Exterior Access**

Applicable to

Healthcare (1 point)

Purpose:

To direct access to the natural environment to provide patients and staff with the related health benefits.

Credit Path:

Offer direct access to an outdoor terrace, courtyard, garden, or balcony. The space must be a minimum of 5 square feet (0.5 square meters) per patient for 75% of all inpatients and 75% of eligible outpatients whose clinical length of stay (**LOS**) exceeds four hours.

Patients whose LOS surpasses four hours and whose treatment makes them unable to move, such as emergency, stage 1 surgical recovery, and critical care patients, can be excluded. Places of respite outside the building and meeting the criteria of SSC: Places of Respite that are right next to clinical areas or with direct access from inpatient units can be included.

Qualifying spaces have to be assigned as nonsmoking. The spaces have to also meet the criteria for outdoor air contaminant concentrations detailed in EQC: Enhanced Indoor Air Quality Strategies, Choice 2 and situate more than 100 feet (30 meters) from loading docks, building exhaust air locations, and roadways with idling vehicles.

Submittals:

- Area and patient calculations
- Site plan showing locations of building air exhausts, exterior exhaust vents, accessible outdoor areas, area takeoffs, and access points and distances to outdoor areas

Synergies:

- SSC: Places of Respite
- SSC: Rainwater Management
- EQC: Enhanced Indoor Air Quality Strategies, Choice 2

Extra Credit (Exemplary Performance):

None

Project Phase:

Schematic Design

LEED Submittal Phase:

Design

Related Code or Standard:

None

Responsible Party:

Architect & Landscape Architect

*SSC: **Joint Use of Facilities**

Applicable to

Schools (1 point)

Purpose:

Share the school's building and its playing fields for nonschool functions and events to assimilate the school with the community.

Credit Path:

Choice 1. Make Building Space Open to the General Public (1 point)

In partnership with the school authorities, ensure that a minimum of three of the following types of spaces in the school are available for and accessible to shared use by the general public:

- auditorium;
- cafeteria;
- gymnasium;
- joint parking;
- one or more classrooms; and
- playing fields and stadiums.

Provide access to toilets after regular school hours in joint-use areas.

OR

Choice 2. Contract with Specific Organizations to Share Building Space (1 point)

In partnership with the school authorities, contract with other organizations or community to offer a minimum of two types of dedicated-use spaces in the building like the following:

- commercial office;
- community service centers (provided by state or local offices);
- health clinic;
- library or media center;
- one or more commercial businesses;
- parking lot; and
- police office.

Provide access to toilets after regular school hours in joint-use areas.

OR

Choice 3. Use Shared Space Owned by Other Organizations (1 point)

In partnership with the school authorities, ensure that a minimum of two of the following six types of spaces that are owned by other agencies or organizations are accessible to students:

- auditorium;
- cafeteria;
- gymnasium;
- playing fields and stadiums;
- one or more classrooms; and
- swimming pool.

Offer direct pedestrian access to these spaces from the school. Furthermore, present signed joint-use agreements with the other agencies or organizations that specify how these spaces will be shared.

Submittals:

Submittals	Choice 1	Choice 2	Choice 3
Floor plan highlighting joint-use spaces, room names, and restroom facilities	x	x	
Shared-use policy with conditions, terms, and narrative of communication to public	x		
Signed agreement between occupying organization(s) and school authorities		x	
Signed agreement specifying how spaces will be shared with students			x
Site plan showing pedestrian access route and distance from school to joint-use spaces			x

Synergies:

- LTC: Surrounding Density and Diverse Uses
- LTC: Reduced Parking Footprint
- SSC: Site Master Plan

Extra Credit (Exemplary Performance):

None

Project Phase:

Pre-design

LEED Submittal Phase:

Design

Related Code or Standard:

None

Responsible Party:

Owner

Chapter 8
Water Efficiency (WE)

Overall Purpose
This section looks at metering, outdoor use, indoor use, and specialized uses, and deals with water holistically. It is based on an "efficiency first" approach. Each prerequisite looks at reductions in potable water use and water efficiency alone. The WE credits recognize the use of alternative and non-potable sources of water.

Only 3% of Earth's water is fresh water, and over two-thirds of fresh water is trapped in glaciers, therefore, the creative reuse and conservation of water are important. Typically, most of water is used by the building users and then flows off-site as wastewater. In a developed country, potable water normally comes through a public water supply system from a remote site, and wastewater is piped to a remote processing plant, and then discharged into a distant water body. This pass-through system depletes freshwater aquifers and reduces stream flow in rivers, causing wells to go dry and water tables to drop. In 60% of European cities with a population over 100,000, groundwater is used too fast to be completely replenished.

Additionally, treating water for drinking and before disposal, as well as piping it to and from a building requires a significant amount of energy, which is not gauged by a building's utility meter. Water treatment and pumping consumes about 19% of all energy used in California.

Behind thermoelectric power and irrigation, buildings use 13.6% of potable water in the United States. Project teams can reuse wastewater for non-potable water needs, install water efficient fixtures, incorporate native landscapes that require no irrigation, and construct green buildings that use much less water. LEED projects saved a total of 1.2 trillion gallons (4.54 trillion liters) of water per the 2009 Green Building Market Impact Report. LEED WE credits encourage significant reduction of total water use.

Cross-Cutting Issues
The WE category includes three main components: water metering, irrigation water, and indoor water (used by appliances, fixtures, and processes, such as cooling). Several kinds of documentation are required based on the specific water-saving strategies of the project.

Site plans are used to document the locations of meters and submeters and the location and size of vegetated areas. Inside the building, floor plans show the location of indoor submeters, appliances, fixtures, and process water equipment (e.g., evaporative condensers, cooling towers). Project teams can use the same documentation for the credits in SS category.

Fixture cut sheets are manufacturers' literature, which provide specifications for each product. These must be used to document the fixtures (and appliances as applicable). The Indoor Water Use Reduction prerequisite and credit require this documentation.

Alternative water sources include rainwater harvesting, graywater reuse, municipally supplied wastewater (purple pipe water), or other reused sources. A project may earn credit in the following categories:

- WEC: Outdoor Water Use Reduction
- WEC: Indoor Water Use Reduction
- WEC: Cooling Tower Water Use
- WEC: Water Metering

However, the same water should NOT be applied to multiple credits unless it has sufficient volume to cover the demand of all the uses (e.g., toilet flushing plus irrigation demand).

Occupancy calculations are estimates based on occupant usage and are required for the Indoor Water Use Reduction prerequisite and credit. The LT and SS categories also use project occupancy calculations. You must understand how occupants are classified and counted. See WE Prerequisite Indoor Water Use Reduction for additional information.

The following are some specific measures:

1) water efficient landscaping (outdoor water reduction from a calculated midsummer baseline, that has no potable water, or irrigation use)
2) innovative wastewater technologies (indoor water that is reused when it's legal, safe, and appropriate)
3) water use reduction (indoor water)

Mnemonic

Love In Universe, or LIU (See underlined letters above.)

Core Concepts

1) Regulation of *indoor* water
   - Save as much *indoor* potable water as possible
   - Use water efficiently
2) *Outdoor* water
   - Save as much *outdoor* potable water as possible
   - Use water efficiently
3) *Process* water
   - Reduce the need for potable water when supplying *process* water
   - Use water efficiently

Recognition, Regulation, and Incentives

1) Recognition
   - WaterSense is a product label sponsored by the EPA.
2) Regulation (requirements and goals)
   - Mandatory federal water efficiency requirements per the Energy Policy Act(EPAct) of 2005 and Executive Order 13423 (2007) state that all federal facilities shall reduce water use intensity by 2% per year between 2006 and 2015 to reach a total reduction of 20%.
   - Energy Policy Act (1992) has mandatory requirements concerning the use of water conserving plumbing fixtures in industrial, commercial, and residential buildings.
3) Financial Incentives
   - There are local or state rebates and credits for water saving devices.

Overall Strategies and Technologies

Note: Not *all* strategies and technologies have to be used simultaneously for your project development.

1) **Reduce *indoor* potable water demand**
   Use non-potable water, by reusing graywater, and capturing and using rainwater; reduce water use via innovative wastewater treatment; use water efficiently through waterless or high efficiency fixtures
2) **Reduce *outdoor* potable water demand**
   Use native and/or adapted and drought-tolerant plants; use non-potable water by capturing and using storm water for landscape irrigation; use water efficiently through drip-irrigation or other high efficiency technologies.
3) **Reduce potable water use for *process* water**
   Use *process* water efficiently through the use of controls and sensors; efficient management of cooling tower water; and use non-potable water.

Useful Information for the WE Category

You can identify the number of occupants by **occupancy type**, i.e., two people for a one-bedroom unit, and three people for a two-bedroom unit, etc. If you do not know the occupancy (like CS projects or mixed-use projects in the early design stages where you do not know who will be the tenants), then you can use the "Default Occupancy Factors" found in the appendixes.

FTE = number of hours of occupancy/8

You can estimate the number of transients for your projects. Use a daily average number over a one-year period.

Use your best judgment to decide if someone should be reported as a FTE or a transient. For example, a volunteer who works at the school 4 hours each day can be considered a FTE with a value of 0.5, and an individual who attends a basketball game can be reported as a visitor.

Use a 1 to 1 male to female ratio for your projects unless they have a specific ratio. You will need to describe special ratios with a narrative.

WE Outline:

WE Prerequisite or Credit Name	Extra Credit	Responsible Party
WE Prerequisite (WEP): Outdoor Water Use Reduction	0	Landscape Architect
WEP: Indoor Water Use Reduction	0	Plumbing Engineer
WEP: Building-Level Water Metering	0	Owner & Plumbing Engineer
WEC: Outdoor Water Use Reduction	0	Landscape Architect
WEC: Indoor Water Use Reduction	Achieve 55% water use reduction	Plumbing Engineer
WEC: Cooling Tower Water Use	0	Plumbing Engineer
WEC: Water Metering	0	Plumbing Engineer

WE Prerequisite (WEP): **Outdoor Water Use Reduction**

Mandatory for:

New Construction (0 point)
Core and Shell (0 point)
Schools (0 point)
Retail (0 point)
Data Centers (0 point)
Warehouses and Distribution Centers (0 point)
Hospitality (0 point)
Healthcare (0 point)

Purpose:

To reduce outdoor water use.

Prerequisite:

Choice 1. No Irrigation Required

Demonstrate that the landscape does not require a permanent irrigation system after an establishment period (not to exceed two years).

OR

Choice 2. Reduced Irrigation

Decrease the project's landscape water use by 30% or more from the calculated baseline for the site's peak watering month. Water savings have to be achieved through irrigation system efficiency and plant species selection, as calculated using the Environmental Protection Agency (EPA) WaterSense Water Budget Tool.

Campus

Group Approach

All buildings in the group can be submitted as one. Use the total landscaped area of the whole campus. The results of the Water Budget Tool apply to all buildings within the group.

Campus Approach

Qualified.

Submittals:

Submittals	Choice 1	Choice 2
Site plan indicating vegetated areas	x	
Description for plant species and water criteria	x	
Site plan indicating size and location of landscape zones		x
Water Budget Tool report		x

Synergies

- WEP: Building-Level Water Metering

Extra Credit (Exemplary Performance):

None

Project Phase:

Schematic Design

LEED Submittal Phase:
Design

Related Code or Standard:
None

Responsible Party:
Landscape Architect

WEP: **Indoor Water Use Reduction**

Mandatory for

New Construction (0 points)
Core and Shell (0 points)
Schools (0 points)
Retail (0 points)
Data Centers (0 points)
Warehouses and Distribution Centers (0 points)
Hospitality (0 points)
Healthcare (0 points)

Purpose

To reduce indoor water use.

Prerequisite:

Building Water Use

For the fittings fixtures listed in Table 1, as related to the project scope, reduce total water use by 20% from the baseline. Base calculations on the flow rates and volumes shown in Table 1.

All newly installed urinals, toilets, private lavatory faucets, and showerheads that qualify for labeling *must* be **WaterSense** labeled (or a local equivalent for international projects).

Important Data to Memorize (The numbers in Table 1 and Table 6 are very important. Almost every LEED exam tests them.)

Table 1 Flow Rates (GPF or GPM or GPC):

	Water Closet	**Urinal**	**Lavatory**	**Shower**	**Kitchen Sink**
Conventional (baseline)	1.6 gpf except blow-out fixture at 3.5 gpf	1.0	**Residential**2.2gpm at 60psi **Commercial** 2.2 gpm at 60 psi for private app. 0.5gpm at 60 psi for public use 0.25gpc (gallons per cycle) for metering faucets	2.5 gpm at 80psi per shower stall	2.2 gpm at 60 psi
EPA Water-Sense Standard or High-efficiency	1.28 gpf	0.5 gpf	1.5 gpm for private lavatory faucets and aerators	≤2.0gpm	
	Water	**Urinal**	**Lavatory**	**Shower**	**Kitchen Sink**

HET= high efficiency toilet

	Closet				
HET, single flush pressure assist	1 gpf	0.5 gpf for HEU			
HET, dual flush (full-flush)	1.6 gpf				
HET, dual flush (low-flush)	1.1 gpf				
HET, foam flush	0.05 gpf				
Low-Flow	1.1 gpf	0.5 gpf	1.8 gpm	1.8 gpm	≤2.2 gpm
Ultra Low- Flow	0.8 gpm		0.5 gpm		
Non-Water Urinal or Composting Toilet		0			

Note:

1) gpf = gallons per flush, gpm = gallons per minute, psi = pounds per square inch
2) Private app. (application) means hospital patient rooms, motel, and hotel rooms, etc.
3) Commercial **pre-rinse spray valves** for food service application **≤1.6gpm**
4) This table applies to **non-residential** (NC, CS, school, commercial, etc.) projects and **residential** projects. I have combined several tables into one table to save you time.
5) This table is based on the **Energy Policy Act of 1992**, **EPA WaterSense** Standard, Uniform Plumbing Code (**UPC**) and International Plumbing Code (**IPC**) standards for plumbing fixture water use. **WaterSense** is a partnership program sponsored by the **EPA.** The **EPA WaterSense** standard exceeds the IPC and UPC requirements in some cases.
6) The following fixtures shall not be included in the water use calculations for this credit, but they may be included for extra ID points for WRc3, Water Use Reduction:
   Automatic commercial ice makers, commercial dishwashers, commercial steam cooker, residential clothes washers, commercial (family-size) clothes washers, standard and compact residential dishwashers.
7) High-efficiency (HE) fixtures include: single-flush gravity fed, high-efficiency toilets (HET), high-efficiency urinals (HEU), etc.
8) HETs are available in different flush types: single-flush gravity fed (like a conventional toilet), single flush pressure assist, and dual-flush in both gravity fed and pressure assist.

Appliance and Process Water Use

Install equipment, appliances, and processes within the project scope to meet the criteria in the tables below.

Table 2. Standards for appliances	
Appliance	**Criteria**
Residential clothes washers	ENERGY STAR or performance equivalent
Commercial clothes washers	Consortium for Energy Efficiency (CEE) Tier 3A
Residential dishwashers (standard and compact)	ENERGY STAR or performance equivalent
Pre-rinse spray valves	≤ 1.3 gpm
Ice machine	ENERGY STAR or performance equivalent and use either air-cooled or closed-loop cooling, such as chilled or condenser water system

Table 3. Standards for processes	
Process	**Criteria**
Heat rejection and cooling	No once-through cooling with potable water for any equipment or appliances that reject heat
Evaporative condensers and cooling towers	Equip with • conductivity controllers and overflow alarms • makeup water meters • efficient drift eliminators that reduce drift to maximum of 0.002% of recirculated water volume for counterflow towers and 0.005% of recirculated water flow for cross-flow towers

Healthcare, Retail, Schools, and Hospitality Only
Water-consuming equipment, appliances, and processes must meet the additional criteria in Tables 4 and 5.

Table 4. Standards for appliances		
Kitchen equipment		**Criteria**
Dishwasher	Undercounter	≤ 1.6 gal/rack
	Stationary, single tank, door	≤ 1.4 gal/rack
	Single tank, conveyor	≤ 1.0 gal/rack
	Multiple tank, conveyor	≤ 0.9 gal/rack
	Flight machine	≤ 180 gal/hour
Food steamer	Batch	≤ 6 gal/hour/pan
	Cook-to-order	≤ 10 gal/hour/pan
Combination oven	Countertop or stand	≤ 3.5 gal/hour/pan
	Roll-in	≤ 3.5 gal/hour/pan

Table 5. Process Criteria	
Process	**Criteria**
Discharge water temperature tempering	Where local criteria regulate discharge temperature of fluids into drainage system, use tempering device that runs water only when equipment releases hot water OR Offer thermal recovery heat exchanger that cools drained discharge water below code-required maximum discharge temperatures while simultaneously preheating inlet makeup water OR If fluid is steam condensate, return it to boiler
Venturi-type flow-through vacuum generators or aspirators	Use no device that generates vacuum by water flow through device into drain

Table 6. Fixture uses per day:

Non-residential Projects					
	Water Closet	**Urinal**	**Lavatory**	**Shower**	**Kitchen Sink**
FTE (including Student FTE)					
Female	3	0	3	0.1 0 for student FTE	1
Male	1	2	3	0.1 0 for student FTE	1
Visitors					
Female	0.5	0	0.5	0	0
Male	0.1	0.4	0.5	0	0
Retail Customers					
Female	0.2	0	0.2	0	0
Male	0.1	0.1	0.2	0	0
Students					
Female	3	0	3	0	0
Male	1	2	3	0	0
Residential Projects					
	Water Closet	Urinal	Lavatory	Shower	Kitchen Sink
Female	5	N/A	5	1	4
Male	5	N/A	5	1	4

Note:

1) Lavatory faucets are counted as a 60 second duration per use for *private* uses, a 30 second duration for *public* uses, and a 12 second duration when equipped with an autocontrol.
2) Kitchen sink faucets are counted as a 60 second duration per use for *residential* projects, and a 15 second duration for *non-residential* projects
3) Showers are counted as a 480 second duration for *residential* projects, and a 300 second duration for *non-residential* projects.
4) This table applies to NC, CS, schools, commercial and residential projects. I have combined several tables into one table to save you time.

Submittals:

Submittals	**All projects**		**Projects with appliance or process water**	**Core and Shell Prescriptive Usage-based projects only**
	Prescriptive	**Usage-based calculation**		
Manufacturers' information, product cutsheets	x	x	x	
Indoor water use calculator		x		
Tenant lease agreement				x
Tenant scope of work narrative				x

Synergies

- WEP: Building-Level Water Metering
- WEC: Water Metering

Extra Credit (Exemplary Performance):

None

Project Phase:

Schematic Design

LEED Submittal Phase:

Design

Related Code or Standard:

- **Energy Policy Act (EPAct) of 1992 and as amended:**eere.energy.gov/femp/regulations/epact1992.html
- **EPAct 2005:** eere.energy.gov/femp/regulations/epact2005.html
- **International Association of Plumbing and Mechanical Officials Publication IAPMO/ANSI UPC 1-2006, Uniform Plumbing Code 2006, Section 402.0, Water-Conserving Fixtures and Fittings:** iapmo.org
- **International Code Council, International Plumbing Code 2006, Section 604, Design of Building Water Distribution System:** iccsafe.org
- **ENERGY STAR:** energystar.gov
- **Consortium for Energy Efficiency:** cee1.org
- **WaterSense:** epa.gov/watersense
- **IgCC/ASHRAE 189.1 cooling tower and evaporative condenser requirements:** ashrae.org/resources--publications/bookstore/standard-189-1

Responsible Party:

Plumbing Engineer

WEP: **Building-Level Water Metering**

Mandatory for

New Construction (0 points)
Core and Shell (0 points)
Schools (0 points)
Retail (0 points)
Data Centers (0 points)
Warehouses and Distribution Centers (0 points)
Hospitality (0 points)
Healthcare (0 points)

Purpose

Tracks water consumption to identify opportunities for additional water savings and supports water management.

Prerequisite:

Building Water Use

Install permanent water meters to measure the overall potable water use for the building and related grounds. Meter readings can be automated or manual; meter data have to be organized as monthly and annual summaries.

Starting on the date the project accepts LEED certification or typical occupancy, whichever comes first, commit to sharing with USGBC the resulting whole-project water usage data for a five-year period.

This commitment must last for five years or until the building changes lessee or ownership.

Campus

Group Approach

Separate submittal for each building. Project team must track potable water used for landscape irrigation in any of three ways: by installing a dedicated meter, by including it with a single building, or by installing multiple meters.

Campus Approach

Unqualified. Each LEED project may be submitted individually.

Submittals:

- Meter declaration
- Sharing commitment

Synergies

- WEP: Indoor Water Use Reduction
- WEC: Water Metering
- EAP: Building-Level Energy Metering

Extra Credit (Exemplary Performance):

None

Project Phase:

Pre-design

LEED Submittal Phase:
Design

Related Code or Standard:
None

Responsible Party:
Owner & Plumbing Engineer

WEC: **Outdoor Water Use Reduction**

Applicable to

New Construction (1-2 points)
Core and Shell (1-2 points)
Schools (1-2 points)
Retail (1-2 points)
Data Centers (1-2 points)
Warehouses and Distribution Centers (1-2 points)
Hospitality (1-2 points)
Healthcare (1 point)

Purpose

Reduces outdoor water use.

Credit Path:

Select one of the following choice to reduce outdoor water use. Permeable or impermeable pavement or other non-vegetated surfaces should be excluded from landscape area calculations. The project team can decide whether to include or exclude playgrounds (if vegetated), athletic fields, and food gardens.

Choice 1. No Irrigation Required (2 points except Healthcare, 1 point Healthcare)
Demonstrate that no permanent irrigation system is needed for the landscape after a maximum two-year establishment period.

Choice 2. Reduced Irrigation (2 points except Healthcare, 1 point Healthcare)
Decrease the project's landscape water requirement (LWR) by a minimum of 50% from the calculated baseline for the site's peak watering month. Reductions must first be achieved through irrigation system efficiency and plant species selection as calculated in the Environmental Protection Agency (EPA) WaterSense Water Budget Tool.

Further reductions above 30% may be accomplished using any combination of alternative water sources, efficiency, and smart scheduling technologies.

Table 1. Points for reducing irrigation water		
Percentage reduction from baseline	Points (except Healthcare)	Points (Healthcare)
50%	1	1
100%	2	-

Campus
Group Approach
All buildings in the group can be submitted as one. Use the total landscaped area of the whole campus. The results of the Water Budget Tool apply to all buildings in the group.

Campus Approach
Qualified.

Submittals:

- For Choice 2:Alternative water source and controls calculations

Synergies

- SSC: Rainwater Management
- WEP: Indoor Water Use Reduction
- WEC: Cooling Tower Water Use
- WEP: Building-Level Water Metering
- WEC: Water Metering

Extra Credit (Exemplary Performance):
None

Project Phase:
Schematic Design

LEED Submittal Phase:
Design

Related Code or Standard:
None

Responsible Party:
Landscape Architect

WEC: **Indoor Water Use Reduction**

Applicable to

New Construction (1-6 points)
Core and Shell (1-6 points)
Schools (1-7 points)
Retail (1-7 points)
Data Centers (1-6 points)
Warehouses and Distribution Centers (1-6 points)
Hospitality (1-6 points)
Healthcare (1-7 points)

Purpose

Reduces indoor water use.

Credit Path:

Further decrease fitting and fixture water use from the calculated baseline in WEP: Indoor Water Use Reduction. Further potable water savings can be achieved above the prerequisite level using alternative water sources. Include fittings and fixtures necessary to meet the needs of the occupants. Some of these fittings and fixtures can be outside the project boundary. Points are awarded according to Table 1.

Table 1. Points for reducing water use

Percentage reduction	Points (BD+C)	Points (Schools, Retail, Hospitality, Healthcare)
25%	1	1
30%	2	2
35%	3	3
40%	4	4
45%	5	5
50%	6	-

Schools, Retail, Hospitality, and Healthcare only
Satisfy the percentage reduction criteria above.

AND
Appliance and Process Water
Install equipment within the project scope that satisfies the criteria in Table 2, 3, 4, or 5. One point is granted for satisfying all applicable requirements in any one table. All pertinent equipment listed in each table must meet the criteria.

Schools, Retail, and Healthcare projects can earn a second point for meeting the criteria of two tables.

To use Table 2, the project must process at least 120,000 lbs (57 606 kg) of laundry per year.

Table 2. Compliant commercial washing machines

Washing machine	Criteria	Points (Schools, Retail, Hospitality, Healthcare)
On-premise, minimum capacity 2,400 lbs (1 088 kg) per 8-hour shift	Maximum 1.8 gals per pound *	Maximum 7 liters per 0.45 kilograms *

* Based on equal quantities of heavy, medium, and light soil laundry.

To use Table 3, the project has to provide at least 100 meals per day of operation. All appliance and process equipment present on the project and listed in the category of kitchen equipment must obey the criteria.

Table 3. Criteria for commercial kitchen equipment

Kitchen equipment		Criteria (IP units)
Dishwasher	Undercounter	Energy Star
	Stationary, single tank, door	
	Single tank, conveyor	
	Multiple tank, conveyor	
	Flight machine	
Food steamer	Batch (no drain connection)	≤ 2 gal/hour/pan including condensate cooling water
	Cook-to-order (with drain connection)	≤ 5 gal/hour/pan including condensate cooling water
Combination oven	Countertop or stand	≤ 1.5 gal/hour/pan including condensate cooling water
	Roll-in	
Food waste disposer	Disposer	3-8 gpm, full load condition, 10 minute automatic shutoff; or 1 gpm, no-load condition
	Scrap collector	Maximum 2 gpm makeup water
	Pulper	
	Strainer basket	No additional water usage

Note: gpm = gallons per minute gph = gallons per hour

To use Table 4, the project must be a medical or laboratory facility.

Table 4. Compliant laboratory and medical equipment

Lab equipment	Criteria (IP units)	Points (Schools, Retail, Hospitality, Healthcare)
Reverse-osmosis water purifier	75% recovery	75% recovery
Steam sterilizer	For 60-inch sterilizer, 6.3 gal/U.S. tray For 48-inch sterilizer, 7.5 gal/U.S. tray	For 1520-mm sterilizer, 28.5 liters/DIN tray For 1220-mm sterilizer, 28.35 liters/DIN tray
Sterile process washer	0.35 gal/U.S. tray	1.3 liters/DIN tray
X-ray processor, 150 mm or more in any dimension	Film processor water recycling unit	
Digital imager, all sizes	No water use	

To use Table 5, the project must be connected to a municipal or district steam system that does not allow the return of steam condensate.

Table 5. Compliant municipal steam systems	
Steam system	**Criteria**
Steam condensate disposal	Cool municipally supplied steam condensate (no return) to drainage system with heat recovery system or reclaimed water
OR	
Reclaim and use steam condensate	100% recovery and reuse

Campus
Group Approach
Separate submittal for each building. If non-potable water systems will be shared by multiple projects, ensure there is enough non-potable water to satisfy the demands of all projects. The non-potable water should not be double-counted among projects.

Campus Approach
Unqualified.

Submittals:

Submittals	Fixtures	Appliances	Process water
		(Retail, Healthcare, Hospitality, and Schools projects only)	
Alternative water source calculations (if applicable)	x		
Plumbing system design drawings (if applicable)	x		
Alternative water narrative	x		
Cut sheets, manufacturers' information	x	x	x
Indoor water use calculator	x		

Synergies
- WEP: Building-Level Water Metering
- WEC: Water Metering

Extra Credit (Exemplary Performance):
- Achieve 55% water use reduction.

Project Phase:
Schematic Design

LEED Submittal Phase:
Design

Related Code or Standard:

- **The Energy Policy Act (EPAct) of 1992 and as amended:** eere.energy.gov/femp/regulations/epact1992.html
- **EPAct 2005:** eere.energy.gov/femp/regulations/epact2005.html

- **International Association of Plumbing and Mechanical Officials Publication IAPMO / ANSI UPC 1-2006, Uniform Plumbing Code 2006, Section 402.0, Water-Conserving Fixtures and Fittings:** iapmo.org
- **International Code Council, International Plumbing Code 2006, Section 604, Design of Building Water Distribution System:** iccsafe.org
- **ENERGY STAR:** energystar.gov
- **WaterSense:** epa.gov/watersense
- **IgCC/ASHRAE 189.1 – cooling tower and evaporative condenser requirements:** ashrae.org/resources--publications/bookstore/standard-189-1

Responsible Party:

Plumbing Engineer

WEC: **Cooling Tower Water Use**

Applicable to

New Construction (1-2 points)
Core and Shell (1-2 points)
Schools (1-2 points)
Retail (1-2 points)
Data Centers (1-2 points)
Warehouses and Distribution Centers (1-2 points)
Hospitality (1-2 points)
Healthcare (1-2 points)

Purpose

Controls corrosion, microbes, and scale in the condenser water system, and conserves water used for the cooling tower makeup.

Credit Path:

For evaporative condensers and cooling towers, perform a one-time potable water analysis, measuring all five control parameters listed in Table 1.

Table 1. Maximum concentrations for parameters in condenser water

Parameter	Maximum level
Ca (as $CaCO_3$)	1000 ppm
Total alkalinity	1000 ppm
SiO_2	100 ppm
Cl-	250 ppm
Conductivity	2000 µS/cm

ppm = parts per million
µS/cm = micro siemens per centimeter

Determine the number of cooling tower cycles by dividing the maximum allowed concentration level of each parameter by the actual concentration level of each parameter found in the potable makeup water. Limit cooling tower cycles to avoid surpassing maximum values for any of these parameters.

Table 2. Points for cooling tower cycles

Cooling tower cycles	Points
Maximum number of cycles achieved without exceeding any filtration levels or affecting operation of condenser water system (up to maximum of 10 cycles)	1
Achieve a minimum 10 cycles by increasing the level of treatment in condenser or make-up water OR Meet the minimum number of cycles to earn 1 point and use a minimum 20% recycled non-potable water	2

CAMPUS

Group Approach

All buildings in the group project may be submitted as one.

Campus Approach

Qualified.

Submittals:

Submittals	1 point	2 points
Potable water analysis results	X	X
Potable water analysis description	X	X
Cycles of concentration calculations	X	X
Non-potable water calculations		X
Water treatment calculations		X
Non-potable water analysis (if using 100% non-potable water)		X

Synergies

- WEP: Indoor Water Use Reduction
- WEC: Water Metering

Extra Credit (Exemplary Performance):

None

Project Phase:

Construction Documents

LEED Submittal Phase:

Design

Related Code or Standard:

None

Responsible Party:

Plumbing Engineer

WEC: **Water Metering**

Applicable to

New Construction (1 point)
Core and Shell (1 point)
Schools (1 point)
Retail (1 point)
Data Centers (1 point)
Warehouses and Distribution Centers (1 point)
Hospitality (1 point)
Healthcare (1 point)

Purpose

Tracks water use to identify opportunities for additional water savings and supports water management.

Credit Path:

Install permanent water meters for *two* or more of the following water subsystems, as pertinent to the project:

- **Irrigation.** Meter water systems for 80% or more of the irrigated landscaped area. Calculate the percentage as the total metered irrigated landscape area divided by the total irrigated landscape area. Landscape areas fully covered with native vegetation or xeriscaping that requires no routine irrigation can be excluded from the calculation.
- **Indoor plumbing fixtures and fittings.** Meter water systems for 80% or more of the indoor fixtures and fittings described in WEP: Indoor Water Use Reduction, either directly or by deducting all other measured water use from the measured total water consumption of the building and grounds.
- **Domestic hot water.** Meter water use for 80% or more of the installed domestic hot water heating capacity (including both tanks and on-demand heaters).
- **Boiler with aggregate projected annual water use of 100,000 gallons (378 500 liters) or more, or boiler of more than 500,000 BtuH (150 kW).** A single makeup meter may record flows for multiple boilers.
- **Reclaimed water.** Meter reclaimed water, regardless of rate. A reclaimed water system with a makeup water connection must also be metered so that the true reclaimed water component can be determined.
- **Other process water.** Meter 80% or more of expected daily water consumption for process end uses, such as dishwashers, clothes washers, humidification systems, pools, and other subsystems using process water.

Healthcare Projects only

In addition to the criteria above, install water meters in any *five* of the following:

- purified water systems (reverse-osmosis, de-ionized);
- filter backwash water;
- water use in dietary department;
- water use in laundry;
- water use in laboratory;
- water use in central sterile and processing department;
- water use in hydrotherapy and physiotherapy and treatment areas;
- water use in surgical suite;
- closed-looped hydronic system makeup water; and
- cold-water makeup for domestic hot water systems.

Campus
Group Approach
Separate submittal for each building. Each building in the group must have a separate whole-building water meter. Each individual building in the group must satisfy the credit criteria for submetering of domestic hot water, indoor plumbing fixtures and fittings, and other process water. All buildings in the group can be served by the same submeter for boilers, irrigation systems, and reclaimed water if all the water used by the group is captured.

Campus Approach
Unqualified.

Submittals:
- Water metering strategy description

Synergies
- WEP: Building-Level Water Metering
- WEP: Indoor Water Use Reduction
- WEP: Outdoor Water Use Reduction

Extra Credit (Exemplary Performance):
None

Project Phase:
Schematic Design

LEED Submittal Phase:
Design

Related Code or Standard:
None

Responsible Party:
Plumbing Engineer

Chapter 9

Energy and Atmosphere (EA)

Overall Purpose

The EA category addresses energy holistically, covering energy-efficient design strategies, energy use reduction, and renewable energy sources. Currently, a large percentage of the worldwide energy resources are from coal, oil, and natural gas. These resources are limited, nonrenewable, and emit greenhouse gases. The current energy practice involves escalating market prices due to uncertain supplies, destructive extraction processes, and national security vulnerability. This practice is not sustainable. Buildings use about 40% of the total energy, and are a major contributor to these problems

Energy efficiency design concentrates on reduction of overall energy needs through the choice of climate-appropriate building materials, glazing selection, and building orientation. Natural ventilation, passive heating and cooling, high-efficiency HVAC systems, and smart controls can reduce a building's energy use. The purchase of green power or on-site renewable energy also lowers the demand for fossil fuel energy.

An important step to ensuring high-performing buildings is the commissioning process. Get a **commissioning authority (CxA)** on board early. The CxA verifies that the design functions as intended and meets the owner's project requirements, helps to reduce wasted energy, and prevents long-term maintenance issues. The staff should understand the installed systems and their function in an operationally efficient and effective building. They should be willing to learn new methods for optimizing system performance, and must be trained so that efficient design is carried through to efficient performance.

The reduction of fossil fuel use is not limited to buildings only. The EA category recognizes this fact. Enrolling projects in a **demand response program** can help to increase electric grid efficiency.

Once enrolled in a demand response, the utility companies can decrease the building's electricity usage during peak times, which reduces the demand on the grid and the need to construct new plants. In the same way, on-site renewable energy avoids transmission losses and strain on the grid, and moves the market away from dependence on fossil fuels.

Between now and 2030, if cost-effective energy efficiency measures are employed in buildings as their lighting, cooling, heating, and other equipment is replaced, the growth in the building sector energy demand could fall from a projected 30% increase to 0% according to the American Physical Society. The EA section use credits related to designing for efficiency, reducing usage, and supplementing the energy supply with renewable energy to support the goal of reduced energy demand.

Overall, the following goals are important to the EA category:
1) Saved energy
2) Promotion of renewable energy supply
3) Fundamental commissioning for building energy systems
4) Minimum energy performance
5) Fundamental refrigerant management
6) Optimized energy performance
7) On-site renewable energy
8) Enhanced commissioning
9) Enhanced refrigerant management
10) Measurement and verification
11) Green power

Core Concepts
1) Energy Efficiency and Demand
   - Understand energy criteria
   - Save energy
   - Measure the performance of energy
2) The Supply of Energy
   - Buy off-site renewable energy
   - Generate on-site renewable energy

Recognition, Regulation, and Incentives
1) **Recognition** through the Energy Star Program, Target Finder Rating Tool, etc.
2) **Regulation (Requirements and Goals)** See detailed discussion under each credit.
3) **Incentives**
   - Private Sector: lower risk and lower premiums for property insurance, social responsibility of corporations, and availability of money
   - Public Sector: tax rebates and credits, incentive for development, expedited plan review and permit processing, and technology-based measures.

Overall Strategies and Technologies
Note: Not **all** strategies and technologies have to be used simultaneously for your project.
1) Utilize typical energy use patterns for various building types.
2) Use statistical databases such as performance-based or prescriptive approaches.
3) Use code-based energy models.

Typical energy use pattern matrix

Building Type	Median Electrical Intensity (kWh/sf-yr)
Education	6.6
Office	11.7
Retail (except mall)	8.0
Food Sales	58.9
Food Service	28.7
Lodging	12.6

4) Reduce energy use through the use of artificial HVAC and lighting. Use energy-efficient equipment with feedbacks and controls.
5) Consider building orientation and improve building envelope performance.
6) Use Energy Star appliances and energy-efficient equipment.
7) Measure and verify building energy performance by building and operating as designed (commissioning, and continuous and retro-commissioning); monitoring performance; and improving over time (monitoring and verification).
8) Generate on-site renewable energy such as geothermal, solar PV, and wind energy.
9) Take advantage of the site's passive solar energy, natural ventilation, and passive cooling.
10) Buy off-site renewable energy.

Some Important Concepts

Process energy includes energy required for refrigeration and kitchen cooking, laundry washing and drying, elevators and escalators, computers, office and general miscellaneous equipment, lighting not included in the lighting power allowance (such as lighting that is part of the medical equipment), other uses like water pumps, etc.

Regulated (non-process) energy includes energy required for HVAC; exhaust fans and hoods; lighting for interiors, surface parking, garage parking, building façade, and grounds; space heating; service water heating; etc.

To achieve EA Credit Optimize Energy Performance, you should use the same process loads for your proposed building performance rating and the baseline performance building rating. You can use the Exceptional Calculation Method (ANSI/ASHRAE/IESNA 90.1-2007 G2.5) to record measures of reducing process loads. Include the assumptions made for both your proposed design and base building, as well as related supporting empirical and theoretical information in your documentation of process load energy savings.

Combined heat and power systems (**CHP**) capture the heat that would have been wasted in the process of generating electricity via fossil fuel. They are much more efficient than separate thermal systems and central power plants. They reduce peak demand, generate fewer emissions, reduce loss in electricity transmission and distribution, and release electrical grid capacity for other uses.

EA Outline:

EA Prerequisite or Credit Name	Extra Credit	Responsible Party
EA Prerequisite (EAP): Fundamental Commissioning and Verification	0	CxA
EAP: Minimum Energy Performance	0	Mechanical Engineer
EAP: Building-Level Energy Metering	0	Owner or leasee
EAP: Fundamental Refrigerant Management	0	Mechanical Engineer
EAC: Enhanced Commissioning	0	CxA, owner, contractor, and design team
EAC: Optimize Energy Performance	Choice 1. New construction, major renovation, and core and shell projects: Achieve at least 54% energy savings.	Mechanical Engineer
EAC: Advanced Energy Metering	0	Mechanical Engineer
EAC: Demand Response	0	Mechanical Engineer
EAC: Renewable Energy Production	Renewable energy has to comprise 15% of total energy. For Core and Shell projects, the threshold is 10%.	Mechanical Engineer
EAC: Enhanced Refrigerant Management	0	Mechanical Engineer
EAC: Green Power and Carbon Offsets	0	Mechanical Engineer

EA Prerequisite (EAP): **Fundamental Commissioning and Verification**

Mandatory for

New Construction (0 points)
Core and Shell (0 points)
Schools (0 points)
Retail (0 points)
Data Centers (0 points)
Warehouses and Distribution Centers (0 points)
Hospitality (0 points)
Healthcare (0 points)

Purpose

Meets the owner's project requirements (OPR) for water, energy, durability, and indoor environmental quality; and supports the design, construction, and operation of a project to meet the OPR.

Prerequisite:

Commissioning (Cx) is a process to ensure that the project meets both the owner's operational needs and the design intent. An owner's objectives and goals should be the driving force for the project team. The Cx verifies that that building systems perform as intended and those objectives and goals are met.

Commissioning Process Scope

Your commissioning team shall complete the following commissioning plan/process for mechanical, electrical, plumbing, and renewable energy systems and assemblies, in accordance with ASHRAE Guideline 0-2005 and ASHRAE Guideline 1.1–2007 for HVAC&R Systems, as they relate to indoor environmental quality, energy, water, and durability:

Criteria for exterior enclosures are limited to inclusion in the **basis of design (BOD)** and **owner's project requirements (OPR)**, as well as the review of the BOD, OPR, and project design. NIBS Guideline 3-2012 for Exterior Enclosures has additional guidance:

- Develop the OPR.
- Develop a BOD.

The **commissioning authority (CxA)** must do the following:

- Review the OPR, BOD, and project design.
- Develop and implement a Cx plan.
- Confirm incorporation of Cx criteria into the construction documents.
- Develop construction checklists.
- Develop a system test procedure.
- Verify system test execution.
- Maintain an issues and benefits log throughout the Cx process.
- Prepare a final Cx process report.
- Document all findings and recommendations and report directly to the owner throughout the process.

A qualified member of the design or construction team (or an employee of that firm) who is not directly responsible for design of the building envelope can perform the review of the exterior enclosure design.

Commissioning Authority
By the end of the design development (DD) phase, hire a commissioning authority with the following qualifications.

- The CxA has to have verified commissioning process experience on two or more building projects with a similar scope of work. The experience must extend from early design phase through a minimum of 10 months of occupancy;
- The CxA can be an independent consultant, a qualified employee of the owner, or an employee of the design or construction firm who is not part of the project's design or construction team or a disinterested subcontractor of the design or construction team.
- For projects that are smaller than 20,000 square feet (1 860 square meters), the CxA can be a qualified member of the design or construction team. In all cases, the CxA must report his or her findings directly to the owner. Project teams that intend to pursue EA Credit Enhanced Commissioning should note a difference in the CxA qualifications: for the credit, the CxA may not be a subcontractor to the construction firm or an employee of the design or construction firm.

The CxA shall finish a summary commissioning report. The report shall include:

1) Executive summary
2) Test results and evaluation
3) History of deficiencies
4) Confirmation from the CxA whether the systems meet the Basis of Design (BOD), Owner's Project Requirements (OPR), and Constructions Documents (CD)

If you are pursuing credit for EAC Enhanced Commissioning, also include:

5) Submittal process summary
6) Design review summary
7) Operations and maintenance documentation and training process
8) As-built drawings

The design team needs to create the Basis of Design (BOD). The owner needs to document the Owner's Project Requirements (OPR). The CxA needs to review these for clarity and completeness. The design team and owner are responsible for updating their own documents.

You shall finish the commissioning process activities for at least the following systems:

a. Wind, solar, or other renewable energy systems.
b. Daylighting and lighting controls (Electrical).
c. Mechanical and passive HVAC and refrigeration systems and related controls.
d. Domestic hot water systems (Plumbing).

Mnemonics: REMP (See underlined letters above)

Current Facilities Requirements and Operations and Maintenance Plan
Create and maintain a current facilities requirements and operations and maintenance plan that contains the information necessary to operate the building efficiently. The plan must include the following:

- a sequence of operations for the building;
- the building occupancy schedule;
- equipment run-time schedules;
- setpoints for all HVAC equipment;
- set lighting levels throughout the building;
- minimum outside air requirements;

- any changes in schedules or setpoints for different days of the week, times of day, and seasons;
- a systems narrative describing the electrical and mechanical systems and equipment;
- a preventive maintenance plan for building equipment described in the systems narrative; and
- a commissioning program that includes ongoing commissioning tasks, periodic commissioning requirements, and continuous tasks for critical facilities.

Data Centers only
For a total computer room peak cooling load less than 600,000 Btu/h (175 kW) or small projects with computer room peak cooling loads less than 2,000,000 Btu/h (600 kW), the CxA can be a qualified employee of the design or construction team.

Campus
Group Approach
Separate submittal for each building.

Campus Approach
Qualified.

Submittals:

Submittals	All projects
CxA previous experience	x
Confirmation of OPR and BOD contents	x
List of systems to be commissioned	x
Verification of CxA activities and reviews	x
Cx plan	x
Documentation of testing and verification	x
CFR, O&M plan	x
Cx report	x

Synergies
- IPC: Integrative Process
- EAC: Advanced Energy Metering
- EAC: Renewable Energy Production
- EAC: Enhanced Commissioning

Extra Credit (Exemplary Performance):
None

Project Phase:
Construction Administration and Occupation/Operation.

LEED Submittal Phase:
Construction

Related Code or Standard:

ASHRAE Guideline 0–2005, The Commissioning Process: ashrae.org

ASHRAE Guideline 1.1–2007, HVAC&R Technical Requirements for the Commissioning Process: ashrae.org

NIBS Guideline 3–2012, Exterior Enclosure Technical Requirements for the Commissioning Process: wbdg.org/ccb/NIBS/nibs_gl3.pdf

Responsible Party:

CxA

EAP: **Minimum Energy Performance**

Mandatory for

New Construction (0 points)
Core and Shell (0 points)
Schools (0 points)
Retail (0 points)
Data Centers (0 points)
Warehouses and Distribution Centers (0 points)
Hospitality (0 points)
Healthcare (0 points)

Purpose

Achieves a minimum level of energy efficiency for the building and its systems to reduce excessive energy use and the related economic and environmental harms.

Prerequisite:

New Construction, Core and Shell, Schools, Retail, Healthcare, Warehouses and Distribution Centers, Hospitality

Choice 1. Whole-Building Energy Simulation

Show an improvement of 2% for core and shell projects, 3% for major renovations, or 5% for new construction in the proposed building performance rating compared with the baseline building performance rating. Calculate the baseline building performance per ANSI/ASHRAE/IESNA Standard 90.1–2010, Appendix G, with errata (or a USGBC-approved equivalent standard for projects outside the U.S.), using a simulation model.

Before obtaining credit for renewable energy systems, projects must meet the minimum percentage savings.

The proposed design has to meet these requirements:

- meet the mandatory provisions of **ANSI/ASHRAE/IESNA Standard 90.1–2010**, with errata (or a USGBC-approved equivalent standard for projects outside the U.S.);
- inclusion of all energy costs and consumption within and related to the building project; and
- comparison against a baseline building that meets Standard 90.1–2010, Appendix G, with errata (or a USGBC-approved equivalent standard for projects outside the U.S.).

Specify the energy modeling input assumptions for **unregulated loads**. Unregulated loads should be modeled accurately to show the actual expected energy consumption of the building.

If unregulated loads are not identical for both the baseline and the proposed building performance rating and the simulation program cannot accurately model the savings, follow the **exceptional calculation method** (ANSI/ASHRAE/IESNA Standard 90.1–2010, G2.5). Otherwise, use the **COMNET Modeling Guidelines and Procedures** to document measures that reduce unregulated loads.

Retail only

For Choice 1, Whole-Building Energy Simulation, process loads for retail can include clothes washing, cooking and food preparation, refrigeration equipment, and other major support appliances. Many of the industry standard baseline conditions for commercial kitchen equipment and refrigeration are defined in Appendix 3, Tables 1–4 of the USGBC reference. You do not need to memorize the information in these tables; you can look it up when you work on a LEED project. We are not going to repeat all of the tables in this book because these details are not likely to be tested on the LEED AP BD+C Exam. If the information is needed in the exam, the GBCI will provide a table for your use. No additional documentation is necessary to substantiate these predefined baseline systems as industry standard.

OR

Choice 2. Prescriptive Compliance: ASHRAE 50% Advanced Energy Design Guide

Meet the mandatory and *prescriptive* provisions of ANSI/ASHRAE/IESNA Standard 90.1–2010, with errata (or a USGBC-approved equivalent standard for projects outside the U.S.).

Meet the service water heating and HVAC requirements, including economizers, ventilation, equipment efficiency, and ducts and dampers, in Chapter 4, Design Strategies and Recommendations by Climate Zone, for the appropriate ASHRAE 50% Advanced Energy Design Guide and climate zone:

- ASHRAE 50% Advanced Energy Design Guide for Small to Medium Office Buildings, for office buildings smaller than 100,000 square feet (9,290 square meters);
- ASHRAE 50% Advanced Energy Design Guide for Medium to Large Box Retail Buildings, for retail buildings with 20,000 to 100,000 square feet (1,860 to 9,290 square meters);
- ASHRAE 50% Advanced Energy Design Guide for K–12 School Buildings; or
- ASHRAE 50% Advanced Energy Design Guide for Large Hospitals. Over 100,000 square feet (9,290 square meters).

For international projects, refer to ASHRAE/ASHRAE/IESNA Standard 90.1–2010, Appendixes B and D, to determine the proper climate zone.

Choice 3. Prescriptive Compliance: Advanced Buildings™ Core Performance™ Guide

Meet the mandatory and prescriptive provisions of ANSI/ASHRAE/IESNA Standard 90.1-2010, with errata (or USGBC approved equivalent standard for projects outside the U.S.).

Meet Section 1: Design Process Strategies, Section 2: Core Performance Requirements, and the following three strategies from Section 3: Enhanced Performance Strategies, as applicable. Where standards conflict, comply with the more stringent of the two. For international projects, refer to ASHRAE/ASHRAE/IESNA Standard 90.1-2010, Appendixes B and D, to determine the proper climate zone.

3.5 Supply Air Temperature Reset (VAV)
3.9 Premium Economizer Performance
3.10 Variable Speed Control
To qualify for Choice 3, the project must be less than 100,000 square feet (9,290 square meters).

Note: *Healthcare, Warehouse, or Laboratory projects cannot qualify for choice 3.*

Data Centers

Whole-Building Energy Simulation

Show a 5% improvement in the proposed performance rating over the baseline performance rating. To determine total energy cost savings, create **two models**: one for IT equipment energy cost and the other for building energy cost. Calculate the baseline building performance per ANSI/ASHRAE/IESNA Standard 90.1–2010, Appendix G, with errata (or a USGBC-approved equivalent standard for projects outside the U.S.), using a simulation model for the whole building and data center modeling guidelines.
Establish the **power utilization effectiveness (PUE)** value of the proposed design.

For this prerequisite, at least 2% of the 5% energy savings must come from cooling infrastructure and building power.

Projects must comply with the minimum percentage savings before taking credit for renewable energy systems.

The proposed design must comply with the following standards:
- meet the mandatory provisions of ANSI/ASHRAE/IESNA Standard 90.1–2010, with errata (or a USGBC-approved equivalent standard for projects outside the U.S.);
- inclusion of all energy costs and consumption within and related to the building project; and
- comparison against a baseline building that meets ANSI/ASHRAE/IESNA Standard 90.1–2010, Appendix G, with errata (or a USGBC-approved equivalent standard for projects outside the U.S.) and data center modeling guidelines

For data centers, regulated energy includes critical distribution equipment, critical power conditioning equipment, cooling units for computer and data processing rooms, heat rejection plants, and mechanical and electrical support rooms.

Include in process loads both the IT equipment load and the unregulated load. The IT load includes electrical power transformation and critical systems, which may include storage and networking power use, servers, and operations affecting monthly server CPU utilization percentages.

Create two sets of IT load models using two scenarios: one at the maximum estimated IT load rating and the second at the startup IT rating expected at the time of commissioning.

Establish the energy modeling input assumptions for unregulated loads. Unregulated loads should be modeled accurately to show the actual expected energy consumption of the building.

If unregulated loads are not the same for both the baseline and the proposed building performance rating and the simulation model cannot accurately model the savings, follow the **exceptional calculation method** (ANSI/ASHRAE/ IESNA Standard 90.1–2010, G2.5) to document measures that reduce unregulated loads.

Campus
Group Approach
Separate submittal for each building.

Campus Approach
Unqualified.

Note:
*A **prescriptive approach** has a limited set of system choices with mandatory performance characteristics. It is simplified and applicable to smaller buildings, retail stores, offices, schools, and some other building types. It is ideal for projects with straightforward design, smaller budgets, and packaged equipment and also provides energy-saving guidance for many simple buildings with standard energy systems. However, it can be inflexible because all the listed requirements must be achieved to meet the prerequisite. There are two prescriptive options available: one based on building size and the second on other factors.*

*A **performance approach** is more flexible, and evaluates the interactive effects of efficiency measures. It uses energy modeling to simulate the overall energy performance of a building. Project teams can then evaluate complex systems and make efficiency trade-offs among components and systems. The prescriptive options do not allow these trade-offs.*

Submittals:

Submittals	Choice 1	Choice 2	Choice 3
Appendix G energy modeling inputs	x		
Input-output reports from modeling software	x		
Exceptional calculations (if applicable)	x		
Energy consumption and demand for each building end use and fuel type	x		
Fuel rates	x		
AEDG compliance tables		x	
Target Finder results, summary			x
Confirmation that all aspects of CPG Sections 1 and 2 were met			x
Building configuration analysis			x
Building loads and mechanical system design capacity			x
Insulation installation details			x
Building envelope details			x
Domestic hot water efficiency			x
Narrative or calculations for CPG enhanced performance strategies			x
Data center calculator (if applicable)	x		
Retail process energy calculator (if applicable)	x		

Synergies

- IPC: Integrative Process
- WEP: Indoor Water Use Reduction
- EAC: Optimize Energy Performance
- EAC: Demand Response
- EAC: Renewable Energy Production
- EAC: Green Power and Carbon Offsets
- EQP: Minimum Indoor Air Quality Performance

Extra Credit (Exemplary Performance):

None

Project Phase:

Construction Documents

LEED Submittal Phase:

Design

Related Code or Standard:

- ASHRAE 90.1–2010 and ASHRAE 90.1–2010 User's Manual: ashrae.org
- ASHRAE 50% Advanced Energy Design Guides: ashrae.org
- Advanced Buildings Core Performance Guide: advancedbuildings.net/core-performance
- COMNET Commercial Buildings Energy Modeling Guidelines: comnet.org/mgp-manual

Responsible Party:

Mechanical Engineer

EAP: **Building-Level Energy Metering**

Mandatory for

New Construction (0 points)
Core and Shell (0 points)
Schools (0 points)
Retail (0 points)
Data Centers (0 points)
Warehouses and Distribution Centers (0 points)
Hospitality (0 points)
Healthcare (0 points)

Purpose

Tracks building-level energy use and identifies opportunities for additional energy savings and support energy management.

Prerequisite:

New Construction, Core and Shell, Schools, Retail, Data Centers, Warehouses and Distribution Centers, Hospitality, Healthcare

Use existing or install new building-level energy meters or submeters that can be collected to provide building-level data of total building energy consumption (natural gas, electricity, chilled water, steam, biomass, fuel oil, propane, etc.). Utility-owned meters that can collect building-level resource use are acceptable.

Project owner should commit to share with USGBC the resulting energy consumption data and electrical demand data (if metered) for a five-year period starting on the date the project accepts LEED certification. Energy consumption must be tracked monthly at a minimum.

This commitment must be valid for five years or until the building changes lessee or ownership.

Campus

Group Approach

Separate submittal for each building.

Campus Approach

Unqualified.

Submittals:

- Confirmation of permanently installed meters
- Letter of commitment
- Confirmation of data sharing source

Synergies

- EAC: Advanced Energy Metering
- EAC: Enhanced Commissioning Option 1, Path 2

Extra Credit (Exemplary Performance):

None

Project Phase:

Occupation/Operation

LEED Submittal Phase:
Construction

Related Code or Standard:

- **Electricity. American National Standards Institute, ANSI C12.20, Class 0.2 (± 0.2):** ansi.org
- **Natural gas. American National Standards Institute, ANSI B109:** ansi.org
- **Thermal energy (Btu meter or heat meter). EN Standard, EN-1434:** cen.eu

Responsible Party:
Owner or leasee

EAP: **Fundamental Refrigerant Management**

Mandatory for

New Construction (0 points)
Core and Shell (0 points)
Schools (0 points)
Retail (0 points)
Data Centers (0 points)
Warehouses and Distribution Centers (0 points)
Hospitality (0 points)
Healthcare (0 points)

Purpose

Reduces depletion of the stratospheric ozone.

Prerequisite:

For new heating, ventilating, air-conditioning, and refrigeration (HVAC&R) systems, do not use chlorofluorocarbon (CFC)-based refrigerants. For existing HVAC&R equipment reuse, before project completion, finalize a comprehensive CFC phase-out conversion. Phase-out plans extending beyond the project completion date will be considered on their merits.

Existing small HVAC&R units containing less than 0.5 pound [225 grams] of refrigerant and other equipment, such as small water coolers and standard refrigerators are exempt.

Campus
Group Approach
Separate submittal for each building.

Campus Approach
Qualified.

Submittals:

Submittals	All equipment	Phase out required
Equipment type		x
Refrigerant type		x
CFC conversion or replacement plan		x
Refrigerant leakage rate, quantity		x
Phase-out completion date		x
Confirmation that no new or existing equipment contains CFCs	x	

Synergies

- EAC: Enhanced Refrigerant Management
- EAC: Optimize Energy Performance

Extra Credit (Exemplary Performance):
None

Project Phase:
Pre-design

LEED Submittal Phase:
Design

Related Code or Standard:
U.S. EPA Clean Air Act, Title VI, Section 608, Refrigerant Recycling Rule: epa.gov/air/caa/

Responsible Party:
Mechanical Engineer

EAC: **Enhanced Commissioning**

Applicable to

New Construction (2-6 points)
Core and Shell (2-6 points)
Schools (2-6 points)
Retail (2-6 points)
Data Centers (2-6 points)
Warehouses and Distribution Centers (2-6 points)
Hospitality (2-6 points)
Healthcare (2-6 points)

Purpose

Expands support for the design, construction, and eventual operation of a project to meet the OPR for durability, water, energy, and indoor environmental quality

Credit Path:

In addition to those required under EAP: Fundamental Commissioning and Verification, perform, or have in place a contract to perform, the following commissioning process activities:

Commissioning Authority (CxA)

- The CxA should have documented commissioning process (CxP) experience on two or more similar building projects. The experience should span from the early design phase to at least 10 months of occupancy;
- The CxA may be an independent consultant, a qualified employee of the owner, or a disinterested subcontractor of the design team.

Choice 1. Enhanced Systems Commissioning (3-4 points)
Path 1: Enhanced Commissioning (3 points)
Finish the following commissioning process (CxP) activities for mechanical, electrical, plumbing, (MEP) and renewable energy systems and assemblies in accordance with **ASHRAE Guideline 0–2005 and ASHRAE Guideline 1.1–2007** for HVAC&R systems, as they relate to water, energy, indoor environmental quality, and durability.

The CxA must do the following:

- Create an on-going commissioning plan.
- Review contractor submittals.
- Verify inclusion of systems manual criteria in construction documents.
- Verify inclusion of operator and occupant training criteria in construction documents.
- Verify systems manual updates and delivery.
- Verify operator and occupant training delivery and effectiveness.
- Verify seasonal testing.
- Review building operations 10 months after substantial completion.

Include all enhanced commissioning tasks in the OPR and BOD.

OR
Path 2: Enhanced and Monitoring-Based Commissioning (4 points)
Achieve Path 1.

AND
Create monitoring-based procedures and identify points to be measured and assessed to evaluate

performance of energy- and water-consuming systems.

Discuss the procedures and measurement points in the commissioning plan. Include the following:

- roles and responsibilities;
- measurement criteria (meters, metering systems, points, data access);
- the points to be tracked, with frequency and duration for trend monitoring;
- the limits of acceptable values for tracked points and metered values (predictive algorithms may be used to compare ideal values with actual values where appropriate);
- the elements used to evaluate performance, including out-of-sequence operation of systems components, conflict between systems, and energy and water usage profiles;
- an action plan for identifying and correcting operational errors and deficiencies;
- training to prevent errors;
- planning for repairs needed to maintain performance; and
- the frequency of analyses in the first year of occupancy (at least quarterly).

Update the systems manual with any new settings or modifications and provide the justification for any modifications from the original design.

AND/OR
Choice 2. Envelope Commissioning (2 points)
Meet the criteria in EAP: Fundamental Commissioning and Verification as they apply to the building's thermal envelope in addition to mechanical and electrical systems and assemblies.

Finish the following CxP activities for the building's thermal envelope in accordance with **ASHRAE Guideline 0–2005 and the National Institute of Building Sciences (NIBS) Guideline 3–2012**, Exterior Enclosure Technical Requirements for the Commissioning Process, as they relate to water, energy, indoor environmental quality, and durability.

CxA must complete the following:

- Create an on-going commissioning plan.
- Review contractor submittals.
- Verify inclusion of systems manual requirements in construction documents.
- Verify inclusion of operator and occupant training requirements in construction documents.
- Verify systems manual updates and delivery.
- Verify operator and occupant training delivery and effectiveness.
- Verify seasonal testing.
- Review building operations 10 months after substantial completion.

For projects with peak cooling loads of 2,000,000 Btu/h (600 kW) or more or a total computer room peak cooling load of 600,000 Btu/h (175 kW) or more, the CxA must conduct at least three verification reviews of the basis of design:

- one verification review of design documents before the start of design development;
- one verification review of design documents before mid-construction documents; and
- one final verification review of 100% complete design documents, verifying achievement of the OPR and adjudication of previous review comments.

Data Centers only

Projects that select Choice 1 must complete the following commissioning process:

For small projects with peak cooling loads less than 2,000,000 Btu/h (600 kW), or a total computer room peak cooling load less than 600,000 Btu/h (175 kW), the CxA must perform the following activities:

- perform one or more commissioning verification review of the OPR, BOD, and design documents before mid-construction documents development;
- back-check the review comments in all subsequent design submissions; and
- perform an additional full verification review at 95% completion of the design documents and BOD.

Campus

Group Approach

All buildings in the group may be one submittal.

Campus Approach

Unqualified.

Submittals:

Submittals	Choice 1, Path 1	Choice 1, Path 2	Choice 2
List of all tasks completed as part of Cx activities	x	x	x
Training outline and participation list	x	x	x
Confirmation of systems manual delivery	x	x	x
Ongoing Cx plan	x	x	x
Inclusion of monitoring and tracking in Cx plan		x	
Inclusion of envelope in Cx plan			x
Verification of additional reviews per Data Center requirements (data centers only)	x	x	

Synergies

- EAP: Fundamental Commissioning and Verification
- EAC: Renewable Energy Production
- EAC: Demand Response
- EAC: Advanced Energy Metering

Extra Credit (Exemplary Performance):

None

Project Phase:

From Pre-Design to Occupation/Operation.

LEED Submittal Phase:

Construction

Related Code or Standard:

- **ASHRAE Guideline 0–2005, The Commissioning Process:** ashrae.org
- **ASHRAE Guideline 1.1–2007, HVAC&R Technical Requirements for the Commissioning Process:** ashrae.org
- **NIBS Guideline 3–2012, Exterior Enclosure Technical Requirements for the Commissioning Process:** nibs.org

Responsible Party:

CxA, owner, contractor, and design team

EAC: **Optimize Energy Performance**

Applicable to

New Construction (1-18 points)
Core and Shell (1-18 points)
Schools (1-16 points)
Retail (1-18 points)
Data Centers (1-18 points)
Warehouses and Distribution Centers (1-18 points)
Hospitality (1-18 points)
Healthcare (1-20 points)

Purpose

Reduces economic and environmental harms related to excessive energy use by achieving advanced levels of energy performance beyond the prerequisite standard.

Credit Path:

New Construction, Core and Shell, Schools, Retail, warehouses and distribution centers, Hospitality, healthcare

Set an energy performance target at the schematic design phase or earlier. The target has to be set as Btu per square foot-year (kW per square meter-year) of source energy use.

Choose one of the following:

Choice 1. Whole-Building Energy Simulation (1–18 points except Schools and Healthcare, 1–16 points Schools, 1–20 points Healthcare)

Analyze efficiency measures throughout the design process and justify the results in design decision making. Use energy simulation of efficiency opportunities, published data (e.g., Advanced Energy Design Guides) from analyses for similar buildings or past energy simulation analyses for similar buildings.

Focus on load reduction and HVAC-related strategies (passive measures are acceptable) appropriate for the facility, analyze efficiency measures. Calculate holistic project cost implications and potential energy savings related to all affected systems.

Project teams pursuing the IPC: Integrative Process has to finish the basic energy analysis for that credit before conducting the energy simulation.

Comply with the criteria in EAP: Energy Performance to show a percentage improvement in the proposed building performance rating related to the baseline. Points are awarded per Table 1.

Table 1. Points for percentage improvement in energy performance

New Construction	Major Renovation	Core and Shell	Points (except Schools, Healthcare)	Points (Healthcare)	Points (Schools)
6%	4%	3%	1	3	1
8%	6%	5%	2	4	2
10%	8%	7%	3	5	3
12%	10%	9%	4	6	4
14%	12%	11%	5	7	5
16%	14%	13%	6	8	6
18%	16%	15%	7	9	7
20%	18%	17%	8	10	8
22%	20%	19%	9	11	9

24%	22%	21%	10	12	10
26%	24%	23%	11	13	11
29%	**27%**	**26%**	12	14	12
32%	30%	29%	13	15	13
35%	33%	32%	14	16	14
38%	36%	35%	15	17	15
42%	**40%**	**39%**	16	18	16
46%	44%	43%	17	19	-
50%	48%	47%	18	20	-

Retail only
Define a clear baseline for all process loads. The baselines in the USGBC reference Appendix 3, Tables 1–4, represent industry standards and can be used without additional documentation.

Note:
We are not going to repeat the tables here. If the LEED AP BD+C exam requires you to calculate the information in the tables, the ratio should be provided in the exam. If you are working on a LEED project, you can look up the information from the table in the USGBC reference guide.

Calculate the baseline and design as follows:

- **Appliances and equipment:** Specify hourly energy use for proposed and budget equipment, with estimated daily use hours for appliances and equipment not covered in Tables 1–4. Include the total estimated appliance/equipment energy use in the energy simulation model as a **plug load**. For this credit, schedule change or reduced use time is not a category of energy improvement. **ENERGY STAR** ratings and evaluations are a valid basis for performing this calculation.
- **Display lighting:** Use the space-by-space method of determining allowed lighting power under ANSI/ASHRAE/IESNA Standard 90.1–2010, with errata (or a USGBC-approved equivalent standard for projects outside the U.S.), to determine the appropriate baseline for both the display lighting and the general building space.
- **Refrigeration:** Use a simulation program designed to account for refrigeration equipment to model the effect of energy performance improvements for hard-wired refrigeration loads.

Note:
***Plug load** is the energy used by products powered by means of an ordinary **AC (alternating current) plug** (e.g., 100, 115, or 230 V). This term typically excludes building energy that is assigned to major end uses (HVAC, water heating, lighting, etc.)*

Choice 2. Prescriptive Compliance: ASHRAE Advanced Energy Design Guide (1–6 points)
To be eligible for Choice 2, projects must use Choice 2 in EAP: Minimum Energy Performance.

Instigate and verify compliance with the pertinent recommendations and standards in Design Strategies and Recommendations by Climate Zone, for the appropriate ASHRAE 50% Advanced Energy Design Guide and climate zone. For international projects, consult ASHRAE/ASHRAE/IESNA Standard 90.1–2010, Appendixes B and D, to determine the proper climate zone.

ASHRAE 50% Advanced Energy Design Guide for Small to Medium Office Buildings

- *Building envelope, opaque*: roofs, walls, floors, slabs, doors, and continuous air barriers (1 point)
- *Building envelope, glazing*: vertical fenestration (1 point)
- *Interior lighting*, including interior finishes and daylighting (1 point)
- *Exterior lighting* (1 point)
- **Plug loads**, including controls and equipment (1 point)

ASHRAE 50% Advanced Energy Design Guide for Medium to Large Box Retail Buildings

- *Building envelope, opaque*: slabs, floors, walls, roofs, doors, and vestibules (1 point)
- *Building envelope, glazing*: fenestration - all orientations (1 point)
- *Interior lighting*, excluding lighting power density for sales floor (1 point)
- *Additional interior lighting* for sales floor (1 point)
- *Exterior lighting* (1 point)
- **Plug loads**, including controls and equipment (1 point)

ASHRAE 50% Advanced Energy Design Guide for K–12 School Buildings

- *Building envelope, opaque*: slabs, floors, walls, roofs, and doors (1 point)
- *Building envelope, glazing*: vertical fenestration (1 point)
- *Interior lighting*, including interior finishes and daylighting (1 point)
- *Exterior lighting* (1 point)
- **Plug loads**, including controls, equipment choices, and kitchen equipment (1 point)

ASHRAE 50% Advanced Energy Design Guide for Large Hospitals

- *Building envelope, opaque*: slabs, floors, walls, roofs, doors, vestibules, and continuous air barriers (1 point)
- *Building envelope, glazing*: vertical fenestration (1 point)
- *Interior lighting*, including daylighting (form or nonform driven) and interior finishes (1 point)
- *Exterior lighting* (1 point)
- **Plug loads**, including controls, equipment choices, and kitchen equipment (1 point)

Retail only

Comply with the criteria of **Choice 2** and the prescriptive measures in Appendix 3, Tables 1–4, for 90% of total energy consumption for all process equipment.

Data Centers

Whole-Building Energy Simulation

Analyze efficiency measures focused on HVAC-related strategies (air-side economizers, hot aisle–cold aisle, etc.) and IT load reduction. Predict the cost implications and potential energy savings for all affected systems.

Follow the criteria in EAP: Minimum Energy Performance to show a percentage improvement in the proposed performance rating compared with the baseline.

Use energy cost savings from both the IT and building to determine the total percentage reduction.

Campus
Group Approach
All buildings in the group may be documented as one.

Campus Approach
Unqualified.

Submittals:

Submittals	Choice 1	Choice 2
Appendix G energy modeling inputs	x	
Input and output reports from modeling software	x	
Renewable energy (if applicable)	x	
Exceptional calculations (if applicable)	x	
Target Finder results and summary	x	x
Energy consumption and demand for each building end use and fuel type	x	
Fuels rates	x	
AEDG compliance tables		x
List of process equipment efficiencies (retail only)		x

Synergies
- EAP: Minimum Energy Performance
- EAC: Renewable Energy Production

Extra Credit (Exemplary Performance):
- Choice 1. New construction, major renovation, and core and shell projects: Achieve at least 54% energy savings.

Project Phase:
Construction Documents

LEED Submittal Phase:
Design

Related Code or Standard:
ASHRAE 90.1–2010 and ASHRAE 90.1–2010 User's Manual: ashrae.org
ASHRAE 50% Advanced Energy Design Guides: ashrae.org
COMNET Commercial Buildings Energy Modeling Guidelines: comnet.org/mgp-manual

Responsible Party:
Mechanical Engineer

EAC: **Advanced Energy Metering**

Mandatory for

New Construction (1 point)
Core and Shell (1 point)
Schools (1 point)
Retail (1 point)
Data Centers (1 point)
Warehouses and Distribution Centers (1 point)
Hospitality (1 point)
Healthcare (1 point)

Purpose

Tracks building-level and system-level energy use, identifies opportunities for additional energy savings, and supports energy management.

Credit Path:

New Construction, Schools, Retail, Data Centers, Warehouses and Distribution Centers, Hospitality, Healthcare

Set up advanced energy metering for:

- all whole-building energy sources; and
- any individual energy end uses that is at least10% of the total annual building consumption.

The advanced energy metering should have the following features:

- Meters have to be permanently installed, transmit data to a remote location, and be record at intervals of not more than one hour.
- Electricity meters have to record both demand and consumption. Whole-building electricity meters should record the power factor, if applicable.
- The data collection system has to use a building automation system, LAN (local area network), wireless network, or comparable communication infrastructure.
- The system has to be able to store all meter data for at least 36 months.
- The data has to be remotely accessible.
- All meters in the system have to be able to report hourly, daily, monthly, and annual energy use.

Core and Shell

Set up meters for future tenant spaces for tenants to independently meter energy consumption (chilled water, electricity, etc.) for all systems dedicated to their space. Provide a sufficient number of meters to capture total tenant energy use with at least one meter per energy source per floor.

Set up advanced energy metering for all base building energy sources.

The advanced energy metering should have the following features:

- Meters have to be permanently installed, transmit data to a remote location, and be recorded at intervals of not more than one hour.
- Electricity meters have to record both demand and consumption. Whole-building electricity meters should record the power factor, if applicable.
- The data collection system has to use a building automation system, LAN (local area network), wireless network, or comparable communication infrastructure.
- The system has to be able to store all meter data for at least 36 months.
- The data has to be remotely accessible.
- All meters in the system have to be able to report hourly, daily, monthly, and annual energy use.

Campus
Group Approach
Separate submittal for each building.

Campus Approach
Unqualified. Separate submittal for each building.

Submittals:

- List of all advanced meters to be installed, including energy source metered and type
- Manufacturers' cut sheets

Synergies

- EAP: Minimum Energy Performance
- EAP: Building-Level Metering
- EAC: Demand Response
- EAC: Renewable Energy Production

Extra Credit (Exemplary Performance):
None

Project Phase:
Construction Documents

LEED Submittal Phase:
Design

Related Code or Standard:
None

Responsible Party:
Mechanical Engineer

EAC: **Demand Response**

Applicable to

New Construction (1-2 points)
Core and Shell (1-2 points)
Schools (1-2 points)
Retail (1-2 points)
Data Centers (1-2 points)
Warehouses and Distribution Centers (1-2 points)
Hospitality (1-2 points)
Healthcare (1-2 points)

Purpose

Reduces greenhouse gas emissions, increases grid reliability, and increases participation in demand response programs and technologies that make distribution systems and energy generation more efficient.

Credit Path:

Design equipment and building for participation in demand response programs through load shifting or shedding.

On-site electricity generation does not meet the intent of this credit.

Choice 1. Demand Response Program Available (2 points)

- Join an existing demand response (DR) program and complete the following activities. Design a system that is capable of fully-automated, real-time DR based on external initiation by a DR program provider. Semi-automated DR can be utilized in practice.
- Enroll in a one-year-minimum DR participation amount contractual commitment with a qualified DR program provider, for the purpose of multiyear renewal, for a minimum of 10% of the estimated peak electricity demand. Peak demand is determined under EAP: Minimum Energy Performance.
- Create a comprehensive plan for meeting the contractual commitment during a DR event.
- Incorporate the DR processes in the scope of work for the commissioning authority (CxA), including participation in a minimum of one full test of the DR plan.

Choice 2. Demand Response Program Not Available (1 point)

Offer infrastructure to utilize future demand response programs or real-time pricing, dynamic programs, and finish the following activities.

- Instate interval recording meters with ability and communications for the building automation system to accept an external control signal or price.
- Create a comprehensive plan for shedding a minimum of 10% of building estimated peak electricity demand. Peak demand is determined under EAP: Minimum Energy Performance.
- Incorporate the DR processes in the scope of work for the commissioning authority (CxA), including participation in a minimum of one full test of the DR plan.
- Communicate with local utility representatives to discuss participation in future DR programs.

Campus
Group Approach
All buildings in the group may be submitted as one.

Campus Approach
Unqualified. Separate submittal for each building.

Submittals:

Submittals	Choice 1	Choice 2
Evidence of enrollment in DR program	x	
Proof of ability to shed 10% of peak demand	x	x
Confirmation that system can receive and act on external signal	x	x
Action plan to comply with reduction criteria during event	x	x
Inclusion of DR in CxA systems testing plan	x	x

Synergies:
- EAP: Fundamental Commissioning and Verification

Extra Credit (Exemplary Performance):
None

Project Phase:
Construction Documents

LEED Submittal Phase:
Design

Related Code or Standard:
None

Responsible Party:
Mechanical Engineer

EAC: **Renewable Energy Production**

Applicable to

New Construction (1-3 points)
Core and Shell (1-3 points)
Schools (1-3 points)
Retail (1-3 points)
Data Centers (1-3 points)
Warehouses and Distribution Centers (1-3 points)
Hospitality (1-3 points)
Healthcare (1-3 points)

Purpose

Increases self-supply of renewable energy, and reduces the economic environmental harms related to fossil fuel energy.

Credit Path:

Use renewable energy systems to reduce or eliminate building energy costs. Use the following equation to calculate the percentage of renewable energy:

$$\% \text{ renewable energy} = \frac{\text{Equivalent cost of usable energy produced by the renewable energy system}}{\text{Total building annual energy cost}}$$

Use the building's annual energy cost, calculated in EAP: Minimum Energy Performance, if Choice 1 was selected.

OR

Use the U.S. Department of Energy's **Commercial Buildings Energy Consumption Survey (CBECS)** database to estimate energy use and cost.

The USGBC allows the use of solar gardens or community renewable energy systems if both of the following criteria are met.

- The project has signed a lease agreement for a minimum of 10 years or owns the system.
- The system is in the same utility service area as the facility claiming the use.

Credit is based on the percentage of use assigned in the lease agreement or the percentage of ownership. Points are awarded per Table 1.

Table 1. Points for renewable energy		
Percentage renewable energy	**Points (All, except Core and Shell)**	**Points (Core and Shell)**
1%	1	1
3%	-	2
5%	2	3
10%	3	-

Campus

Group Approach

All buildings in the group may be submitted as one.

Campus Approach

Unqualified. Separate submittal for each building.

Submittals:

Submittals	On-site system	Third-party system ownership	Community system
Renewable system rated capacity	x	x	x
Calculations to determine energy generated	x	x	x
Equivalent cost of renewable energy produced	x	x	x
Documentation of annual energy costs	x	x	x
Contract indicating duration		x	x
Documentation indicating percentage owned or leased of community system			x

Synergies

- EAC: Advanced Energy Metering
- EAC: Green Power and Carbon Offsets

Extra Credit (Exemplary Performance):

- Renewable energy has tocomprise15% of total energy. For Core and Shell projects, the threshold is 10%.

Project Phase:

Construction Documents

LEED Submittal Phase:

Design

Related Code or Standard:

- **Center for Resource Solutions Green-e Program:** green-e.org
- **Commercial Building Energy Consumption Survey (CBECS):** eia.gov/consumption/commercial

Responsible Party:

Mechanical Engineer

EAC: **Enhanced Refrigerant Management**

Applicable to

New Construction (1 point)
Core and Shell (1 point)
Schools (1 point)
Retail (1 point)
Data Centers (1 point)
Warehouses and Distribution Centers (1 point)
Hospitality (1 point)
Healthcare (1 point)

Purpose

Minimizes direct contributions to climate change, reduces depletion of ozone layer, and supports early compliance with the Montreal Protocol.

Credit Path:

New Construction, Core and Shell, Schools, Data Centers, Warehouses and Distribution Centers, Hospitality, HealthCare

Choice 1. No Refrigerants or Low-Impact Refrigerants (1 point)

Use no refrigerants, or use only refrigerants (synthetic or naturally occurring) that have a global warming potential (**GWP**) of less than 50 and an ozone depletion potential (**ODP**) of zero.

OR

Choice 2. Calculation of Refrigerant Impact (1 point)

Choose refrigerants for heating, ventilating, air-conditioning, and refrigeration (**HVAC&R**) equipment to eliminate or minimize the emission of compounds that contribute to ODP and climate change. The combination of all existing and new base building and tenant HVAC&R equipment for the project have to comply with the following formulas:

English System (IP Units)	Metric System (SI Units)
Calculation definitions for LCGWP + LCODP $\times 10^5 \leqslant 100$ (IP units)	Calculation definitions for LCGWP + kg CFC 11/(kW/year) x $10^5 \leqslant 13$ (SI units)
LCODP = [ODPr × (Lr × Life + Mr) × Rc] / Life	kg CFC 11/(kW/year) = [ODPr × (Lr × Life + Mr) × Rc] / Life
LCGWP = [GWPr × (Lr × Life + Mr) × Rc] / Life	LCGWP = [GWPr × (Lr × Life + Mr) × Rc] / Life
LCODP: Lifecycle Ozone Depletion Potential (lb CFC 11/Ton-Year)	kg CFC 11/(kW/year): Lifecycle Ozone Depletion Potential (lb CFC 11/Ton-Year)
LCGWP: Lifecycle Direct Global Warming Potential (lb CO_2 /Ton-Year)	LCGWP: Lifecycle Direct Global Warming Potential (kg CO_2/kW-year)
GWPr: Global Warming Potential of Refrigerant (0 to 12,000 lb CO_2/ lbr)	GWPr: Global Warming Potential of Refrigerant (0 to 12,000 kg CO_2/kg r)
ODPr: Ozone Depletion Potential of Refrigerant (0 to 0.2 lb CFC 11/lbr)	ODPr: Ozone Depletion Potential of Refrigerant (0 to 0.2 kg CFC 11/kg r)
Lr: Refrigerant Leakage Rate (2.0%)	Lr: Refrigerant Leakage Rate (2.0%)
Mr: End-of-life Refrigerant Loss (10%)	Mr: End-of-life Refrigerant Loss (10%)
Rc: Refrigerant Charge (0.5 to 5.0 lbs of refrigerant per ton of gross AHRI rated cooling capacity)	Rc: Refrigerant Charge (0.065 to 0.65 kg of refrigerant per kW of AHRI rated or Eurovent Certified cooling capacity)
Life: Equipment Life (10 years; default based on equipment type, unless otherwise demonstrated)	Life: Equipment Life (10 years; default based on equipment type, unless otherwise demonstrated)

For multiple types of equipment, use the following formula to calculate a weighted average of all base building HVAC&R equipment:

IP Units	SI Units
$\frac{\Sigma [(LCGWP+LCODP \times 10^5) Qunit]}{Qtotal} \leq 100$	$\frac{\Sigma [(LCGWP+LCODP \times 10^5) Qunit]}{Qtotal} \leq 13$

Qunit = Gross AHRI rated cooling capacity of an individual HVAC or refrigeration unit (Tons) **Qtotal**= Total gross AHRI rated cooling capacity of all HVAC or refrigeration	**Qunit** = Eurovent Certified cooling capacity of an individual HVAC or refrigeration unit (kW) **Qtotal** = Total Eurovent Certified cooling capacity of all HVAC or refrigeration (kW)

Retail
Meet Choice 1 or 2 for all HVAC systems.

Stores with commercial refrigeration systems have to meet the following criteria.

- Use non-ozone-depleting refrigerants only.
- Choose equipment with an average HFC refrigerant charge of 1.75 pounds of refrigerant or less per 1,000 Btu/h (2.72 kg of refrigerant per kW) total evaporator cooling load.
- Show a predicted store-wide annual refrigerant emissions rate of 15% or less. Conduct leak testing using the procedures in GreenChill's best practices guideline for leak tightness at installation.

As an alternate, stores with commercial refrigeration systems can provide proof of attainment of EPA GreenChill's silver-level store certification for newly constructed stores.

Campus
Group Approach
Separate submittal for each building.

Campus Approach
Choice 1: Qualified.
Choice 2: Unqualified. Separate submittal for each building.

Submittals:

Submittals	Choice 1	Choice 2
Confirmation that only no or low-impact refrigerants are used	x	
Equipment type		x
Refrigerant charge calculations (for VRF systems only)		x
Equipment cooling capacity		x
Provide refrigerant equipment schedule or GreenChill certification (commercial refrigeration systems)		x
Equipment quantity		x
Refrigerant type		x
Refrigerant charge (plus supporting documentation, if applicable)		x
Equipment life (plus supporting documentation, if applicable)		x
Leak test results (commercial refrigeration systems only)		x

Synergies

- EAC: Optimize Energy Performance

Extra Credit (Exemplary Performance):

None

Project Phase:

Schematic Design & Construction Documents,

LEED Submittal Phase:

Design

Related Code or Standard:

None

Responsible Party:

Mechanical Engineer

EAC: **Green Power and Carbon Offsets**

Applicable to

New Construction (1-2 points)
Core and Shell (1-2 points)
Schools (1-2 points)
Retail (1-2 points)
Data Centers (1-2 points)
Warehouses and Distribution Centers (1-2 points)
Hospitality (1-2 points)
Healthcare (1-2 points)

Purpose

Promotes the use of carbon mitigation projects, renewable energy grid-source technologies, and the reduction of greenhouse gas emissions.

Credit Path:

Sign a contract for qualified resources for a minimum of five years to be delivered at least annually. The resources must have come online since January 1, 2005. The contract has to stipulate the provision of a minimum of 50% or 100% of the project's energy from carbon offsets, green power, or renewable energy certificates (**RECs**).

Green power and RECs have to be **Green-e Energy certified** or the equivalent. The project team can only use RECs to mitigate the effects of Scope 2, electricity use.

Carbon offsets can be Green-e Climate certified, or the equivalent, and be used to mitigate Scope 1 or Scope 2 emissions on a metric ton of carbon dioxide–equivalent basis.

Establish the percentage of green power or offsets per the **quantity** of energy consumed, not the cost. For U.S. projects, the offsets have to be from greenhouse gas emissions reduction projects within the U.S. Points are awarded according to Table 1.

Table 1. Points for energy from green power or carbon offsets

Percentage of total energy addressed by green power, RECs, and/or offsets	Points
50%	1
100%	2

If Choice 1 was pursued, use the project's annual energy consumption, calculated in EAP: Minimum Energy Performance; otherwise, use the U.S. Department of Energy's Commercial Buildings Energy Consumption Survey (CBECS) database to estimate energy use.

Core and Shell Only

A **core and shell building's energy** is the energy usage of the core and shell floor area per the Building Owners and Managers Association (BOMA) standards, but not less than 15% of the project's floor area.

Campus

Group Approach

All buildings in the group may be submitted as one.

Campus Approach

Unqualified. Separate submittal for each building.

Submittals:

- Annual electricity and nonelectricity energy use calculations
- Calculations showing required REC, green power, or carbon offsets for targeted point threshold
- Purchase contract or letter of commitment showing REC, green power, or carbon offsets for targeted point threshold
- Green-e equivalency documentation, if not Green-e certified

Synergies:

- EAP: Minimum Energy Performance
- EAC: Optimize Energy Performance
- EAC: Renewable Energy Production

Extra Credit (Exemplary Performance):

None

Project Phase:

Pre-Design

LEED Submittal Phase:

Design

Related Code or Standard:

- **Green-e Energy and Green-e Climate:** green-e.org
- **U.S. Department of Energy's Commercial Buildings Energy Consumption Survey (CBECS):** eia.gov/consumption/commercial/index.cfm
- **Building Owners and Managers Association (BOMA):** boma.org
- **ENERGY STAR Portfolio Manager: Methodology for Greenhouse Gas Inventory and Tracking Calculations:** energystar.gov/ia/business/evaluate_performance/Emissions_Supporting_Doc.pdf?72c6-8475
- **Inventory of U.S. Greenhouse Gas Emissions and Sinks: 1990–2010. Annex 2 Methodology and Data for**
- **Estimating CO_2 Emissions from Fossil Fuel Combustion:** epa.gov/climatechange/ghgemissions/usinventoryreport/archive.html
- **2006 IPCC Guidelines for National Greenhouse Gas Inventories:** ipcc-nggip.iges.or.jp/public/2006gl/index.html
- **eGRID2012 Version 1.0—U.S. Environmental Protection Agency:** epa.gov/cleanenergy/energy-resources/egrid/index.html
- **WRI-WBCSD Greenhouse Gas Protocol:** ghgprotocol.org/standards

Responsible Party:

Mechanical Engineer

Chapter 10

Materials and Resources (MR)

Overall Purpose

The MR credit category emphasizes minimizing the impacts such as the embodied energy that is associated with the maintenance, processing, extraction, transport, and disposal of building materials. The criteria are set up to encourage resource efficiency and support a **life-cycle approach,** which in turn improves performance. Each criterion recognizes a particular action that is part of a life-cycle approach to embodied impact reduction.

The Hierarchy of Waste Management

About 25% of the total waste stream in the European Union and about 40% of the total solid waste stream in the United States is construction and demolition waste. **Source reduction, reuse, recycling, and waste to energy** are the four preferred strategies for reducing waste in the **solid waste management hierarchy** for the US Environmental Protection Agency (EPA) ranks. The MR section directly covers each of these recommended strategies.

Source reduction prevents environmental damages in a material's entire life cycle, from the supply chain, to actual use, and finally to recycling and waste disposal. It is at the top of the hierarchy in regards to efficiency. Source reduction promotes designing and prefabrication of dimensional construction materials and other innovative construction strategies to minimize inefficiencies and material cutoffs.

Building and material **reuse** prevents environmental harms caused by the manufacturing process, and is the second most effective strategy. Production and transportation of new materials are required to replace existing materials with new ones. The process generates greenhouse gases and takes many years of increased building efficiency to be offset. LEED v4 is more flexible and rewards all material reuse in a project, including both in situ and from off site, as well as building reuse and salvaging strategies. Rewarding material reuse is a consistent LEED strategy.

Recycling is the most common practice to divert waste from landfills. Traditionally, most waste is sent to a landfill and with time is becoming more and more of an unsustainable solution. Landfill space is being used up in urban areas, requires more land elsewhere, and raises the waste transportation costs. Recycling technology innovations improve processing and sorting, keep the materials in the production stream for longer, and supply raw material to secondary markets.

Secondary markets only exist for some materials. The conversion of energy is its next most beneficial use. Many countries use a waste-to-energy solution to alleviate the burden on landfills. In Saudi Arabia, Sweden, and some other countries, there are far more waste-to-energy facilities than landfills. Waste-to-energy can be a feasible alternative to energy production by extracting fossil fuels when air quality control measures are strict.

Overall, LEED projects have diverted more than 80 million tons (72.6 million tonnes) of waste from landfills, and are expected to divert 540 million tons (489.9 million tonnes) by 2030. LEED projects in Seattle diverted 175,000 tons (158,757.3 tonnes), which is an average of 90% of their construction waste from the landfill from 2000 to 2011. The result would be astounding if all newly constructed buildings can achieve the 90% diversion rate. Construction debris is a resource instead of waste.

Life-Cycle Assessment in LEED

Using MR category credits, LEED has created a cycle of end user demand and industry distribution of environmentally preferable products, and started to transform the building products market. LEED has generated demand for increasingly sustainable products, and designers, manufacturers, and suppliers are responding. LEED has measurably increased the supply of sustainable materials, such as bio-based materials, increased recycled content, and harvested wood. Some MR credits promote the use of products that meet specific criteria. However, some products that have different sustainable attributes are hard to compare. For instance, solid wood cabinets made from local timber versus cabinets bound together in resin and made of wheat husks sourced from no local areas. **Life-cycle assessment (LCA)** offers a more complete picture of products and materials, allows project teams to make more informed choices that will have greater overall benefit for the human health, environmental, and communities, while promoting innovation and encouraging manufacturers to improve their products.

According to ISO 14040 International Standard, Environmental management, Life cycle assessment, principles and framework (Geneva, Switzerland: International Organization for Standardization, 2006), **LCA** is a "compilation and evaluation of the inputs and outputs and the potential environmental impacts of a product system throughout its life cycle." Project teams examine the entire life cycle of a building or product, identify the constituents and processes, and assess their environmental effects both upstream and downstream, from the point of raw materials extraction or manufacture, to transportation, use, maintenance, and end of life. LCA is also called **"cradle to grave."** Going one step further, **"cradle to cradle"** emphasizes reuse and recycling instead of disposal.

LCA started with carbon accounting models in the 1960s. LCA practices and standards have been refined and developed since then. Regulators, specifiers, manufacturers, and consumers in many fields have been using life-cycle information to improve their product environmental profiles and product selections in Europe and some other places. However, the United States lacked the tools and data that support LCA until recently. Now more and more manufacturers are ready to detail and publicly release the environmental profiles of their products, and programs are available to help users understand the results and assist this effort.

LEED strives to speed up the use of LCA-based decision-making and LCA tools, so as to improve the quality of databases and stimulate market transformation. Because of the limitations of LCA for dealing with the ecosystem consequences and human health of raw material extraction, LEED uses different, complementary approaches to LCA in credits covering these topics.

Cross-Cutting Issues

Required Products and Materials

The MR credit category includes the portions of the building or the whole building that are being renovated or constructed. Unless otherwise noted, project teams typically exclude portions of an existing building that are not in the renovation scope from MR documentation. See the minimum program requirements (MPR) for information on additions.

Qualifying Products and Exclusions

The MR section covers "permanently installed building products," which means materials and products that are attached to a building or that create the building. These include enclosure and structural elements, framing, interior walls, installed finishes, cabinets and casework, doors, and roofs, etc. Most of these materials belong to Construction Specifications Institute (CSI) 2012 MasterFormat Divisions 3-10, 31, and 32. Some products covered by MR credits may be outside these divisions.

Project teams do not have to include furniture in credit calculations. Nevertheless, if project teams include furniture in MR credit calculations, they must include all furniture consistently in all cost-based credits.

In previous versions of LEED, the USGBC excluded all mechanical, plumbing, and electrical equipment (MEP), part of CSI MasterFormat divisions 11, 21-28, and other specialty divisions from MR credits. In LEED v4, some specific products that are "passive" parts of the system (not part of the active portions of the system) may be included. This allows optional assessment of ducts, duct insulation, conduit, lamp housings, piping, pipe insulation, plumbing fixtures, showerheads, and faucets. If project teams include them in credit calculations, they must include them consistently in relevant MR credits. Nevertheless, unlike furniture, if project teams include some of these products in credit calculations, they do NOT have to include all products of that type. For instance, if project teams include the cost of ducts in the MR calculations for recycled content, they do NOT have to include the cost of ducts that do not meet the credit requirement in the denominator or numerator of the credit calculation. Nevertheless, cost-based credits (all Building Product Disclosure and Optimization credits) calculations must have the same denominator.

Process equipment, fire suppression systems, elevators, escalators, and other special equipment, is not included in the credit calculations. Concrete formwork and other products purchased for temporary use on the project are also excluded.

For healthcare projects, the MR Credit Medical Furniture and Furnishings includes all freestanding medical furnishings and furniture. To avoid double-counting, freestanding furniture items counted in this credit cannot be included in any Building Product Disclosure and Optimization credit. Built-in millwork, casework and other permanently installed items must be counted in the Building Product Disclosure and Optimization credits, not MR Credit Medical Furniture and Furnishings.

Defining a Product

Some credit calculations in this category are based on the number of products instead of product cost. In these cases, a "permanently installed building product" or a "product" is defined by its function. A product includes the necessary services and physical components to serve its function. For similar products within a specification, each is counted as a separate product. Here are a few samples.

Products shipped to the project site ready for installation-

- Concrete masonry units, wallboard, and metal studs are all separate products.
- For wallboard, the binder, the gypsum, and backing are all required for its function, so each ingredient is not a separate product.

Products shipped to the project site as a component or ingredient used in a site-assembled product-

- Since each component in concrete (aggregate, admixture, and cement) serves a different function, each component is considered a separate product.

  Similar products from the same manufacturer with reconfigurations or aesthetic variations versus similar products from the same manufacturer with different formulations-

- Since paint types of distinct gloss levels, such as gloss, semi-gloss, and flat paint, are specified to serve a specific function, such as water resistance, they are separate products. Since different colors of the same paint serve the same function, they are not separate products.
- Since carpets of different pile heights are used for different kinds of foot traffic, they are separate products. Since the carpets in the same product line but in a different color serve the same function, they are not separate products.
- Since side chairs and desk chairs in the same product line serve different functions, they are different products. Since two side chairs with only different aesthetic aspects, such as the presence of arms, serve the same function, they are not different products.

Determining Product Cost

Product and material cost includes all contractor expenses and taxes to ship the material to the project site but does *not* include any cost for equipment and labor necessary for installation after the material is shipped to the site.

Use either the default materials cost or the actual materials cost to calculate the total materials cost of a project.

Default materials cost calculates 45% of the total construction costs as an option to determine the total materials cost. It can replace the actual cost for most products and materials, as listed above. If optional products and materials, such as MEP items and furniture are included, project teams should add the actual value of those items to the default value for all other materials and products.

Actual materials cost is the cost of all the materials used on the job site, including delivery and taxes, but excluding labor.

Location Valuation Factor

Some MR category credits include a location valuation factor which adds value to locally produced materials and products. The purpose is to encourage the purchase of products and support the local economy. Materials and products manufactured, extracted, and purchased within 100 miles (160 kilometers) of the project are valued at two times their cost.

To qualify for the location valuation factor, a product must meet two conditions:

1) All manufacture, extraction, and purchase (including distribution) of the product and its materials must occur within 100 miles (160 kilometers) of the project.
2) The product (or portion of an assembled product) have to meet a minimum of one of the sustainable criteria (e.g., recycled content, FSC certification) listed in the credit.

   Materials and products that do not meet the location criteria but do meet a minimum of one of the sustainability criteria are valued at one times their cost.

The distance should be measured with a straight line instead of actual travel distance. The location of the purchase transaction is considered the point of purchase. The location of product distribution is considered the point of purchase for transactions that do not occur in person such as online purchase.

See MRC: Building Product Disclosure and Optimization, Sourcing of Raw Materials, for the location valuation factor of reused and salvaged materials.

Determining Material Contributions of an Assembly
Many MR category sustainability criteria are applicable for the entire product, as is the case for programs and product certifications. Nevertheless, some criteria are only applicable for a portion of the product. The portion of the product that helps to earn points for the credit could be either the percentage of qualifying components permanently or mechanically attached together or a percentage of a homogeneous material. In either situation, the project teams should use *weight* to calculate the contributing value. Assemblies (parts permanently or mechanically attached together) include demountable partition walls, premade window assemblies, office chairs, doors, etc. Homogeneous materials include ceiling tiles, composite flooring, and rubber wall base, etc.

Based on weight, project teams can calculate the value that contributes to the credit as the percentage of the component or material meeting the criteria, multiplied by the total product cost.

Product value ($) = Total product cost ($) x (%) product component by weight x (%) meeting sustainable criteria

Below is some useful information.
The MR category has many purposes including the following:
1) minimize material use (**reduce**)
2) environmentally friendly materials
3) waste management and reduction (**recycle**)
4) storage and collection of recyclables
5) building **reuse** (maintain existing walls, floors and roof)
6) building reuse (maintain interior nonstructural elements)
7) construction waste management
8) materials reuse
9) recycled content
10) regional materials
11) rapidly renewable materials
12) certified wood

Mnemonic
My effortless work at SBBC
MR Regan Ray Carter (See underlined letters.)

Core Concepts
1) Manage waste
   - Reduce waste
   - Reuse and divert waste

2) Reduce and reuse materials
   - Reduce materials used
   - Reuse of building and materials
   - Choose rapidly renewable materials

Recognition, Regulation, and Incentives

1) Recognition
   - Cradle to Cradle, Green Seal and other product certifications
2) Regulation (requirements and goals)
   - Rare
   - Internal policy for supply chain and materials management in some organizations
3) Financial Incentives
   - Recycling incentive

Overall Strategies and Technologies

Note: Not **all** strategies and technologies have to be used simultaneously for your project.

1) **Reduce** waste.
2) Purchase sustainable materials.
3) **Reuse** and divert waste. **Recycle** solid waste and demolition waste.
4) Reduce life cycle impact.
5) Reduce demand for materials. (Implement in design and construction and use new technologies.)
6) Reuse all or a portion of the existing building.
7) Reuse materials. (Use refurbished, salvaged, and reclaimed materials; purchase refurbished and reclaimed materials.)
8) Use **rapidly renewable materials** such as wool carpeting, cork flooring, sunflower seed board panels, linoleum flooring, bamboo flooring, and cotton Batt insulation.
   Mnemonic: WC on SLAB (See underlined letters above.)
9) Choose materials with a reduced life cycle impact such as regional materials, certified wood, and materials containing pre- and post-consumer recycled content.

Important Notes for MR Category

1. Provide an easily accessible designated area for separation, collection, storage, and recycling of non-hazardous materials, like **p**aper, corrugated **c**ardboard, **m**etals, **g**lass, and **p**lastics for the entire building.

Mnemonic: People Can Make Green Promises (See **bold** letters at the last part of the sentence listing the recycled materials.

Note: *These five materials required for recycling (as listed above) make up 59% of the total municipal solid waste stream. Food scraps (12%) and yard trimmings (13%) make up for 25% of the total. (The GBCI encourages you to compost these types of waste on-site if possible.) The remaining waste is wood (6%); textiles, leather, and rubber (7%); and other (3%).*

2. Encourage the **3 R's**: reduce, reuse, and recycle.
3. Rapidly renewable materials include wool, bamboo, cotton, wheatboard, cork, strawboard, cotton insulation, agrifiber, linoleum, etc.

MR Outline:

MR Prerequisite or Credit Name	Extra Credit	Responsible Party
MR Prerequisite (MRP): Storage and Collection of Recyclables	0	Owner or tenant
MRP: Construction and Demolition Waste Management Planning	0	Contractor
*MRP: PBT Source Reduction—Mercury	0	Electrical Engineer & Contractor
MRC: Building Life-Cycle Impact Reduction	Choices 1& 2: Not available. Choice 3: Reuse 95% of the building. Choice 4: Achieve any improvement over the required credit thresholds in all six impact measures	Architect
MRC: Building Product Disclosure and Optimization— Environmental Product Declarations	Choice 1: Source at least 40 qualifying products from five manufacturers. Choice 2: Purchase 75%, by cost, of permanently installed building products that meet the required attributes.	Architect
MRC: Building Product Disclosure and Optimization—Sourcing of Raw Materials	Choice 1: Source a minimum of 40 products from five manufacturers. Choice 2: By cost, purchase 50% of the total value of permanently installed building products that meet the responsible extraction criteria.	Contractor
MRC: Building Product Disclosure and Optimization—Material Ingredients	Choice 1: Purchase 40 or more permanently installed building products that meet the credit criteria. Choice 2: By cost, Purchase 50% or more of permanently installed building products that meet the credit criteria.	Contractor
*MRC: PBT Source Reduction—Mercury	0	Electrical Engineer
*MRC: PBT Source Reduction—Lead, Cadmium, and Copper	0	Electrical and Plumbing Engineers
*MRC: Furniture and Medical Furnishings	0	Interior Designer or Architect
*MRC: Design for Flexibility	0	Architect & Contractor
MRC: Construction and Demolition Waste Management	Achieve both Choice 1 (either Path 1 or Path 2) and Choice 2	Contractor

Note: * indicates prerequisite or credit NOT applicable to all LEED rating systems. Refer to the specific prerequisite or credit for more information.

MR Prerequisite (MRP): **Storage and Collection of Recyclables**

Mandatory for

New Construction (0 points)
Core and Shell (0 points)
Schools (0 points)
Retail (0 points)
Data Centers (0 points)
Warehouses and Distribution Centers (0 points)
Hospitality (0 points)
Healthcare (0 points)

Purpose

Reduces the waste generated by building users, and diverts solid waste from landfills.

Prerequisite:

New Construction, Core and Shell, Schools, Data Centers, Warehouses and Distribution Centers, Hospitality, Healthcare

Offer dedicated areas accessible to building occupants and waste haulers for the collection and storage of recyclable materials for the entire building. Provide separate locations for collection and storage areas. Recyclable materials have to include corrugated cardboard, glass, mixed paper, plastics, and metals. Take proper measures for the safe collection, storage, and disposal of two of the following: mercury-containing lamps, batteries, and electronic waste.

Retail

Do a waste stream study to pinpoint the retail project's top five recyclable waste streams, by either volume or weight, using consistent metrics. Offer collection and storage space the top four waste streams identified by the waste study. Use data from similar operations to make estimates if no information is available on waste streams for the project. Retailers with existing stores of similar function and size can use historical information from their other locations.

Offer dedicated areas accessible to building occupants and waste haulers for the separation, collection, and storage of recyclable materials for at least the top four recyclable waste streams identified by the waste study. Place the collection and storage bins close to the source of recyclable waste. Take proper measures for safe collection, storage, and disposal if any of the top four waste streams are batteries, mercury-containing lamps, or electronic waste.

Campus

Group Approach

All buildings in the group may be submitted as one. For campuses, a shared central recycling facility for haulers is acceptable if the space accommodates recycling produced by all buildings served.

Campus Approach

Qualified.

Submittals:

Submittals	All projects	Retail only
Verification of recycled material types	x	
Description of recycling storage and collection strategies	x	
Floor plans showing recycling storage and collection areas	x	
Methodology of waste stream study		x

Synergies

- MRP: PBT Source Reduction—Mercury (Healthcare)

Extra Credit (Exemplary Performance):

None

Project Phase:

Schematic Design

LEED Submittal Phase:

Design

Related Code or Standard:

None

Responsible Party:

Owner/Developer, tenant or architect

MRP: **Construction and Demolition Waste Management Planning**

Mandatory for

New Construction (0 points)
Core and Shell (0 points)
Schools (0 points)
Retail (0 points)
Data Centers (0 points)
Warehouses and Distribution Centers (0 points)
Hospitality (0 points)
Healthcare (0 points)

Purpose

Recovers, reuses, and recycles materials, and also diverts demolition and construction waste from landfills and incineration facilities.

Prerequisite:

Create and instigate a construction and demolition waste management plan:

- Identify a minimum of five materials (both structural and nonstructural) targeted for diversion and set up waste diversion goals for the project. Estimate a percentage of the overall project waste that these materials represent.
- Stipulate whether materials will be separated or commingled and clarify the diversion strategies planned for the project. Explain where the material will be taken and how the recycling facility will process the material.

Offer a final report specifying all major waste streams generated, including disposal and diversion rates.

Alternative daily cover (ADC) cannot be included as material diverted from disposal. Land-clearing debris is not counted as construction, demolition, or renovation waste that can contribute to waste diversion.

Campus

Group Approach

All buildings in the group may be submitted as one. Campus buildings may develop one comprehensive plan for construction waste.

Campus Approach

Qualified.

Submittals:

- Construction waste management plan
- Total construction waste

Synergies

- MRC: Construction and Demolition Waste Management

Extra Credit (Exemplary Performance):

None

Project Phase:

Construction Administration

LEED Submittal Phase:
Construction

Related Code or Standard:

- **European Commission Waste Framework Directive 2008/98/EC:** www.ec.europa.eu/environment/waste/framework/index.htm
- **European Commission Waste Incineration Directive 2000/76/EC:** www.europa.eu/legislation_summaries/environment/waste_management
- **EN 303-1—1999/A1—2003, Heating boilers with forced draught burners, Terminology, general requirements, testing and marking:** www.cen.eu/cen/Products
- **EN 303-2—1998/A1—2003, Heating boilers with forced draught burners, Special requirements for boilers with atomizing oil burners:** www.cen.eu/cen/Products
- **EN 303-3—1998/AC—2006, Gas-fired central heating boilers, Assembly comprising a boiler body and a forced draught burner**: www.cen.eu/cen/Products
- **EN 303-4—1999, Heating boilers with forced draught burners, Special requirements for boilers with forced draught oil burners with outputs up to 70 kW and a maximum operating pressure of 3 bar, Terminology, special requirements, testing and marking**: www.cen.eu/cen/Products
- **EN 303-5—2012, Heating boilers for solid fuels, manually and automatically stoked, nominal heat output of up to 500 kW:** www.cen.eu/cen/Products
- **EN 303-6—2000, Heating boilers with forced draught burners, Specific requirements for the domestic hot water operation of combination boilers with atomizing oil burners of nominal heat input not exceeding 70 kW:** www.cen.eu/cen/Products
- **EN 303-7—2006, Gas-fired central heating boilers equipped with a forced draught burner of nominal heat output not exceeding 1000 kW**: www.cen.eu/cen/Products

Responsible Party:
Contractor

*MRP: **PBT Source Reduction—Mercury**

Applicable to

Healthcare (0 points)

Purpose:

To promote product substitution, capture, and recycling to reduce mercury-containing products and devices and mercury release.

Prerequisite:

Specify the following as part of the project's recycling collection system:

- types of mercury-containing devices and products to be collected;
- requirements governing how they are to be managed by a recycling program; and
- disposal methods for captured mercury.

Related mercury-containing products and devices include, but are not limited to, dental wastes (such as chair side traps, scrap amalgam, and separator wastes) and lamps (such as integrally ballasted and nonintegrally ballasted compact fluorescents and HIDs, linear and circular fluorescents). Specify and install amalgam separation devices that meet or exceed the **ISO-11143** standard in facilities delivering dental care

Meet the mercury elimination requirements listed below, from the **2010 FGI Guidelines for Design and Construction of Health Care Facilities, Section A1.3- 4b, Mercury Elimination**.

- 4.2.1.1. New construction: healthcare facilities may not use mercury-containing equipment, including thermostats, switching devices, and other building system sources. Lamps are excluded.
- 4.2.1.2. Renovation: healthcare facilities must develop a plan to phase out mercury-containing products and upgrade current mercury-containing lamps to high-efficiency, low-mercury, or mercury-free lamp technology.

Do not specify or install mercury vapor high-intensity discharge (HID) lamps or preheat T-9, T-10, or T-12 fluorescents in the project. Do not specify probe-start metal halide HID lamps in any interior spaces.

Specify and install illuminated exit signs that use less than 5 watts of electricity and contain no mercury. High-pressure sodium and fluorescent lamps must meet the criteria in Table 1.

Table 1. Maximum mercury content of lamps

Lamp	Maximum content
T-8 fluorescent, eight-foot	10 mg mercury
T-8 fluorescent, four-foot	3.5 mg mercury
T-8 fluorescent, U-bent	6 mg mercury
T-5 fluorescent, linear	2.5 mg mercury
T-5 fluorescent, circular	9 mg mercury
Compact fluorescent, nonintegral ballast	3.5 mg mercury
Compact fluorescent, integral ballast	3.5 mg mercury, ENERGY STAR qualified
High-pressure sodium, up to 400 watts	10 mg mercury
High-pressure sodium, above 400 watts	32 mg mercury

mg = milligram

Note: *Mercury is a neurotoxin and a* ***persistent bioaccumulative toxic (PBT)*** *chemical element. It breaks down extremely slowly in the environment, accumulates within animal tissues in increasing concentrations up the food chain. Once present in an organism, mercury can influence the central nervous system, ultimately damaging the spinal cord, brain, kidneys, and liver. It is difficult to contain once released into the environment.*

Campus

Group Approach

All buildings in the group may be submitted as one. Projects that are part of large health care systems or on existing campuses can coordinate lamp selection with purchasing protocols to ensure continuously meeting prerequisites.

Campus Approach

Qualified.

Submittals:

- Phase-out plan and existing inventory (for renovation projects)
- Recycling plan for mercury-containing lamps
- Lighting schedule including mercury content and lamp type
- USGBC's PBT source reduction calculator (or equivalent documentation)

Synergies:

- MRP: Storage and Collection of Recyclables
- MRC: PBT Source Reduction—Mercury

Extra Credit (Exemplary Performance):

None

Project Phase:

Construction Documents & Occupation/Operation

LEED Submittal Phase:

Design

Related Code or Standard:

None

Responsible Party:

Electrical Engineer & Contractor

MRC: **Building Life-Cycle Impact Reduction**

Applicable to

New Construction (2-5 points)
Core and Shell (2-6 points)
Schools (2-5 points)
Retail (2-5 points)
Data Centers (2-5 points)
Warehouses and Distribution Centers (2-5 points)
Hospitality (2-5 points)
Healthcare (2-5 points)

Purpose

Takes full advantage of the environmental performance of materials and products, and promotes adaptive reuse.

Credit Path:

During initial project decision-making, choose to reuse existing building resources or demonstrate a reduction in materials use through life-cycle assessment to show reduced environmental effects. Achieve one of the following choices.

Choice 1. Historic Building Reuse (5 points BD+C, 6 points Core and Shell)

Preserve the existing building envelope, structure, and interior nonstructural elements of a contributing building in a historic district or a historic building. To qualify, the historic district or building must be eligible for listing or listed in the national, state, or local register of historic places. Do not demolish any part of a contributing building in a historic district or a historic building unless it is deemed hazardous or structurally unsound. For locally listed buildings, only local historic preservation review board can grant approval of any demolition. For buildings listed in a the U.S. National Register or state register of historic places (or local equivalent for international projects), an approval has to appear in a programmatic agreement with the state historic preservation office or National Park Service (or local equivalent for international projects).

Any change (preservation, restoration, or rehabilitation) to a contributing building in a historic district or a historic building on the project site must be performed per national or local standards for rehabilitation, whichever are applicable. If a building is not subject to historic review, include on the project team a preservation professional who meets U.S. federal requirements for historic architects (or local equivalent for international projects); the preservation professional must confirm conformance to the Secretary of Interior's Standards for the Treatment of Historic Properties (or local equivalent for international projects).

OR

Choice 2. Renovation of Abandoned or Blighted Building (5 points BD+C, 6 points Core and Shell)

By surface area, maintain a minimum of 50%, of the existing building enclosure, structure, and interior structural elements for buildings that are considered to be blighted or meet local criteria to be considered abandoned. The building should be renovated to a state of productive occupancy. A maximum of 25% of the building surface area can be excluded from credit calculation due to deterioration or damage.

OR

Choice3. Building and Material Reuse (2–4 points BD+C, 2-5 points Core and Shell)
Salvage or reuse building materials from on site or off site as a percentage of the surface area, as listed in Table 1.
Include enclosure materials (e.g., skin, framing), structural elements (e.g., floors, roof decking), and permanently installed interior elements (e.g., doors, walls, floor coverings, ceiling systems). Do not include window assemblies and any hazardous materials that are remediated as a part of the project in the calculation. Materials contributing toward this credit cannot contribute toward MRC: Material Disclosure and Optimization.

Table 1. Points for Reuse of Building Materials

Percentage of completed project surface area reused	Points BD+C	Points BD+C (Core and Shell)
25%	2	2
50%	3	3
75%	4	5

OR
Choice 4. Whole-Building Life-Cycle Assessment (3 points)
For new construction (buildings or portions of buildings), perform a life-cycle assessment of the project's enclosure and structure that shows at least 10% reduction, compared with a baseline building, in a minimum of three of the six impact categories listed below, one of which must be global warming potential. No impact category assessed as part of the life-cycle assessment can increase by 5% or more compared with the baseline building.

The buildings must be proposed and baseline of similar function, size, orientation, and operating energy performance as defined in EAP: Minimum Energy Performance. The service life of the proposed and baseline buildings should be the same and at least 60 years to fully account for maintenance and replacement. Use the same life-cycle assessment software data sets and tools to evaluate both the baseline building and the proposed building, and report all listed impact categories. Data sets must be compliant with **ISO 14044**.

Choose a minimum of three of the following impact categories for reduction:

- global warming potential (greenhouse gases), in CO_2e;
- depletion of the stratospheric ozone layer, in kg CFC-11;
- acidification of land and water sources, in kg SO2 or moles H+;
- **eutrophication**, in kg phosphate or kg nitrogen;
- formation of **tropospheric ozone**, in kg ethene or kg NOx; and
- depletion of nonrenewable energy resources, in MJ.

Note: *Per Wikipedia:*
"Eutrophication (Greek: eutrophia—healthy, adequate nutrition, development; German: Eutrophie) or more precisely hypertrophication, is the ecosystem's response to the addition of artificial or natural substances, mainly phosphates, through detergents, fertilizers, or sewage, to an aquatic system."
*"**Ozone (O3)** is a constituent of the troposphere (it is also an important constituent of some regions of the stratosphere commonly known as the ozone layer). The **troposphere** extends from a certain place of the Earth to between 12 and 20 kilometers above the surface of the Earth and consists of many layers. Ozone is more concentrated above the mixing layer, or ground layer. Ground-level ozone, though less concentrated than ozone aloft, is more of a problem because of its health effects."*

HEALTHCARE only
For all choices in this credit, building materials demolished to create courtyards to increase daylighting can be counted as retained in calculations if the new courtyards meet the requirements of EQC: Daylight and Quality Views.

Campus
Group Approach
Choices 1 & 2. Separate submittal for each building.
Choice 3. All buildings in the group may be submitted as one.
Choice 4. All buildings in the group may be submitted as one. Although each building will need to be modeled separately, each with a baseline and proposed building, the end results may be aggregated across multiple buildings.

Campus Approach
Unqualified. Separate submittal for each building.

Submittals:

Submittals	Choice 1	Choice 2	Choice 3	Choice 4
Documentation of historic designation status	X			
Description of demolition (if any)	X			
Documentation of how additions and alterations (if any) meet local review board requirements	X			
Description of blighted or abandoned status		X		
Reused elements table and calculations		X	X	
Description of LCA assumptions, scope, and analysis process for baseline building and proposed building				X
Life-cycle impact assessment summary showing outputs of proposed building with percentage change from baseline building for all impact indicators.				X

Synergies
- LTC: High-Priority Site
- MRP: Construction and Demolition Waste Management Planning
- MRC: Construction and Demolition Waste Management
- MRC: Building Product Disclosure and Optimization—Sourcing of Raw Materials
- MRC: Building Product Disclosure and Optimization—Environmental Product Declarations
- MRC: Building Product Disclosure and Optimization—Material Ingredients

Extra Credit (Exemplary Performance):
- Choices 1& 2: Not available.
- Choice 3: Reuse 95% of the building.
- Choice 4: Achieve any improvement over the required credit thresholds in all six impact measures.

Project Phase:
Construction Documents

LEED Submittal Phase:
Design

Related Code or Standard:
- **ISO 14044:** iso.org/
- **National Register of Historic Places:** nrhp.focus.nps.gov/
- **Secretary of Interior's Standards for the Treatment of Historic Properties:** nps.gov/ and nps.gov/hps/tps/standguide/

Responsible Party:
Architect

MRC: **Building Product Disclosure and Optimization—Environmental Product Declarations**

Applicable to

New Construction (1-2 points)
Core and Shell (1-2 points)
Schools (1-2 points)
Retail (1-2 points)
Data Centers (1-2 points)
Warehouses and Distribution Centers (1-2 points)
Hospitality (1-2 points)
Healthcare (1-2 points)

Purpose

Encourages selection of manufacturers and products with verified improved environmental life-cycle impacts. Rewards project teams for using materials and products with life-cycle information that have social, economical, and environmental preferred life-cycle impacts.

Credit Path:

Select one or more of the following choices, for a maximum of 2 points.

Choice 1. Environmental Product Declaration (EPD) (1 point)

Use a minimum of 20 different permanently installed products sourced from a minimum of five different manufacturers that comply with one of the following disclosure criteria.

1) **Product-specific declaration.**
   Products with a critically reviewed, publicly available life-cycle assessment conforming to ISO 14044 with at least a cradle to gate scope are valued as1/4 of a product for the purposes of credit achievement calculation.

   Note: *"**Cradle-to-gate** is an assessment of a partial product life cycle from resource extraction (cradle) to the factory gate (i.e., before it is transported to the consumer). The use phase and disposal phase of the product are omitted in this case."*
   –quoted from Wikipedia (http://en.wikipedia.org/wiki/Life-cycle_assessment)

2) **Environmental Product Declarations that meet ISO 14025, 14040, 14044, and EN 15804 or ISO 21930 and have at least a cradle to gate scope.**
   - Industry-wide (generic) EPD –Project team can value products with third-party certification (Type III), including external verification, as 1/2 of a product for purposes of credit achievement calculation if the manufacturer is explicitly recognized as a participant by the program operator.
   - Product-specific Type III EPD –Project team can value products with third-party certification (Type III), including external verification as one whole product for purposes of credit achievement calculation if the manufacturer is explicitly recognized as the participant by the program operator.

3) **USGBC approved program – Products that meet other USGBC approved environmental product declaration frameworks.**

Choice 2. Multi-Attribute Optimization (1 point)

Use products that meet one of the requirements below for 50%, by cost of the total value of permanently installed products in the project. Products will be valued as follows.

1) **Third party certified products that show impact reduction below industry average in a minimum of three of the following categories are valued at 100% of their cost for credit achievement calculations.**
   - acidification of land and water sources, in moles H+ or kg SO_2;
   - depletion of the stratospheric ozone layer, in kg CFC-11;
   - eutrophication, in kg nitrogen or kg phosphate;
   - formation of tropospheric ozone, in kg NOx or kg ethene and depletion of nonrenewable energy resources, in MJ;
   - global warming potential (greenhouse gases), in CO_2e;

   Note: *MJ is megajoules. "The **joule**, symbol **J**, is a derived unit of energy, work, or amount of heat in the International System of Units. It is equal to the energy transferred (or work done) when applying a force of one newton through a distance of one metre (1 newton metre or N·m), or in passing an electric current of one ampere through a resistance of one ohm for one second." –quoted from Wikipedia (http://en.wikipedia.org/wiki/Joule)*

2) **USGBC approved program -- Products that comply with other USGBC approved multi-attribute frameworks.**
   For credit achievement calculation, products sourced (manufactured, extracted, purchased) within 100 miles (160 km) of the project site are counted at 200% of their base contributing cost.

   Structure and enclosure materials cannot be counted as more than 30% of the value of compliant building products.

Campus
Group Approach
All buildings in the group may be submitted as one.
Campus Approach
Unqualified. Separate submittal for each building.

Note: Environmental product declarations (EPDs) *are a standardized method of conveying the environmental effects related to a system or product's energy use, waste generation, chemical makeup, raw material extraction, and emissions to air, soil, and water. Even though many EPD programs are available, the credit requires that EPDs originate from program operators who abide by the **International Organization for Standardization (ISO)** standards, the internationally recognized norm for EPDs.*

Submittals:

Submittals	Choice 1	Choice 2
MR building product disclosure and optimization calculator or equivalent tracking tool	x	x
EPD and LCA reports or compliant summary documents for 100% of products contributing toward credit	x	
Documentation of compliance with USGBC-approved program		x

Synergies

- MRC: Building Product Disclosure and Optimization—Sourcing of Raw Materials
- MRC: Building Product Disclosure and Optimization—Material Ingredients
- MRC: Building Life-Cycle Impact Reduction

Extra Credit (Exemplary Performance):

- Choice 1. Source at least 40 qualifying products from five manufacturers.
- Choice 2. Purchase 75%, by cost, of permanently installed building products that meet the required attributes.

Project Phase:

Construction Documents

LEED Submittal Phase:

Design

Related Code or Standard:

- **International Standard ISO 14021–1999, Environmental labels and declarations—Self Declared Claims (Type II Environmental Labeling):** iso.org
- **International Standard ISO 14025–2006, Environmental labels and declarations (Type III Environmental Declarations—Principles and Procedures):** iso.org
- **International Standard ISO 14040–2006, Environmental management, Life cycle assessment principles, and frameworks:** iso.org
- **International Standard ISO 14044–2006, Environmental management, Life cycle assessment requirements, and guidelines:** iso.org
- **CEN Comité Européen de Normalisation (European Committee for Standardization) EN 15804—2012 Sustainability of construction works, Environmental product declarations, Core rules for the product category of construction products:** cen.eu
- **International Standard ISO 21930–2007 Sustainability in building construction—Environmental declaration of building products:** iso.org
- **Federal Trade Commission, Guides for the Use of Environmental Marketing Claims, 16 CFR 260.7 (e):** ftc.gov/bcp/grnrule/guides980427.htm

Responsible Party:

Architect

MRC: **Building Product Disclosure and Optimization— Sourcing of Raw Materials**

Applicable to

New Construction (1-2 points)
Core and Shell (1-2 points)
Schools (1-2 points)
Retail (1-2 points)
Data Centers (1-2 points)
Warehouses and Distribution Centers (1-2 points)
Hospitality (1-2 points)
Healthcare (1-2 points)

Purpose

Encourages project teams to select products confirmed to have been sourced or extracted in a responsible manner. To reward the use of materials and products with life cycle information which have social, economical, and environmental preferable life cycle effects.

Credit Path:

Choice 1. Raw Material Source and Extraction Reporting (1 point)

Use a minimum of 20 different permanently installed products from a minimum of five different manufacturers that have published a report from their raw material suppliers that include a commitment to reducing environmental harms from extraction and/or manufacturing processes, a commitment to long-term ecologically responsible land use, raw material supplier extraction locations, and a commitment to meeting applicable programs or standards voluntarily that address responsible sourcing criteria.

1) Products sourced from manufacturers with self-declared reports are counted as one half (1/2) of a product for credit achievement.
2) Third-party verified **corporate sustainability reports (CSR)** that include activities associated with the manufacturer's product and the product's supply chain and environmental impacts of extraction operations are counted as one whole product for credit achievement calculation. Acceptable CSR frameworks include the following:
   - **Global Reporting Initiative (GRI) Sustainability Report**
   - **ISO 26000:** 2010 Guidance on Social Responsibility
   - **Organization for Economic Co-operation and Development (OECD) Guidelines for Multinational Enterprises**
   - **U.N. Global Compact:** Communication of Progress
   - **USGBC approved program:** Other USGBC approved programs meeting the CSR criteria.

Choice2. Leadership Extraction Practices (1 point)

Use products that meet one or more of the following responsible extraction criteria for at least 25%, by cost of the total value of permanently installed building products in the project.

- **Extended producer responsibility**. Products purchased from a producer (manufacturer) that is directly responsible for extended producer responsibility or participates in an extended producer responsibility program. Products meeting extended producer responsibility criteria are counted at 50% of their cost for credit achievement calculation.
- **Bio-based materials.** Bio-based products should comply with the **Sustainable Agriculture Network's Sustainable Agriculture Standard**. Bio-based raw materials should be tested using **ASTM Test Method D6866** and be legally harvested, as defined by the receiving and exporting country. Exclude hide products, such as leather. Products meeting bio-based materials criteria are counted at 100% of their cost for credit achievement calculation.
- **Wood products.** Wood products should be certified by the **Forest Stewardship Council** or

USGBC-approved equivalent. Products meeting wood products criteria are counted at 100% of their cost for the credit achievement calculation.

- **Materials reuse.** Reuse includes refurbished, salvaged, or reused products. Products meeting materials-reuse criteria are counted at 100% of their cost for credit achievement calculation.
- **Recycled content.** Recycled content is the sum of 50% of the preconsumer recycled content plus 100% of the postconsumer recycled content, based on cost. Products meeting recycled content criteria are counted at 100% of their cost for credit achievement calculation
- **USGBC approved program.** Other USGBC approved programs meeting leadership extraction criteria.

For credit achievement calculation:
Products sourced (manufactured, extracted, purchased) within 100 miles (160 km) of the project site are counted at 200% of their base contributing cost. The base contributing cost of individual products compliant with multiple responsible extraction criteria cannot exceed 100% its total actual cost (before regional multipliers), and single product components compliant with multiple responsible extraction criteria cannot be double counted. A product shall never be permitted to contribute more than 200% of its total actual cost.

Enclosure materials and structure cannot constitute over 30% of the value of compliant building products.

Campus
Group Approach
All buildings in the group may be submitted as one.

Campus Approach
Unqualified. Separate submittal for each building.

Note: Corporate sustainability reports (CSRs), *based on generally accepted standards and frameworks, can identify sources of raw material extraction and provide information on product supply chains.*

Submittals:

Submittals	Choice 1	Choice 2
MR building product disclosure and optimization calculator or equivalent tracking tool	x	x
Corporate sustainability reports for 100% of products contributing toward credit	x	
Documentation of product claims for credit requirements or other USGBC-approved program		x

Synergies

- MRC: Building Life Cycle Impact Reduction
- MRC: Building Product Disclosure and Optimization—Environmental Product Declarations
- MRC: Building Product Disclosure and Optimization—Material Ingredients

Extra Credit (Exemplary Performance):

- Choice 1. Source a minimum of 40 products from five manufacturers.
- Choice 2. By cost, purchase 50% of the total value of permanently installed building products that meet the responsible extraction criteria.

Project Phase:

Construction Administration

LEED Submittal Phase:

Construction

Related Code or Standard:

- **ASTM Test Method D6866:** astm.org/Standards/D6866.htm
- **Forest Stewardship Council:** ic.fsc.org
- **Global Reporting Initiative (GRI) Sustainability Report:** globalreporting.org/
- **International Standards ISO 14021–1999, Environmental Labels and Declarations—Self Declared Environmental Claims (Type II Environmental Labeling):** iso.org/iso/catalogue_detail.htm?csnumber=23146
- **ISO 26000—2010 Guidance on Social Responsibility:** iso.org/iso/home/standards/iso26000.htm
- **Organization for Economic Co-operation and Development (OECD) Guidelines for Multinational Enterprises:** oecd.org/daf/internationalinvestment/guidelinesformultinationalenterprises/
- **U.N. Global Compact, Communication of Progress:** unglobalcompact.org/cop/
- **Sustainable Agriculture Network:** sanstandards.org
- **The Rainforest Alliance:** rainforest-alliance.org/

Responsible Party:

Contractor

MRC: **Building Product Disclosure and Optimization— Material Ingredients**

Applicable to

New Construction (1-2 points)
Core and Shell (1-2 points)
Schools (1-2 points)
Retail (1-2 points)
Data Centers (1-2 points)
Warehouses and Distribution Centers (1-2 points)
Hospitality (1-2 points)
Healthcare (1-2 points)

Purpose

Encourages raw material manufacturers to produce products confirmed of having improved life-cycle effects. Rewards the use of materials and products with life cycle information and that have socially, economically, and environmentally preferable life cycle effects. To encourage project teams to select products confirmed to minimize the generation and use of harmful substances, and products whose chemical ingredients are inventoried via an established methodology.

Credit Path:

Choice 1. Material Ingredient Reporting (1 point)

Use 20 or more different permanently installed products from a minimum of five different manufacturers that use any of the following programs to demonstrate the chemical inventory of the product to at least 0.1% (1000 ppm).

1) **Manufacturer Inventory.** The manufacturer has published complete content inventory for the product per these guidelines:
    - A publicly available inventory of all ingredients labeled by **Chemical Abstract Service Registration Number (CASRN)** and name.
    - Materials defined as intellectual property or trade secret can withhold the CASRN and/or name but should disclose amount, role, and **GreenScreen** benchmark, as defined in GreenScreen v1.2.
2) **Health Product Declaration.** The end use product has a complete, published Health Product Declaration with full disclosure of known risks per the Health Product Declaration open standard.
3) **Cradle to Cradle.** The end use product has been certified at the Cradle to Cradle v3 Bronze level or Cradle to Cradle v2 Basic level.
4) **USGBC approved program.** Other USGBC-approved programs that satisfy the material ingredient reporting requirements.

AND/OR

Choice 2. Material Ingredient Optimization (1 point)

By cost, use products that detail their material ingredient optimization using the following paths for at least 25% of the total value of permanently installed products in the project.

1) **GreenScreen v1.2 Benchmark**. Products that have completely listed chemical ingredients to 100 ppm that have no Benchmark 1 hazards:
    - Value the products at 100% of cost if *any* ingredients are assessed with the GreenScreen List Translator.
    - Value the products at 150% of cost if *all* ingredients have undergone a full GreenScreen Assessment.

2) **Cradle to Cradle Certified.** End use products are certified Cradle to Cradle. Products will be valued per these criteria:
   - Cradle to Cradle v2 Gold: 100% of cost
   - Cradle to Cradle v2 Platinum: 150% of cost
   - Cradle to Cradle v3 Silver: 100% of cost
   - Cradle to Cradle v3 Gold or Platinum: 150% of cost
3) **International Alternative Compliance Path – REACH Optimization.** End use products and materials that contain *no* substances that meet REACH criteria for substances of very high concern. Value the product at 100% of cost if it contains *no* ingredients listed on the REACH Authorization or Candidate list.
4) **USGBC approved program.** Products that meet USGGBC approved building product optimization criteria.

AND/OR

Choice3. Product Manufacturer Supply Chain Optimization (1 point)

By cost, use building products for 25% or more of the total value of permanently installed products in the project that:

1) Are sourced from product manufacturers who engage in robust validated health, safety, hazard, and risk programs which at least document 99% or more (by weight) of the ingredients used to make the building material or building product, and
2) Are sourced from product manufacturers with independent third party verification of their supply chain that at least verifies:
   - processes are set up to transparently prioritize chemical ingredients and communicate along the supply chain per available exposure, hazard and use information to identify those that require more detailed evaluation;
   - processes are set up to document, identify, and communicate information on safety, health, and environmental characteristics of chemical ingredients;
   - processes are set up to implement measures to manage the safety, health, and environmental hazard and risk of chemical ingredients;
   - processes are set up to optimize safety, health, and environmental impacts when designing and improving chemical ingredients;
   - processes are set up to receive, communicate, and evaluate chemical ingredient stewardship and safety information along the supply chain; and
   - stewardship and safety information about the chemical ingredients is publicly available from all points along the supply chain.

Products meeting Choice 3 criteria are valued at 100% of their cost for credit achievement calculation.

For credit achievement calculation of choices 2 and 3, products sourced (manufactured, extracted, purchased) within 100 miles (160 km) of the project site are valued at 200% of their base contributing cost. For credit achievement calculation, the value of individual products compliant with either choice 2 or 3 can be combined to reach the 25% threshold, but products compliant with both choice 2 and 3 may only be counted once.

Structure and enclosure materials cannot be more than 30% of the value of compliant building products.

Campus
Group Approach
All buildings in the group may be submitted as one.

Campus Approach
Unqualified. Separate submittal for each building.

Note: *Many building materials and products contain* ***persistent bioaccumulative and toxic chemicals (PBTs)*** *and* ***persistent organic pollutants (POPs)****. PBTs can cause damage even in very small amount, build up in humans and other life forms high on the food chain, and remain in the environment.*

Submittals:

Submittals	Choice 1	Choice 2	Choice 3
MR building product disclosure and optimization calculator or equivalent tracking tool	x	x	
Documentation of chemical inventory through Health Product Declaration, manufacturers' lists of ingredients with GreenScreen assessment reports for confidential ingredients, Cradle to Cradle certification labels, or USGBC-approved programs (if applicable)	x		
Verification of ingredient optimization through Cradle to Cradle certification labels, manufacturers' lists of ingredients with GreenScreen benchmarks listed for all ingredients, or manufacturers' declaration (for REACH), or USGBC-approved programs (if applicable)		x	
Documentation of supply chain optimization			x

Synergies

- MRC: Building Life-Cycle Impact Reduction
- MRC: Building Product Disclosure and Optimization—Environmental Product Declarations
- MRC: Building Product Disclosure and Optimization—Sourcing of Raw Materials

Extra Credit (Exemplary Performance):

- Choice 1. Purchase 40 or more permanently installed building products that meet the credit criteria.
- Choice 2. By cost, Purchase 50% or more of permanently installed building products that meet the credit criteria.

Project Phase:
Construction Administration

LEED Submittal Phase:
Construction

Related Code or Standard:
Chemical Abstracts Service: cas.org/

Health Product Declaration: hpdcollaborative.org/
Cradle-to-Cradle Certified CM Product Standard: c2ccertified.org/product_certification
Registration, Evaluation, Authorization and Restriction of Chemicals (REACH): echa.europa.eu/support/guidance-on-reach-and-clp-implementation
GreenScreen: cleanproduction.org/Greenscreen.v1-2.php

Responsible Party:
Contractor

*MRC: **PBT Source Reduction—Mercury**

Applicable to

Healthcare (1 point)

Purpose:

To reduce the release of persistent, bioaccumulative, and toxic chemicals (PBTs) related the life cycle of building materials.

Credit Path:

Specify and install fluorescent lamps with both long lamp life and low mercury content (MR Prerequisite PBT Source Reduction—Mercury), as listed in Table 1.

Table 1. Criteria for rated life of low-mercury lamps

Lamp	Maximum content	Lamp life (hrs)
T-8 fluorescent, eight foot	10 mg mercury	Standard output – 24,000 rated hours on instant start ballasts (3-hourstarts) High output – 18,000 rated hours on instant start ballasts or program start ballasts (3-hour starts)
T-8 fluorescent, four-foot	3.5 mg mercury	Both standard and high output – 30,000 rated hours on instant start ballasts or 36,000 rated hours on program start ballasts (3-hour starts)
T-8 fluorescent, two-foot and three-foot	3.5 mg mercury	24,000 rated hours on instant start ballasts or program start ballasts (3-hour starts)
T-8 fluorescent, U-bent	6 mg mercury	18,000 rated hours on instant start ballasts, or 24,000 rated hours on program start ballasts (3-hour starts)
T-5 fluorescent, linear	2.5 mg mercury	Both standard and high-output – 25,000 rated hours on program start ballasts
Compact fluorescent, nonintegral ballast	3.5 mg mercury	12,000 rated hours
Compact florescent, integral ballast, bare bulb	3.5 mg mercury, ENERGY STAR qualified	Bare bulb – 10,000 rated hours Covered models such as globes, reflectors, A-19s – 8,000 hours
High-pressure sodium, up to 400 watts	10 mg mercury	Use noncycling type or replace with LED lamps or induction lamps
High-pressure sodium, above 400 watts	32 mg mercury	Use noncycling type or replace with LED lamps or induction lamps

Do not specify or install probe start metal halide lamps or circular fluorescent lamps.

Campus
Group Approach
All buildings in the group may be submitted as one.
Campus Approach
Qualified.

Submittals:

- Lighting schedule (including lamp life hours)
- Description explaining lamps excluded from credit
- USGBC's MR PBT source reduction calculator (or equivalent documentation)

Synergies:

- MRP: PBT Source Reduction—Mercury

Extra Credit (Exemplary Performance):
None

Project Phase:
Construction Documents

LEED Submittal Phase:
Design

Related Code or Standard:
None

Responsible Party:
Electrical Engineer

*MRC: PBT Source Reduction—Lead, Cadmium, and Copper

Applicable to

Healthcare (2 points)

Purpose:

To reduce the release of persistent, bioaccumulative, and toxic (PBT) chemicals related to the life cycle of building materials.

Credit Path:

Specify substitutes for materials manufactured with cadmium and lead, as follows.

Lead

- For potable water, require and use flux and solder to connect plumbing pipe on site that complies with the California AB1953 standard, which requires that solder contain 0.2% or less lead, and flux a weighted average of 0.25% lead or less for wetted surfaces. The "lead free" label as defined by the Safe Drinking Water Act (SDWA) does not provide acceptable screening for this credit because the SDWA defines "lead free" as flux and solders containing 0.2% lead or less.
- For water intended for human consumption, require and use pipe fittings, pipes, plumbing fittings, and faucets that meet the California law AB1953 of a weighted average lead content of the wetted surface area of 0.25% or less lead.
- Require and use lead-free roofing and flashing.
- Require and use cable and electrical wire with lead content less than 300 parts per million.
- Require no use of exterior or interior paints containing lead.
- For renovation projects, confirm the removal and proper disposal of disconnected wires with lead stabilizers per the 2002 National Electric Code requirements.

Copper used for MRI shielding and lead used for radiation shielding are exempt.

Cadmium

- Require no use of exterior or interior paints containing intentionally added cadmium.

Copper

- For copper pipe applications, eliminate or reduce joint-related sources of copper corrosion:
  - use mechanically crimped copper joint systems; or
  - require and use ASTM B813 2010 for flux, and require that all solder joints comply with ASTM B828 2002.

Campus

Group Approach

All buildings in the group may be submitted as one.

Campus Approach

Unqualified. Separate submittal for each building.

Submittals:

- Product documentation showing credit criteria have been met (proof of certification or manufacturer's data)
- Description explaining any excluded materials
- Description of pipe jointing processes (for copper pipe only)
- Confirmation of appropriate disposal of wires and lead stabilizers (for renovation projects only)

Synergies:

- EQC: Low-Emitting Materials. Specifying exterior and interior paints that are GreenSeal compliant will ensure that they also contain no lead and cadmium.

Extra Credit (Exemplary Performance):

None

Project Phase:

Construction Documents

LEED Submittal Phase:

Construction

Related Code or Standard:

- **ASTM B813 for copper flux:** astm.org/Standards/B813.htm
- **ASTM B828, Standard Practice for Making Capillary Joints by Soldering of Copper and Copper Alloy Tube and Fittings:** www.astm.org/Standards/B828.htm
- **California AB1953 standard for lead water pipes used to convey water for human consumption:** leginfo.ca.gov/pub/05-06/bill/asm/ab_19512000/ab_1953_bill_20060930_chaptered.html
- **GreenSeal:** greenseal.org
- **2002 National Electric Code requirements for removal and disposal of disconnected wires with lead**
- **stabilizers**: nfpa.org

Responsible Party:

Electrical and Plumbing Engineers

*MRC: **Furniture and Medical Furnishings**

Applicable to

Healthcare (1-2 points)

Purpose:

To improve the human health performance and environmental attributes related to freestanding furniture and medical furnishings.

Credit Path:

By cost, use a minimum of 30% (1 point) or 40% (2 points) of all freestanding furniture and medical furnishings (e.g., foams, mattresses, window coverings, cubicle curtains, panel fabrics, other textiles) that comply with the requirements in one of the following three choices.

Include built-in millwork and built-in casework in the base building calculations, even if manufactured off site. The cost of any individual product may be included in the total qualifying value if the product meets the criteria.

Choice 1. Minimal Chemical Content

By weight, all components that equal 5% or more of a medical furnishing assembly or furniture, including finishes, textiles, and dyes, should contain less than 100 parts per million (ppm) of at least four of the five following chemical groups:

- urea formaldehyde;
- heavy metals, including cadmium, lead, mercury, and antimony;
- hexavalent chromium in plated finishes consistent with the European Union Directive on the Restriction of the Use of Certain Hazardous Substances (EU RoHS);
- stain and nonstick treatments derived from perfluorinated compounds (PFCs), including perfluorooctanoic acid (PFOA); and
- added antimicrobial treatments.

AND/OR

Choice 2. Testing and Modeling of Chemical Content

All components of a medical furnishing assembly or furniture, including finishes, textiles, and dyes, must contain less than 100 parts per million (ppm) of at least two of the five chemicals or materials listed in Choice 1.

New medical furnishing assemblies or furniture should comply with ANSI/BIFMA Standard Method M7.1–2011, as well as ANSI/BIFMA e3-2010 Furniture Sustainability Standard, Sections 7.6.1 and 7.6.2, using either the emissions factor approach or the concentration modeling approach . Model the test results using the private office, open plan, or seating scenario in ANSI/BIFMA M7.1, as appropriate. USGBC-approved equivalent contaminant thresholds and testing methodologies are also acceptable. Submittals for furniture should indicate the modeling scenario used to determine compliance.

Salvaged and reused furniture over one year old at the time of use is deemed compliant, if it meets the criteria for any site-applied paints, adhesives, coatings, and sealants.

AND/OR

Choice3. Multi-Attribute Assessment of Products

Use products that comply with one or more of the criteria below. Each product can gain credit for each criterion met. The scope of any environmental product declaration (EPD) should be as a minimum cradle to gate.

- **Product-specific declaration.**
  - Products with a critically reviewed, publicly available life-cycle assessment per ISO 14044 that have as a minimum a cradle to gate scope are counted as one quarter (1/4) of a product for credit achievement calculation.
- **Environmental Product Declarations per ISO 14025, 14040, 14044, and EN 15804 or ISO 21930 and have as a minimum a cradle to gate scope.**
  - Industry-wide (generic) EPD – Products with third-party certification (Type III), including external confirmation in which the manufacturer is clearly acknowledged as a participant by the program operator are counted as one half (1/2) of a product for credit achievement calculation.
  - Product-specific Type III EPD – Products with third-party certification (Type III), including external confirmation in which the manufacturer is clearly recognized as the participant by the program operator are counted as one whole product for credit achievement calculation.
- **Materials reuse.** Use refurbished, salvaged, or reused products.
- **Recycled content.** Use products with recycled content. Recycled content is the sum of post-consumer recycled content plus one-half the pre-consumer recycled content.
- **Extended producer responsibility.** Products purchased from a manufacturer (producer) that is directly responsible for extended producer responsibility or participates in an extended producer responsibility program.
- **Bio-based materials.** Bio-based products should meet the Sustainable Agriculture Network's Sustainable Agriculture Standard. Bio-based raw materials should be tested using ASTM Test Method D6866 and be legally harvested, as defined by the receiving and exporting country. Exclude hide products, such as leather and other animal skin material.
- **Wood products.** Wood products should be certified by the Forest Stewardship Council or USGBC-approved equivalent.

Products that meet the above criteria are counted per source location (manufacture, extraction, and purchase point must be within the distances noted below):
For credit achievement calculation, products sourced (manufactured, extracted, purchased) within 100 miles (160 km) of the project site are counted at 200% of their base contributing cost.

Campus

Group Approach

All buildings in the group may be submitted as one.

Campus Approach

Unqualified. Separate submittal for each building.

Submittals:

- MR furniture and medical furnishings calculator provided by USGBC
- Documentation of product claims for credit criteria

Synergies:

- MRC: Building Product Disclosure and Optimization—Environmental Product Declarations, Sourcing of Raw Materials, and Material Ingredients.

Extra Credit (Exemplary Performance):

None

Project Phase:

Construction Documents & Construction Administration

LEED Submittal Phase:

Design

Related Code or Standard:

- **Restriction of the Use of Certain Hazardous Substances of the European Union Directive (EU RoHS):**eur-lex.europa.eu
- **American National Standard and The Business and Institutional Furniture Manufacturers Association Standard M7.1–2011: ANSI/BIFMA M7-2011:**bifma.org/standards/standards.html
- **Furniture Sustainability Standard and level™ Certification Program. American National Standard and The Business and Institutional Furniture Manufacturers Association Standard e3–2011 for Furniture Sustainability:** ANSI/BIFMA e3–2011: levelcertified.org
- **International Standard ISO 14025–2006, Environmental labels and declarations, Type III environmental declarations, Principles and procedures:** iso.org
- **International Standard ISO 14040–2006, Environmental management, Life cycle assessment principals and frameworks:** iso.org
- **International Standard ISO 14044–2006, Environmental management, Life cycle assessment Requirements and guidelines:** iso.org
- **International Standard ISO 21930–2007, Sustainability in building construction, Environmental declaration of building products:** iso.org
- **International Standards ISO 14021–1999, Environmental Labels and Declarations, Self-Declared Environmental Claims (Type II Environmental Labeling):** iso.org

Responsible Party:

Interior Designer or Architect

*MRC: **Design for Flexibility**

Applicable to

Healthcare (1 point)

Purpose:

Design for the service life of assemblies and components and for flexibility and ease of future adaptation to conserve resources associated with the construction and management of buildings.

Credit Path:

Use at least three of the following strategies to increase ease of adaptive use over the life of the structure and building flexibility.

- Use interstitial space. Design distribution zone utility equipment and systems including electrical, HVAC, plumbing, medical gases, information technology, and life-safety systems to serve the occupied zones and have the ability to control multiple zones in clinical spaces.
- Provide programmed soft space, like storage or administration, equal to 5% or more of departmental gross area (DGA). Locate soft space next to clinical departments that anticipate growth. Determine a strategy to accommodate displaced soft space in the future.
- Provide shell space equal to 5% or more of DGA. Locate it in a way that it can be occupied without displacing occupied space.
- Identify horizontal expansion capacity for clinical spaces, such as diagnostic and treatment, equal to 30% or more of existing floor area (excluding inpatient units) without demolition of occupied space except at the connection point. Additional existing occupied space with demountable partition systems can be reconfigured.
- Design for future vertical expansion on 75% or more of the roof and ensure existing operations and service systems can continue at or near capacity during the expansion.
- Allocate space for future above-grade parking structures equal to 50% of existing on-grade parking capacity, with direct access to circulation or the main hospital lobby. Vertical transportation pathways that lead directly to circulation or the main hospital lobby are acceptable.
- Use demountable partitions for 50% of applicable areas.
- Use modular or movable casework for 50% or more of custom millwork and casework. Base the calculation on the combined value of millwork and casework determined by the contractor or cost estimator.

Campus

Group Approach

All buildings in the group may be submitted as one.

Campus Approach

Qualified.

Submittals:

- Narrative of overall flexible design strategy
- Floor plans or other documentation for areas using flexible design strategies
- Calculations for departmental gross area showing areas required for each selected strategy
- Calculations of linear area for demountable partitions and description of excluded areas (if applicable)

- Calculation of product costs for movable and modular casework (if applicable)

Synergies:
- MRP: Construction and Demolition Waste Management Planning
- MRC: Building Product Disclosure and Optimization—Environmental Product Declarations, Sourcing of Raw Materials, and Material Ingredients

Extra Credit (Exemplary Performance):
None

Project Phase:
Schematic Design

LEED Submittal Phase:
Construction

Related Code or Standard:
None

Responsible Party:
Architect& Contractor

MRC: **Construction and Demolition Waste Management**

Applicable to

New Construction (1-2 points)
Core and Shell (1-2 points)
Schools (1-2 points)
Retail (1-2 points)
Data Centers (1-2 points)
Warehouses and Distribution Centers (1-2 points)
Hospitality (1-2 points)
Healthcare (1-2 points)

Purpose

Utilizes material reuse, recover, and recycle. Diverts demolition and construction waste away from landfills and incineration facilities.

Credit Path:

Recycle and/or salvage nonhazardous demolition and construction materials. Calculations can be by volume or weight but need to be consistent throughout.

Project team can include wood waste converted to fuel (biofuel) in the calculations but should exclude other types of waste-to-energy conversions, land-clearing debris, excavated soil, and alternative daily cover (ADC) from waste diversion.

However, if the European Commission Waste Framework Directive 2008/98/EC and Waste Incineration Directive 2000/76/EC are followed and waste-to-energy facilities meet applicable European Committee for Standardization (CEN) EN 303 standards, for projects that cannot meet credit requirements using recycling and reuse methods, waste-to-energy systems may be considered waste diversion.

Choice 1. Diversion (1–2 points)
Path 1. Divert 50% and Three Material Streams (1 point)
Divert 50% or more of the total demolition and construction material; diverted materials need to include three or more material streams.

OR
Path 2. Divert 75% and Four Material Streams (2 points)
Divert 75% or more of the total construction and demolition material; diverted materials must include four or more material streams.

OR
Choice 2. Reduction of Total Waste Material (2 points)
Generate not more than 2.5 pounds of construction waste per square foot (12.2 kilograms of waste per square meter) of the building's floor area.

Campus
Group Approach
All buildings in the group may be submitted as one. Multiple buildings on a campus may share on-site collection equipment and waste hauling contracts. Data aggregation is allowed if each building included is pursuing the same choice.

Campus Approach
Unqualified. Separate submittal for each building.

Submittals:

Submittals	Choice 1	Choice 2
MR Construction and Demolition Waste Management calculator or equivalent tool, tracking total and diverted waste amounts and material streams	x	
Documentation of recycling rates for commingled facilities (if applicable)	x	
Justification narrative for use of waste-to-energy strategy (if applicable)	x	
Documentation of waste-to-energy facilities adhering to relevant EN standards (if applicable)	x	
Total waste per area		x

Synergies
- MRP: Construction and Demolition Waste Management Planning

Extra Credit (Exemplary Performance):
- Achieve both Choice 1 (either Path 1 or Path 2) and Choice 2

Project Phase:
Construction Administration

LEED Submittal Phase:
Construction

Related Code or Standard:
- **Certification of Sustainable Recyclers:** recyclingcertification.org
- **European Commission Waste Framework Directive 2008/98/EC:**
  - ec.europa.eu/environment/waste/framework/index.htm
  - eur-lex.europa.eu/LexUriServ/LexUriServ.do?uri=OJ:L:2008:312:0003:0030:en:PDF
- **European Commission Waste Incineration Directive 2000/76/EC:**
  - europa.eu/legislation_summaries/environment/waste_management/l28072_en.htm
  - central2013.eu/fileadmin/user_upload/Downloads/Document_Centre/OP_Resources/Incineration_Directive_2000_76.pdf
- **EN 303-1—1999/A1—2003, Heating boilers with forced draught burners, Terminology, general requirements, testing and marking:** cen.eu/cen/Products/Search/Pages/default.aspx
- **EN 303-2—1998/A1—2003, Heating boilers with forced draught burners, Special requirements for boilers with atomizing oil burners:** cen.eu/cen/Products/Search/Pages/default.aspx
- **EN 303-3—1998/AC—2006, Gas-fired central heating boilers, Assembly comprising a boiler body and a forced draught burner:** cen.eu/cen/Products/Search/Pages/default.aspx
- **EN 303-4—1999, Heating boilers with forced draught burners, Special requirements for boilers with forced draught oil burners with outputs up to 70 kW and a maximum operating pressure of 3 bar, Terminology, special requirements, testing and marking:** cen.eu/cen/Products/Search/Pages/default.aspx
- **EN 303-5—2012, Heating boilers for solid fuels, manually and automatically stoked, nominal heat output of up to 500 kW:** cen.eu/cen/Products/Search/Pages/default.aspx

- **EN 303-6—2000, Heating boilers with forced draught burners, Specific requirements for the domestic hot water operation of combination boilers with atomizing oil burners of nominal heat input not exceeding 70kW:** cen.eu/cen/Products/Search/Pages/default.aspx
- **EN 303-7—2006, Gas-fired central heating boilers equipped with a forced draught burner of nominal heat output not exceeding 1000 kW:** cen.eu/cen/Products/Search/Pages/default.aspx

Responsible Party:
Contractor

Chapter 11

Indoor Environmental Quality (EQ)

Overall Purpose

The average American spends about 90% of his time indoors, so indoor environmental quality is very important for quality of life, well-being, and productivity.

The EQ category encourages project teams to improve indoor air quality and visual, thermal, and acoustic comfort. LEED certified buildings protect the comfort and health of building occupants via good indoor environmental quality (EQ). Good EQ also improves the building's value, decreases absenteeism, enhances productivity, and reduces liability for building owners and designers. The EQ category covers many environmental design factors and strategies, such as control over one's surroundings, lighting quality, air quality, and acoustic design. These factors influence the way people live, learn, and work.

Researchers have not fully understood the complex relationship between the health and comfort of building occupants and the indoor environment. It is hard to measure and quantify the direct impact of a building on its occupants because of many variables including the building's site, design, and construction, occupant activities, and local customs and expectations. For this reason, the EQ section uses the performance-oriented credit requirements to balance the need for prescriptive measures. For instance, a prerequisite covers source control first, and a later credit then measures the actual outcome of those strategies with an indoor air quality assessment.

The EQ category takes advantage of both conventional methods, such as thermal and ventilation control, and emerging design strategies, including requirements for lighting quality (Interior Lighting credit), source control and monitoring for user-determined contaminants (Enhanced Indoor Air Quality Strategies credit), an emissions-based, holistic approach (Low-Emitting Materials credit), and advanced lighting metrics (Daylight credit). All projects using a BD+C rating system now have a new credit covering acoustics.

Cross-Cutting Issues

Floor Area Calculations and Floor Plans

The percentage of floor area meeting the credit requirements determines the compliance of many of the credits in the EQ category. Overall, space categorization and floor areas ought to be consistent across EQ credits. The project teams should explain and highlight any discrepancies or excluded spaces in floor area values in the documentation. See Space Categorization for more information on which floor area should be included.

Space Categorization

The EQ category concentrates on the interaction between the indoor spaces and the occupants of the building. Therefore, understanding which spaces are used by the building users and what activities they carry out in each space is critical. The credit requirements may or may not apply based on the space categorization (Table 1).

Occupied Versus Unoccupied Space

A space in a building is either occupied or unoccupied. Occupied spaces are for human activities. Unoccupied spaces are inactive areas for other purposes and occupied only occasionally and briefly. Typical unoccupied spaces include the following:

- electrical and mechanical rooms
- dedicated emergency exit corridor or egress stairway
- closets in a home (a walk-in closet is occupied space)
- data center floor area, including a raised floor area
- inactive storage area in a distribution center or warehouse

For areas with equipment retrieval, the space is unoccupied only if the retrieval is occasional.

Table 1 Space types in EQ credits

Space Category	Prerequisite or Credit
Occupied space	• Minimum Indoor Air Quality Performance, ventilation rate procedure and natural ventilation procedure • Minimum Indoor Air Quality Performance, monitoring requirements • Enhanced Indoor Air Quality Strategies, Options 1C, 1D, 1E, 2B, 2E • Indoor Air Quality Assessment, Option 2, Air Testing (sampling must be representative of all occupied spaces) • Thermal Comfort (New Construction, Schools, Retail, Hospitality), design requirements • Acoustic Performance (New Construction, Data Centers, Warehouses and Distribution Centers, Hospitality)
Regularly occupied space	• Thermal Comfort, design requirements (Data Centers) • Interior Lighting, Option 2, strategies A, D, E, G, H • Daylight • Quality Views
Individual occupant space	• Thermal Comfort, control requirements • Interior Lighting, Option 1
Shared multi-occupant space	• Thermal Comfort, control requirements • Interior Lighting, Option 1
Densely occupied space	• Enhanced Indoor Air Quality Strategies, Option 2 C

Regularly Versus Non-Regularly Occupied Spaces

Occupied spaces are divided into regularly occupied or non-regularly occupied categories according to the duration of the occupancy. **Regularly occupied spaces** are enclosed areas where building users typically spend at least one hour of continuous occupancy per person per day on average; the building users can be standing or seated as they study, work, or carry out other activities. For spaces not used daily, the classification ought to be according to the time a typical building user spends there when it is in use. For instance, a computer workstation can be vacant most the month, but when it is used, an occupant spends one to five hours in the space. It should be considered regularly occupied because that length of stay is sufficient to affect the occupant's health, and she or he would expect to have thermal control and comfort there.

Occupied spaces other than regularly occupied are **non-regularly occupied**; these are spaces that people use for less than one hour per person per day on average or simply pass through.

The following are examples of non-regularly occupied spaces:

• break room • circulation space • copy room • corridor • fire station apparatus bay • hospital linen area • hospital medical record area • hospital patient room bathroom • hospital short-term charting space • hospital prep and cleanup area in surgical suite • interrogation room	• lobby (except hotel lobby)* • locker room • residential bathroom • residential laundry area • residential walk-in closet • restroom • retail fitting area • retail stock room • shooting range • stairway

* Hotel lobbies are considered regularly occupied because people often work and spend more time there than in an office building lobby.

Occupied Space Subcategories

Occupied spaces, or portions of an occupied space, can also be divided into individual or shared multi-occupant per the number of building users and their activities. An **individual occupant space** is a place for someone to carry out distinctive tasks. A **shared multi-occupant space** is a space for congregation or for building users to perform collaborative or overlapping tasks. Non-regularly occupied spaces that are not used for collaborative or distinct tasks are *neither* shared multi-occupant *nor* individual occupant spaces. Occupied spaces can also be divided into **densely** or **non-densely occupied** per the concentration of occupants in the space. A **densely occupied space** has no more than 40 square feet (3.7 square meters) per person, or 25 people or more per 1,000 square feet (93 square meters). A **non-densely occupied space** has more than 40 square feet (3.7 square meters) per person.

Table 2. Rating system–specific space classifications

Rating System	Space Type	Prerequisite or Credit
Schools	classroom and core learning spaces	• Minimum Acoustic Performance • Acoustic Performance (Schools)
Hospitality	guest rooms	• Interior Lighting* • Thermal Comfort, control requirements*
Healthcare	patient rooms	• Thermal Comfort, control requirements • Interior Lighting, Option 2, Lighting Quality
	staff areas	• Interior Lighting, Option 2, Lighting Quality
	perimeter area	• Daylight • Quality Views
	inpatient units	• Quality Views
Warehouses & Distribution Centers	office areas	• Thermal Comfort, control requirements • Quality Views
	areas of bulk storage, sorting, and distribution	
Retail	office and administrative areas	• Thermal Comfort, control requirements • Interior Lighting, Option 2, Lighting Quality
	sales areas	• Interior Lighting, Option 2, Lighting Quality

Space classifications will not affect the following credits:

- Environmental Tobacco Smoke Control
- Enhanced Indoor Air Quality Strategies, Option 1A, 1B, 2A, 2D (There are no specific spaces; applicable spaces are determined by the project team.)
- Low-Emitting Materials
- Construction Indoor Air Quality Management Plan
- Indoor Air Quality Assessment, Option 1, Flush-Out (The floor area from all spaces must be included in calculation for total air volume; the flush-out must be demonstrated at the system level.)
- Interior Lighting, Option 2, strategies B, C, and F
- Acoustic Performance (Healthcare)

The average American spends about 90% of his or her time indoors, so indoor environmental quality is very important for quality of life, well-being, and productivity.

EQ credits cover the following important topics:

1) Indoor environment quality (achieved through properly designed and installed systems)
2) Contaminants (reduce, manage, and eliminate)
3) Minimum IAQ performance
4) Environmental tobacco smoke (ETS) control
5) Outdoor air delivery monitoring
6) Increased ventilation
7) Construction IAQ management plan
8) Low-emitting materials
9) Indoor chemical and pollutant source control
10) Systems control
11) Thermal comfort
12) Daylight and views

Mnemonic

I Called Mike Evans.
Oh! Ian Catches LISTD (See underlined letters.)

Core Concepts

1) Improve indoor air quality
   - Improve building ventilation
   - Choose proper materials
   - Reduce, manage, and eliminate contaminants
   - Advocate green construction practices and green building operation
   - **Active (Mechanical)** Ventilation
   - **Passive (Natural)** Ventilation

2) Improve indoor environmental quality
   - Thermal comfort control
   - Daylight and views
   - Considering acoustics

Recognition, Regulation, and Incentives
Guidance is available from private and public sector organizations such as EPA, Department of Labor or ASHRAE

Overall Strategies and Technologies
1) Choose low-emitting materials, interior finishes, furniture, etc.
2) Reduce, manage, and eliminate contaminants like certain cleaning products, tobacco smoke, and radon.
3) Advocate green construction practices like **Best Management Practices (BMPs)**, outdoor air introduction, green cleaning, and proper handling of exhaust systems.
4) Allow thermal comfort control such as user control and feedback or operations and maintenance management.
5) Provide daylight/views such as north-facing skylight, interior light (reflecting) shelf, interior and exterior permanent shading devices, automatic photocell-based control, and high performance glazing. Try to maximize daylight for interior spaces while avoiding high-contrast conditions.
6) Use light fixtures with sensors and dimming controls.

EQ Outline:

EQ Prerequisite or Credit Name	Extra Credit	Responsible Party
EQP: Minimum Indoor Air Quality Performance	0	Architect
EQP: Environmental Tobacco Smoke Control	0	Landlord or tenant
*EQP: Minimum Acoustic Performance	0	Acoustical Engineer and Architect
EQC: Enhanced Indoor Air Quality Strategies	Achieve both Choice 1 and Choice 2 and incorporate an additional Choice 2 strategy.	Mechanical Engineer
EQC: Low-Emitting Materials	Choice 1. Reach 100% of products & earn all points. Choice 2. Reach 100% of products.	Contractor
EQC: Construction Indoor Air Quality Management Plan	0	Contractor
EQC: Indoor Air Quality Assessment	0	Contractor
EQC: Thermal Comfort	0	Mechanical Engineer
EQC: Interior Lighting	0	Electrical Engineer
EQC: Daylight	0	MEP Engineers & Architect
EQC: Quality Views	**New Construction, Core and Shell, Schools, Retail, Data Centers, Hospitality** • Meet the criteria for 90% of all regularly occupied areas. **Warehouses and Distribution Centers** • Meet the criteria for 90% of the regularly occupied floor area in the office portion of the building, and for • 50% of the regularly occupied floor area in the sorting, bulk storage, and distribution portions of the building. **Healthcare** • For inpatient areas, meet the criteria for 90% of the regularly occupied floor area. • For non-inpatient areas, exceed the area criteria in Table 1 by 10% or more.	Architect
EQC: Acoustic Performance	0	Acoustical Engineer, Mechanical Engineer, and Architect

Note: * indicates prerequisite or credit NOT applicable to all LEED rating systems. Refer to the specific prerequisite or credit for more information.

EQP: **Minimum Indoor Air Quality Performance**

Mandatory for

New Construction (0 points)
Core and Shell (0 points)
Schools (0 points)
Retail (0 points)
Data Centers (0 points)
Warehouses and Distribution Centers (0 points)
Hospitality (0 points)
Healthcare (0 points)

Purpose

Establishes minimum standards for indoor air quality (IAQ), and contributes to the well-being and comfort of building occupants.

Credit Path:

New Construction, Core and Shell, Schools, Retail, Data Centers, Warehouses and Distribution Centers, Hospitality

Meet the criteria for both ventilation and monitoring.

Ventilation

Mechanically Ventilated Spaces

Choice 1. ASHRAE Standard 62.1–2010

For mixed-mode systems when the mechanical ventilation is activated and for mechanically ventilated spaces, use the ventilation rate procedure from ASHRAE 62.1–2010 or a local equivalent, whichever is more stringent, to determine the minimum outdoor air intake flow for mechanical ventilation systems.

Meet the minimum requirements of ASHRAE Standard 62.1–2010, Sections 4–7, Ventilation for Acceptable Indoor Air Quality (with errata), or a local equivalent, whichever is more stringent.

Choice 2. **CEN Standards EN 15251–2007 and EN 13779–2007**

Projects outside the U.S. can meet the minimum outdoor air requirements of Annex B of **Comité Européen de Normalisation (CEN)** Standard EN 15251–2007; indoor environmental input parameters for design and assessment of energy performance of buildings addressing indoor air quality, thermal environment, lighting, and acoustics; and meet the requirements of CEN Standard EN 13779–2007, ventilation for nonresidential buildings, performance requirements for ventilation and room conditioning systems, excluding Section 7.3, Thermal environment; 7.6, Acoustic environment; A.16; and A.17.

Naturally Ventilated Spaces

For mixed-mode systems when the mechanical ventilation is inactivated and for naturally ventilated spaces, use the natural ventilation procedure from ASHRAE Standard 62.1–2010 or a local equivalent, whichever is more stringent, to determine the minimum outdoor air opening and space configuration requirements. Verify that natural ventilation is an effective strategy for the project by following the flow diagram in the Chartered Institution of Building Services Engineers (CIBSE) Applications Manual AM10, March 2005, Natural Ventilation in Nondomestic Buildings, Figure 2.8, and meet the requirements of ASHRAE Standard 62.1–2010, Section 4, or a local equivalent, whichever is more stringent.

All Spaces
The indoor air quality procedure defined in ASHRAE Standard 62.1–2010 cannot be used to meet this prerequisite.

Monitoring

Mechanically Ventilated Spaces
For mixed-mode systems when the mechanical ventilation is activated and for mechanically ventilated spaces, monitor outdoor air intake flow as follows:

For variable air volume systems, provide a direct outdoor airflow measurement device that can measure the minimum outdoor air intake flow. This device must measure the minimum outdoor air intake flow with an accuracy of +/–10% of the design minimum outdoor airflow rate per the ventilation requirements above. An alarm must indicate when the outdoor airflow value varies by 15% or more from the outdoor airflow setpoint.

For constant-volume systems, balance outdoor airflow to the design minimum outdoor airflow rate per ASHRAE Standard 62.1–2010 (with errata), or higher. Install a current transducer on the airflow switch, a supply fan, or similar monitoring device.

Naturally Ventilated Spaces
For mixed-mode systems when the mechanical ventilation is inactivated and for naturally ventilated spaces, comply with a minimum of one of the following strategies.

Provide a direct exhaust airflow measurement device that can measure the exhaust airflow. This device must measure the exhaust airflow with an accuracy of +/–10% of the design minimum exhaust airflow rate. An alarm must indicate when airflow values vary by 15% or more from the exhaust airflow setpoint.

Provide automatic indication devices on all natural ventilation openings intended to meet the minimum opening requirements. An alarm must indicate when any one of the openings is closed during occupied hours.

Monitor carbon dioxide (CO_2) concentrations within each thermal zone. CO_2 monitors must be within the thermal zone and between 3 and 6 feet (900 and 1 800 millimeters) above the floor. CO_2 monitors must have an audible or visual indicator or alert the building automation system if the sensed CO_2 concentration exceeds the setpoint by more than 10%. Use the methods in ASHRAE62.1–2010, Appendix C to calculate appropriate CO_2 setpoints.

Core and Shell only
Based on the requirements of anticipated future tenants, mechanical ventilation systems installed during core and shell construction must be capable to meet projected ventilation levels and monitoring.

Residential only
In addition to the requirements above, if the project building contains residential units, each dwelling unit must meet all of the following criteria.

- Unvented combustion appliances (e.g., decorative logs) are not allowed.
- Carbon monoxide monitors must be installed on each floor of each unit.

- All indoor woodstoves and fireplaces must have solid glass enclosures or doors that seal when closed.
- Any indoor woodstoves and fireplaces that are not closed combustion or power-vented must pass a backdraft potential test to ensure that depressurization of the combustion appliance zone is less than 5 Pa.
- Space- and water-heating equipment that involves combustion must be designed and installed with power-vented exhaust or with closed combustion (i.e., sealed supply air and exhaust ducting) or located in a detached utility building or open-air facility.
- For projects in high-risk areas for radon, EPA Radon Zone 1 (or local equivalent for international projects), design and construct any dwelling unit on levels one through four above grade with radon-resistant construction techniques. Follow the most stringent techniques prescribed in International Residential Code, Appendix F; EPA Building Radon Out; NFPA 5000, Chapter 49; CABO, Appendix F; ASTM E1465; or a local equivalent.

Healthcare
Meet the following requirements for both ventilation and monitoring.

Ventilation

Mechanically Ventilated Spaces
For mixed-mode systems when the mechanical ventilation is activated and for mechanically ventilated spaces, use the most stringent requirements of the 2010 FGI Guidelines for Design and Construction of Health Care Facilities (Table 2.1–2); the ventilation rates in ASHRAE Standard 170–2008, Section 7; or a local equivalent to determine the minimum outdoor air intake flow for mechanical ventilations systems. For any area not covered in 170 or the FGI guidelines, follow the more stringent requirements of ASHRAE 62.1 or a local equivalent, and meet the minimum requirements of ASHRAE Standard 170–2008, Sections 6–8, Ventilation of Health Care Facilities (with errata) or a USGBC-approved equivalent standard for international projects.

Naturally Ventilated Spaces
For mixed-mode systems when the mechanical ventilation is inactivated and for naturally ventilated spaces, use the more stringent natural ventilation procedure of ASHRAE Standard 62.1–2010 (with errata) or a local equivalent to determine the minimum outdoor air opening and space configuration requirements. Verify that natural ventilation is an effective strategy for the project by following the flow diagram in Figure 2.8 of the Chartered Institution of Building Services Engineers (CIBSE) Applications Manual AM10, March 2005, Natural Ventilation in Nondomestic Buildings.

Monitoring
Mechanically Ventilated Spaces
For mixed-mode systems when the mechanical ventilation is activated and for mechanically ventilated spaces, provide a direct outdoor airflow measurement device that can measure the minimum outdoor air intake flow. This device must measure the minimum outdoor air intake flow with an accuracy of +/–10% of the design minimum outdoor airflow rate defined by the ventilation requirements above. An alarm must indicate whenever the outdoor airflow value varies by 15% or more from the outdoor airflow setpoint.

Naturally Ventilated Spaces
For mixed-mode systems when the mechanical ventilation is inactivated and for naturally ventilated spaces, comply with one or more of the following strategies.

- Provide a direct exhaust airflow measurement device that can measure the exhaust airflow with an accuracy of +/–10% of the design minimum exhaust airflow rate. An alarm must signal when airflow values vary by 15% or more from the exhaust airflow setpoint.
- Provide automatic indication devices on all natural ventilation openings intended to meet the minimum opening requirements. An alarm must signal when any one of the openings is closed during occupied hours.
- Monitor carbon dioxide (CO_2) concentrations within each thermal zone. CO_2 monitors must be within the thermal zone and between 3 and 6 feet (900 and 1 800 millimeters) above the floor. CO_2 monitors must have an audible or visual indicator or alert the building automation system if the sensed CO_2 concentration exceeds the setpoint by more than 10%. Calculate appropriate CO_2 setpoints by using the methods in ASHRAE 62.1–2010, Appendix C.

Campus
Group Approach
Separate submittal for each building.

Campus Approach
Unqualified.

Submittals:

New Construction, Core and Shell, Schools, Retail, Data Centers, Warehouses and Distribution Centers, Hospitality				
Submittals	**Choice 1**	**Choice 2**	**Naturally ventilated**	**Mixed Mode**
Verification that project satisfies minimum requirements of ASHRAE 62.1–2010, Sections 4–7, or CEN Standard 13779–2007	X	X		X
Verification that project has MERV 11 or higher filters (if project is in nonattainment area for PM2.5)	X	X		X
Ventilation rate procedure or CEN calculations and documentation of assumptions for calculation variables	X	X		X
Verification that project meets minimum requirements of ASHRAE Standard 62.1–2010, Section 7, and exhaust ventilation requirements of Section 6.5			X	X
Documentation of CIBSE flow diagram process for project			X	X
Natural ventilation procedure calculations and ventilation opening information			X	X
Any natural ventilation exception from mechanical ventilation system (ASHRAE 62.1–2010, Section 6.4)			X	X
Any exception from authority having jurisdiction			X	X
Controls drawing showing monitoring devices (outdoor airflow measuring device, current transducer, airflow switch or similar monitor, automatic indication device, CO_2 sensor)	X	X	X	X

Healthcare			
Submittals	**Mechanically ventilated**	**Naturally ventilated**	**Mixed mode**
Verification that project satisfies minimum requirements of ASHRAE Standard170-2008, Sections 6-8	x		x
If applicable, air balance summary table to show that the min total air changes, minimum OA changes, and space pressurization relationships provided are consistent with the FGI or ASHRAE Standard 170	x		x
If applicable, ventilation rate procedure calculations and documentation of assumptions for calculation variables	x		x
Documentation of CIBSE flow diagram process for project		x	x
Natural ventilation procedure calculations and ventilation opening information		x	x
Any natural ventilation exception from mechanical ventilation system (ASHRAE62.1–2010, Section 6.4)		x	x
Any exception from authority having jurisdiction		x	x
Controls drawing demonstrating monitoring devices (current transducer, outdoor airflow measuring device, airflow switch or similar monitor, automatic indication device, CO_2 sensor)	x	x	x

Synergies

- EAP: Minimum Energy Performance
- EQC: Enhanced Indoor Air Quality Strategies
- EQC: Indoor Air Quality Assessment

Extra Credit (Exemplary Performance):

None

Project Phase:

Construction Documents & Construction Administration

LEED Submittal Phase:

Construction

Related Code or Standard:

ASHRAE 62.1–2010: ashrae.org
ASHRAE Standard 170–2008: ashrae.org
2010 FGI Guidelines for Design and Construction of Health Care Facilities: fgiguidelines.org
CEN Standard EN 15251–2007: cen.eu
CEN Standard EN 13779–2007: cen.eu
CIBSE Applications Manual AM10, March 2005: cibse.org

Responsible Party:

Architect

EQP: **Environmental Tobacco Smoke Control**

Mandatory for

New Construction (0 points)
Core and Shell (0 points)
Schools (0 points)
Retail (0 points)
Data Centers (0 points)
Warehouses and Distribution Centers (0 points)
Hospitality (0 points)
Healthcare (0 point)

Purpose

Minimizes or protects ventilation air distribution systems, indoor surfaces, and building occupants from exposure to environmental tobacco smoke.

Credit Path:

New Construction, Core and Shell, Retail, Data Centers,
Warehouses and Distribution Centers, Hospitality, Healthcare

Ban smoking inside the building.
Ban smoking outside the building except in designated smoking areas located 25 feet (7.5 meters) or more from all outdoor air intakes, entries, and operable windows. Also, ban smoking outside the property line in spaces for business purposes.

If the requirement to ban smoking within 25 feet (7.5 meters) cannot be implemented because of code, provide documentation of these regulations.

Signage must be displayed within 10 feet (3 meters) of all building entrances specifying the no-smoking policy.

Residential only
Choice 1. No Smoking
Meet the requirements above.

OR

Choice 2. Compartmentalization of Smoking Areas
Ban smoking inside all common areas of the building. The ban must be communicated in building lease or rental agreements or coop association or condo covenants and restrictions. Make provisions for enforcement.

Ban smoking outside the building except in designated smoking areas located 25 feet (7.5 meters) or more from all outdoor air intakes, entries, and operable windows. Also, ban smoking outside the property line in spaces for business purposes.

If the requirement to ban smoking within 25 feet (7.5 meters) cannot be implemented because of code, provide documentation of these regulations.

Signage must be displayed within 10 feet (3 meters) of all building entrances specifying the no-smoking policy.

To prevent excessive leakage between units, each unit must be compartmentalized:

- Weather-strip all operable windows and exterior doors in the residential units to minimize leakage from outdoors.
- Weather-strip all doors leading from common hallways into residential units.
- Minimize uncontrolled pathways for the transfer of indoor air pollutants, including smoke between residential units, by sealing penetrations in the ceilings, walls, and floors and by sealing vertical chases (including garbage chutes, utility chases, mail drops, and elevator shafts) adjacent to the units.
- Show a maximum leakage of 0.23 cubic feet per minute per square foot (1.17 liters per second per square meter) at 50 Pa of enclosure (i.e., all surfaces enclosing the apartment, including floors, exterior and party walls, and ceilings).

SCHOOLS
Prohibit smoking on site.
Signage must be posted at the property line indicating the no-smoking policy.

Campus
Group Approach
All buildings in the group may be submitted as one.

Campus Approach
Qualified.

Submittals:

Submittals	All projects where smoking is prohibited	Residential projects where smoking is permitted
Narrative of project's no-smoking policy, including information on how policy is communicated to building occupants and enforced	x	x
Copy of no-smoking policy, copy of any legally binding covenants or restrictions to verify status of residential units as nonsmoking, or signed letter from owner describing project's no-smoking policy and enforcement	x	
Door schedule showing weather-stripping at doors leading from common hallways to units and exterior unit doors		x
Differential air pressure test report for units in project building		x
Scaled map or site plan showing the location of property line, location of designated outdoor smoking and no-smoking areas, and site boundary and indicating 25-foot (7.5-meter) distance from building openings	x	x
Photos, drawings, or other evidence of signage communicating no-smoking policy	x	x
Any landlord or code restrictions that prevent establishment of no-smoking criteria	x	x

Synergies:
None

Extra Credit (Exemplary Performance):
None

Project Phase:
Design Development

LEED Submittal Phase:
Design

Related Code or Standard:

- **Standard Test Method for Determining Air Leakage Rate by Fan Pressurization, ASTM E779-03**: astm.org
- **Standard Test Methods for Determining Airtightness of Buildings Using an Orifice Blower Door, ASTME1827-11**: astm.org
- **Nondestructive testing, Leak testing—Criteria for method and technique selection, CEN Standard EN1779—1999**: cen.eu
- **Nondestructive testing, Leak testing, Tracer gas method, CEN Standard EN 13185—2001**: cen.eu
- **Nondestructive testing, Leak testing, Calibration of reference leaks for gases, CEN Standard EN 13192—2001**:cen.eu
- **RESNET Standards**: resnet.us/standards
- **ENERGY STAR Multifamily Testing Protocol**: energystar.gov/ia/partners/bldrs_lenders_raters

Responsible Party:
Landlord or tenant

*EQP: **Minimum Acoustic Performance**

Applicable to

Schools

Purpose:

Use effective acoustic design to provide classrooms that facilitate student-to student and teacher-to-student communication.

Credit Path:

HVAC Background Noise

In classrooms and other core learning spaces, achieve a background noise level of 40 dBA or less from HVAC systems. Follow the recommended methodologies and best practices for mechanical system noise control in the 2011 HVAC Applications ASHRAE Handbook, Chapter 48, Noise and Vibration Control (with errata); ANSI Standard S12.60–2010, Part 1, Annex A.1; AHRI Standard 885–2008; or a local equivalent for international projects.

Exterior Noise

For high-noise sites (peak-hour L_{eq} above 60 dBA during school hours), use acoustic treatment and other measures to control sound transmission between classrooms and other core learning spaces and minimize noise intrusion from exterior sources. Projects at least 1/2 mile (800 meters) from any significant noise source (e.g., highways, aircraft overflights, trains, industry) are exempt.

Note: *L_{eq} is Equivalent Continuous Sound Level.*

Reverberation Time

Comply with the following reverberation time requirements.

Classrooms and Core Learning Spaces < 20,000 Cubic Feet (566 Cubic Meters)

Design core learning spaces, including classrooms, to incorporate sufficient sound-absorptive finishes for compliance with the reverberation time requirements of ANSI Standard S12.60–2010, Part 1, Acoustical Performance Criteria, Design Requirements and Guidelines for Schools, or a local equivalent for international projects.

Choice 1

For each room, confirm that the total surface area of acoustic wall panels, ceiling finishes, and other sound-absorbent finishes is not less than the total ceiling area of the room (excluding diffusers, lights, and grilles). Materials must have an NRC of 0.70 or higher to be included in the calculation.

OR

Choice 2

Verify through calculations explained in ANSI Standard S12.60-2010 that rooms are designed to meet reverberation time requirements per this ANSI standard.

Classrooms and Core Learning Spaces ⩾ 20,000 Cubic Feet (566 Cubic Meters)

Comply with the recommended reverberation times for classrooms and core learning spaces described in the NRC-CNRC Construction Technology Update No. 51, Acoustical Design of Rooms for Speech (2002), or a local equivalent for international projects.

Exceptions
Exceptions to the requirements will be considered to observe historic preservation requirements or because of a limited scope of work.

Campus
Group Approach
Separate submittal for each building.

Campus Approach
Unqualified. Separate submittal for each building.

Submittals:

- **Background noise:** Summary report of measurements and calculations documenting compliance with selected reference standard
- **Exterior noise:**
  - Description of exterior noise sources (or lack thereof) within 1/2-mile (800-meter) radius
  - L_{eq} calculations and narrative describing when measurements were taken (if required)
  - Description or drawings of measures and strategies implemented to minimize exterior noise (if required)
- **Reverberation time, spaces less than 20,000 ft^2 (1 860 m^2):**
  - Choice 1, documentation showing materials with NRC of 0.70 or higher
  - Choice 2, calculations or measurements showing that reverberation times meet the ANSIS12.60–2010 or requirements
- **Reverberation time, spaces 20,000 ft^2 (1 860 m^2) or larger:** Calculations or measurements showing that reverberation times meet NRC-CNRC Construction Technology Update No. 51 requirements

Synergies:

- EQC: Acoustic Performance.

Extra Credit (Exemplary Performance):
None

Project Phase:
Construction Documents

LEED Submittal Phase:
Design

Related Code or Standard:

- **AHRI Standard 885–2008, Procedure for Estimating Occupied Space Sound Levels in the Application of Air Terminals and Air Outlets:** ahrinet.org
- **American National Standards Institute (ANSI)/ASHRAE Standard S12.60–2010, Acoustical Performance Criteria, Design Requirements, and Guidelines for Schools**: asastore.aip.org

- **2011 HVAC Applications, ASHRAE Handbook, Chapter 48, Noise and Vibration Control**: ashrae.org
- **NRC-CNRC Construction Technology Update No. 51, Acoustic Design of Rooms for Speech, 2002**:nrc-cnrc.gc.ca

Responsible Party:

Acoustical Engineer and Architect

EQC: **Enhanced Indoor Air Quality Strategies**

Applicable to

New Construction (1-2 points)
Core and Shell (1-2 points)
Schools (1-2 points)
Retail (1-2 points)
Data Centers (1-2 points)
Warehouses and Distribution Centers (1-2 points)
Hospitality (1-2 points)
Healthcare (1-2 points)

Purpose

Improves indoor air quality which results in occupant well-being, comfort, and productivity.

Credit Path:

Choice 1. Enhanced IAQ Strategies (1 point)

Meet the following criteria, as applicable.

Mechanically ventilated spaces:

- **entryway systems:** Install permanent entryway systems with a minimum length of 10 feet (3 meters) in the main direction of travel to capture particulates and dirt at regularly used exterior entrances. Acceptable entryway systems include permanently installed grilles, grates, slotted systems that allow for cleaning underneath, rollout mats, and any other materials manufactured as entryway systems with equal or better performance. Maintain all on a weekly basis.

  Warehouses and Distribution Centers only

  Entryway systems are not needed at doors leading from the exterior to the garage or loading dock but must be installed between these spaces and adjacent office areas.

  Healthcare only

  Provide pressurized entryway vestibules at high-volume building entrances in addition to the entryway system.

- **filtration:** Every ventilation system that provides outdoor air to occupied spaces must have air-cleaning devices or particle filters that comply with one of the following filtration media criteria:
  - minimum efficiency reporting value (MERV) of 13 or higher, in accordance with ASHRAE Standard 52.2–2007;
    OR
  - Class F7 or higher as defined by CEN Standard EN 779–2002, Particulate Air Filters for General Ventilation, Determination of the Filtration Performance. Replace all air filtration media after completion of construction and before occupancy.

  Data Centers only

  The above filtration media criteria are required only for ventilation systems serving regularly occupied spaces.

  - **interior cross-contamination prevention:** Sufficiently exhaust each space where hazardous chemicals or gases may be present or used (e.g., housekeeping and laundry areas, garages, copying and printing rooms) using the exhaust rates determined in EQP: Minimum Indoor Air Quality Performance or a minimum of 0.50 cfm per square foot (2.54 l/s per square meter) to create negative pressure to adjacent spaces when the doors to the room are closed.

Provide self-closing doors and a hard-lid ceiling or deck-to-deck partitions for each of these spaces.

Naturally ventilated spaces:

- **entryway systems;** and
- **natural ventilation design calculations:** Show that the system design for occupied spaces employs the appropriate strategies in Chartered Institution of Building Services Engineers (CIBSE) Applications Manual AM10, March 2005, Natural Ventilation in Non-Domestic Buildings, Section 2.4.

Mixed-mode systems:

- **entryway systems;**
- **filtration;**
- **interior cross-contamination prevention;**
- **natural ventilation design calculations;** and
- **mixed-mode design calculations:** Show that the system design for occupied spaces complies with CIBSE Applications Manual 13–2000, Mixed Mode Ventilation.

Choice 2. Additional Enhanced IAQ Strategies (1 point)

Meet the following criteria, as applicable.

Mechanically ventilated spaces (select one):

- **exterior contamination prevention:**
  Design to control and minimize the entry of pollutants into the building. Through the results of Gaussian dispersion analyses, computational fluid dynamics modeling, wind tunnel modeling, or tracer gas modeling, ensure that outdoor air contaminant concentrations at outdoor air intakes are below the thresholds listed in Table 1 (or local equivalent for international projects, whichever is more stringent).

Table 1. Maximum concentrations of pollutants at outdoor air intakes

Pollutants	Maximum concentration	Standard
Those regulated by National Ambient Air Quality Standards (NAAQS)	Allowable annual average OR 8-hour or 24-hour average where an annual standard does not exist OR Rolling 3-month average	National Ambient Air Quality Standards (NAAQS)

- **increased ventilation:**
  Improve breathing zone outdoor air ventilation rates to all occupied spaces by 30% or more above the minimum rates per EQP: Minimum Indoor Air Quality Performance.

- **carbon dioxide monitoring:**
  Monitor CO_2 concentrations in all densely occupied spaces. CO_2 monitors have to be between 3 and 6 feet (900 and 1,800 millimeters) above the floor. CO_2 monitors must alert the building automation system or have an audible or visual indicator if the sensed CO_2 concentration exceeds the setpoint by 10% or more. Calculate appropriate CO_2 setpoints using methods in ASHRAE 62.1–2010, Appendix C.
  OR

- **additional source control and monitoring:**
  Evaluate potential sources of additional air contaminants besides CO_2 for spaces where air contaminants are likely. Create and instigate a materials-handling plan to reduce the likelihood of contaminant release. Establish monitoring systems with sensors designed to detect the specific contaminants. An alarm must signal any unsafe or unusual conditions.

Naturally ventilated spaces (select one):
- exterior contamination prevention;
- additional source control and monitoring; or
- natural ventilation room by room calculations:
  Follow CIBSE AM10, Section 4, Design Calculations, to predict that room-by-room airflows will provide effective natural ventilation.

Mixed-mode systems (select one):
- exterior contamination prevention;
- increased ventilation;
- additional source control and monitoring; or
- natural ventilation room-by-room calculations.

Campus
Group Approach
Separate submittal for each building.

Campus Approach
Unqualified. Separate submittal for each building.

Submittals:

Submittals	Choice 1	Choice 2
Entryway systems: scaled floor plans showing locations and measurements	x	
Interior cross-contamination prevention: list of rooms, exhaust rate, areas, separation method	x	
Filtration: mechanical schedules highlighting MERV or class ratings for all units that supply outdoor air	x	
Natural ventilation design: calculations and narrative demonstrating appropriate strategies per referenced standard	x	
Mixed mode design: calculations and narrative demonstrating appropriate strategies per referenced standard	x	
Exterior contamination prevention: narrative describing type of modeling; model output reports highlighting required thresholds and contaminant levels		x
Increased ventilation: confirmation (calculations are documented under EQP: Minimum Indoor Air Quality Performance)		x
Carbon dioxide monitoring: list of densely occupied spaces, space type, floor plan showing sensor locations, design CO_2 concentrations, narrative describing CO_2 setpoints		x

Additional source control and monitoring: description of materials handling plan, description of likely air contaminants and how they were identified, plans showing installed monitoring system		x
Natural ventilation: narrative, room-by-room calculations, and diagrams demonstrating effective natural ventilation per referenced standard		x

Synergies

- EAP: Minimum Energy Performance
- EAC: Energy Performance
- EQP: Indoor Air Quality Performance

Extra Credit (Exemplary Performance):

Achieve both Choice 1 and Choice 2 and incorporate an additional Choice 2 strategy.

Project Phase:

Construction Documents

LEED Submittal Phase:

Design

Related Code or Standard:

ASHRAE Standard 52.2–2007: ashrae.org
ASHRAE Standard 62.1—2010: ashrae.org
Chartered Institution of Building Services Engineers (CIBSE) Applications Manual AM10, March 2005:
cibse.org
Chartered Institution of Building Services Engineers (CIBSE) Applications Manual 13, 2000:
cibse.org
CEN Standard EN 779–2002: cen.eu
National Ambient Air Quality Standards (NAAQS): epa.gov/air/criteria.html

Responsible Party:

Mechanical Engineer

EQC: **Low-Emitting Materials**

Applicable to

New Construction (1-3 points)
Core and Shell (1-3 points)
Schools (1-3 points)
Retail (1-3 points)
Data Centers (1-3 points)
Warehouses and Distribution Centers (1-3 points)
Hospitality (1-3 points)
Healthcare (1-3 points)

Purpose

Lessens the concentration of chemical pollutants that may harm the environment, air quality, human productivity, and human health.

Credit Path:

This credit includes criteria for project teams as well as product manufacturers. It covers **volatile organic compound (VOC)** content of materials and the VOC emissions into indoor air, as well as the testing methods by which indoor VOC emissions are gauged. Different materials must meet different criteria to be considered compliant for this credit. The building exterior and interior are organized in seven categories, each with different thresholds. The building exterior is inclusive of the primary and secondary weatherproofing system and include outside building elements, such as air- and water-resistive barrier materials and waterproofing membranes. The building interior is everything within the waterproofing membrane.

Choice 1. Product Category Calculations

Realize the threshold level of compliance with content standards and emissions for the number of product categories listed in Table 2.

Table 1. Thresholds of compliance with emissions and content standards for 7 categories of materials

Category	Threshold	Emissions and content criteria
Interior coatings and paints applied on site	100% for VOC content; at least 90%, by volume, for emissions	• General Emissions Evaluation for coatings and paints applied to walls, floors, and ceilings • VOC content criteria for wet applied products
Interior sealants and adhesives applied on site (including flooring adhesive)	100% for VOC content; at least 90%, by volume, for emissions	• General Emissions Evaluation • VOC content criteria for wet applied products
Flooring	100%	General Emissions Evaluation
Composite wood	100% not covered by other categories	Composite Wood Evaluation
Ceilings, walls, thermal, and acoustic insulation	100%	• General Emissions Evaluation • **Healthcare, Schools only** Additional insulation requirements
Furniture (include in calculations if part of scope of work)	At least 90%, by cost	Furniture Evaluation

Healthcare and Schools Projects only: Exterior applied products	At least 90%, by volume	Exterior Applied Products

Table 2. Points for number of compliant categories of products	
Compliant categories	**Points**
New Construction, Core and Shell, Retail, Data Centers, Warehouses and Distribution Centers, Hospitality projects without furniture	
2	1
4	2
5	3
New Construction, Core and Shell, Retail, Data Centers, Warehouses and Distribution Centers, Hospitality projects with furniture	
3	1
5	2
6	3
Schools, Healthcare without furniture	
3	1
5	2
6	3
Schools, Healthcare with furniture	
5	1
6	2
7	3

Choice 2. Budget Calculation Method

For products that do not meet the criteria, the budget calculation method can be used (Table 3).

Table 3. Points for percentage compliance, under budget calculation method	
Percentage of total	**Points**
$\geqslant$ 50% and < 70%	1
$\geqslant$ 70% and < 90%	2
$\geqslant$ 90%	3

The budget method organizes the building interior into six assemblies:

- flooring;
- walls;
- ceilings;
- thermal and acoustic insulation;
- furniture; and
- **Healthcare, Schools only:** exterior applied products.

If furniture is part of the scope of work, include it in the calculations. Walls, ceilings, and flooring are building interior products; each layer of the assembly, including adhesives, paints, coatings, and sealants, must be evaluated for compliance. Insulation is tracked separately.

Determine the total percentage of compliant materials per Equation 1.

Equation 1. Total percentage compliance
Total % compliant for projects without furniture = (% compliant walls + % compliant ceilings + % compliant flooring + % compliant insulation) / 4

Total % compliant for projects with furniture = [(% compliant walls + % compliant ceilings + % compliant flooring + % compliant insulation) + (% compliant furniture)] / 5

Equation 2. System percentage compliant
Flooring, walls, ceilings, insulation % compliant = [(compliant surface area of layer 1 + compliant surface area of layer 2 + compliant surface area of layer 3 +...) / (total surface area of layer 1 + total surface area of layer 2 + total surface area of layer 3 + …)] x 100

Equation 3. Furniture systems compliant, using ANSI/BIFMA evaluation
% compliant for furniture = [(0.5 × cost compliant with §7.6.1 of ANSI/BIFMA e3-2011 + cost compliant with §7.6.2 of ANSI/BIFMA e3-2011) / (total furniture cost)] x 100

Calculate surface area of assembly layers per the manufacturer's documentation for application.

If 90% or more of an assembly meets the criteria, the system is considered 100% compliant. If less than 50% of an assembly meets the criteria, the assembly is considered 0% compliant.

Manufacturers' claims. Both first-party and third-party statements of product compliance must meet the guidelines in CDPH SM V1.1–2010, Section 8. Organizations that certify manufacturers' claims must be accredited under ISO Guide 65.

Laboratory requirements. Laboratories that conduct the tests listed in this credit must be accredited under ISO/IEC 17025 for the test methods they use.

Emissions and Content Requirements
To show compliance, a product or layer must meet all of the following criteria, as applicable.

Inherently nonemitting sources. Products that are inherently nonemitting sources of VOCs (ceramic, stone, concrete, clay brick, plated or anodized metal, powder-coated metals, glass, and unfinished or untreated solid wood flooring) are considered fully compliant without any VOC emissions testing if they do not include integral organic based binders, surface coatings, or sealants.

General emissions evaluation. Project team must have building products test results to determine compliant per **California Department of Public Health (CDPH) Standard Method v1.1–2010**, using the applicable exposure scenario. The default scenario is the private office scenario. The manufacturer's or third-party certification has to specify the exposure scenario used to determine compliance. Claims of compliance for wet-applied products have to specify the amount applied in mass per surface area.

Manufacturers' claims of compliance with the above criteria must also specify the range of total VOCs after14 days (336 hours), measured per the CDPH Standard Method v1.1:

- 0.5 mg/m^3 or less;
- between 0.5 and 5.0 mg/m^3; or
- 5.0 mg/m^3 or more.

International projects may use products tested and deemed compliant in accordance with either
(1) the CDPH standard method (2010)
OR
(2) the German AgBB Testing and Evaluation Scheme (2010).

Test products either with
(1) the CDPH Standard Method (2010)
(2) the German AgBB Testing and Evaluation Scheme (2010)
(3) ISO 16000-3: 2010, ISO 16000-6: 2011, ISO 16000-9: 2006, ISO 16000-11:2006 either in conjunction with AgBB, or with French legislation on VOC emission class labeling
OR
(4) the DIBt testing method (2010). If the applied testing method does not specify testing details for a product group for which the CDPH standard method does provide details, use the specifications in the CDPH standard method. U.S. projects must follow the CDPH standard method.

Additional VOC content requirements for wet-applied products. Besides meeting the general criteria for VOC emissions mentioned earlier, on-site wet-applied products shall not contain excessive levels of VOCs for the health of the installers and others who are exposed to these products. To show compliance, a product or layer shall comply with the following criteria, as applicable. Disclosure of VOC content shall be made by the manufacturer. Any testing shall follow the test method listed in the applicable regulation.

- All coatings and paints wet-applied on site shall comply with the applicable VOC limits of the **California Air Resources Board (CARB)** 2007, the **South Coast Air Quality Management District (SCAQMD)** Rule 1113, effective June 3, 2011, or Suggested Control Measure (SCM) for Architectural Coatings.
- All sealants and adhesives wet-applied on site shall comply with the applicable chemical content requirements of SCAQMD Rule 1168, July 1, 2005, Adhesive and Sealant Applications, as analyzed by the methods listed in Rule 1168. The provisions of SCAQMD Rule 1168 do not apply to sealants and adhesives subject to state or federal consumer product VOC regulations.
- For international projects, all coatings, paints, adhesives, and sealants wet-applied on site must either meet the technical criteria of the afore-mentioned regulations or comply with related national VOC control regulations, such as the Canadian VOC Concentration Limits for Architectural Coatings, the European Decopaint Directive (2004/42/EC), or the Hong Kong Air Pollution Control (VOC) Regulation.
- If the related regulation requires subtraction of exempt compounds, any content of intentionally added exempt compounds larger than 1% weight by mass (total exempt compounds) shall be disclosed.
- If a product cannot reasonably be tested as specified above, testing of VOC content shall comply with ASTMD2369-10; ISO 11890, part 1; ASTM D6886-03; or ISO 11890-2.
- For projects in North America, methylene chloride and perchloroethylene cannot be intentionally added in coatings, paints, adhesives, or sealants.

Composite Wood Evaluation. Composite wood, as defined by the California Air Resources Board, Airborne Toxic Measure to Reduce Formaldehyde Emissions from Composite Wood Products Regulation, shall be documented to have low formaldehyde emissions that meet the **California Air Resources Board ATCM** for formaldehyde criteria for **ultra-low-emitting formaldehyde (ULEF)** resins or no added formaldehyde resins.

Reused and salvaged architectural millwork more than one year old at the time of occupancy is considered compliant if it meets the criteria for any site-applied coatings, paints, adhesives, and sealants.

Furniture evaluation. New furnishing items and furniture shall be tested per ANSI/BIFMA Standard Method M7.1–2011 and must meet ANSI/BIFMA e3-2011 Furniture Sustainability Standard, Sections 7.6.1 and 7.6.2, using either the **concentration modeling approach** or the **emissions factor approach**. The test results must be modeled using the private office, open plan, or seating scenario in ANSI/BIFMA M7.1, as applicable. USGBC-approved equivalent contaminant thresholds and testing methodologies are also acceptable. For classroom furniture, use the standard school classroom model in CDPH Standard Method v1.1. Documentation submitted for furniture shall specify the modeling scenario used to determine compliance.

Reused and salvaged architectural millwork more than one year old at the time of occupancy is considered compliant if it meets the criteria for any site-applied coatings, paints, adhesives, and sealants.

Healthcare, Schools only

Additional insulation criteria. Batt insulation products cannot contain added formaldehyde, including phenol formaldehyde, urea formaldehyde, and urea-extended phenol formaldehyde.

Exterior applied products. Sealants, adhesives, coatings, roofing, and waterproofing materials applied on site shall meet the VOC limits of California Air Resources Board (CARB) 2007 Suggested Control Measure (SCM) for Architectural Coatings, and South Coast Air Quality Management District (SCAQMD), Rule 1168, effective July 1, 2005. Small containers of sealants and adhesives subject to state or federal consumer product VOC regulations are exempt.

Projects outside North America may comply with the European Decopaint Directive (2004/42/EC, to be updated to most current version when available) Phase II or use either the jurisdictional VOC content criteria, for water-borne coatings, as analyzed per ISO 11890 parts 1 and 2, instead of the CARB and SCAQMD regulatory standards.

Two materials are banned and do not count toward total percentage compliance: coal tar sealants for parking lots and other paved surfaces, and hot-mopped asphalt for roofing.

Campus

Group Approach

All buildings in the group may be documented as one.

Campus Approach

Unqualified. Separate submittal for each building.

Submittals:

For both choices:

- USGBC low-emitting materials calculator
- Product information (e.g., MSDS, third-party certifications, testing reports)

Synergies

- MRC: Furniture and Medical Furnishings (Healthcare only)
- EQC: Indoor Air Quality Assessment

Extra Credit (Exemplary Performance):

Choice 1. Reach 100% of products & earn all points.
Choice 2. Reach 100% of products.

Project Phase:

Construction Administration

LEED Submittal Phase:

Construction

Related Code or Standard:

- **AgBB—2010**: umweltbundesamt.de/produkte-e/bauprodukte/agbb.htm
- **ANSI/BIFMA e3–2011 Furniture Sustainability Standard**: bifma.org
- **ANSI/BIFMA M7.1 Standard Test Method for Determining VOC Emissions from Office Furniture Systems, Components and Seating**: bifma.org
- **Canadian VOC Concentration Limits for Architectural Coatings**: ec.gc.ca/lcpe-cepa/eng/regulations/detailReg.cfm?intReg=117
- **CARB 93120 ATCM**: arb.ca.gov/toxics/compwood/compwood.htm
- **CDPH Standard Method v1.1–2010**: cal-iaq.org
- **European Decopaint Directive**: ec.europa.eu/environment/air/pollutants/stationary/paints/paints_legis.htm
- **Hong Kong Air Pollution Control Regulation**: epd.gov.hk/epd/english/environmentinhk/air/air_maincontent.html
- **ISO 17025**: iso.org
- **ISO Guide 65**: iso.org
- **ISO 16000 parts 3, 6, 7, 11**: iso.org
- **South Coast Air Quality Management District (SCAQMD) Rule 1168**: aqmd.gov
- **South Coast Air Quality Management District (SCAQMD) Rule 1113**: aqmd.gov

Responsible Party:

Contractor

EQC: **Construction Indoor Air Quality Management Plan**

Applicable to

New Construction (1 point)
Core and Shell (1 point)
Schools (1 point)
Retail (1 point)
Data Centers (1 point)
Warehouses and Distribution Centers (1 point)
Hospitality (1 point)
Healthcare (1 point)

Purpose

Lessens indoor air quality problems related to renovation and construction; and protects the health of building occupants and construction workers.

Credit Path:

New Construction, Core and Shell, Schools, Retail, Data Centers, Warehouses and Distribution Centers, Hospitality

Create and instigate an indoor air quality (IAQ) management plan for the construction and preoccupancy phases of the building. The plan must address all of the following.

During construction, meet or surpass all applicable recommended control measures of the Sheet Metal and Air Conditioning National Contractors Association (SMACNA) IAQ Guidelines for Occupied Buildings under Construction, 2nd edition, 2007, ANSI/SMACNA 008–2008, Chapter 3.

Protect installed and stored on-site absorptive materials from moisture damage.

Only operate permanently installed air-handling equipment during construction after installation of filtration media with **a minimum efficiency reporting value (MERV) of 8** or more, as determined by ASHRAE 52.2–2007, with errata (or equivalent filtration media class of F5 or higher, as defined by CEN Standard EN 779–2002, Particulate Air Filters for General Ventilation, Determination of the Filtration Performance), at each return or transfer duct inlet opening and return air grille such that there is no bypass around the filtration media. Right before occupancy, replace all filtration media with the final design filtration media, installed per the manufacturer's recommendations.

Ban the use of tobacco products within 25 feet (7.5 meters) of the building entrance and inside the building during construction.

Healthcare

Moisture. Create and instigate a moisture control plan to protect installed and stored on-site absorptive materials from moisture damage. Properly dispose of and instantly remove from site any materials prone to microbial growth and replace with new, uncontaminated materials. Also, incorporate strategies for preventing occupants' exposure to mold spores and protecting the building from moisture intrusion.

Particulates. Only operate permanently installed air-handling equipment during construction after installation of filtration media with a minimum efficiency reporting value (MERV) of 8, as determined by ASHRAE 52.2–2007, with errata (or equivalent filtration media class of F5 or higher, as defined by CEN Standard EN 779–2002, Particulate Air Filters for General Ventilation, Determination of the Filtration Performance), at return or transfer duct inlet opening and return air grille such that there is no bypass around the filtration media. Right before occupancy, replace all filtration media with the final design filtration media, installed in accordance with the manufacturer's recommendations.

VOCs. Manage construction procedures to keep exposure of absorbent materials to VOC emissions to a minimum. Finish sealing and painting before installing or storing "dry" materials, which may accumulate pollutants and release them over time. Store solvents, fuels, and other sources of VOCs separately from absorbent materials.

Outdoor emissions. For renovation projects involving repairing asphalt roofing, waterproofing, sealing parking lots, or other outdoor activities that generate high VOC emissions, create a plan to manage fumes and avoid infiltration to occupied spaces. Follow the procedures established by NIOSH, Asphalt Fume Exposures during the Application of Hot Asphalt to Roofs (Publication 2003–112).

Tobacco. Ban the use of tobacco products within 25 feet (7.5 meters) of the building entrance and inside the building during construction.

Noise and vibration. Create a plan based on the British Standard (BS 5228) to lessen noise emissions and vibration from construction equipment and other nonroad engines by specifying the lowest decibel level available or low-noise emission design that meets performance criteria in the British Standard. In areas where sound levels exceed 85 dB for extended periods, construction crews must wear ear protection.

Infection control. For additions adjacent to occupied facilities and renovations or phased occupancy in new construction, comply with the FGI 2010 Guidelines for Design and Construction of Health Care Facilities and the Joint Commission on Standards to create an integrative infection control team including the designer, owner, and contractor to evaluate infection control risk and document the required precautions in a project-specific plan. Use the infection control risk assessment standard published by the American Society of Healthcare Engineering and the U.S. Centers for Disease Control and Prevention (CDC) as a guideline to evaluate risk and to choose mitigation procedures for construction activities.

Campus

Group Approach

All buildings can be submitted as one. One master indoor air quality management plan is acceptable. The plan should incorporate building specific instructions if necessary. Photo documentation shall include a sampling for all buildings.

Campus Approach

Unqualified. Separate submittal for each building.

Submittals:

Submittals	All projects except Healthcare	Healthcare
Detailed checklist or IAQ management plan, highlighting nonsmoking policy	x	
EQMP or detailed checklist, highlighting nonsmoking policy		x
Narrative describing protection measures for absorbent materials	x	x
Annotated photographs of indoor air and environmental quality measures	x	x
Record of filtration media	x	x

Synergies

- EQC: Enhanced Indoor Air Quality Strategies
- EQC: Low-Emitting Materials
- EQC: Indoor Air Quality Assessment

Extra Credit (Exemplary Performance):

None

Project Phase:

Construction Administration

LEED Submittal Phase:

Construction

Related Code or Standard:

- **Sheet Metal and Air-Conditioning National Contractors Association (SMACNA) IAQ Guidelines for Occupied Buildings under Construction, 2nd edition, 2007, ANSI/SMACNA 008–2008 (Chapter 3)**: smacna.org
- **ASHRAE 52.2–2007**: ashrae.org
- **CEN Standard EN 779–2002**: cen.eu
- **British Standard 5228—2009 (Healthcare)**: bsigroup.com
- **Infection Control Risk Assessment (ICRA) Standard, published by the American Society of Healthcare Engineering (ASHE) and the U.S. Centers for Disease Control and Prevention (CDC) (Healthcare)**:
- ashe.org/advocacy/organizations/CDC
- **NIOSH, Asphalt Fume Exposures During the Application of Hot Asphalt to Roofs, Publication No. 2003-112 (Healthcare)**: cdc.gov/niosh/topics/asphalt

Responsible Party:

Contractor

EQC: **Indoor Air Quality Assessment**

Applicable to

New Construction (1-2 points)
Schools (1-2 points)
Retail (1-2 points)
Data Centers (1-2 points)
Warehouses and Distribution Centers (1-2 points)
Hospitality (1-2 points)
Healthcare (1-2 points)

Purpose

Sets up better IAQ in the building after construction and during occupancy.

Credit Path:

Select one of the following two choices, to be applied after construction ends and the building has been totally cleaned. All interior finishes, such as doors, millwork, carpet, paint, acoustic tiles, and movable furnishings (e.g., partitions, workstations), shall be installed, and major VOC punch list items shall be finished. The choices cannot be combined.

Choice 1. Flush-Out (1 point)
Path 1. Before Occupancy
Install new filtration media and complete a building flush-out by supplying a total air volume of 14,000 cubic feet of outdoor air per square foot (4 267 140 liters per second of outdoor air per square meter) of gross floor area while keeping an internal temperature between 60°F (15°C) and 80°F (27°C) and relative humidity lower than 60%.

OR
Path 2. During Occupancy
If owner wants occupancy before the flush-out is completed, the space can be occupied only after delivery of a minimum of 3,500 cubic feet of outdoor air per square foot (1 066 260 liters per second of outdoor air per square meter) of gross floor area while keeping an internal temperature between 60°F (15°C) and 80°F (27°C) and relative humidity lower than 60%.

Once the space is occupied, it shall be ventilated at a minimum rate of 0.30 cubic foot per minute (cfm) per square foot of outdoor air (1.5 liters of outside air per second per square meter) or the design minimum outdoor air rate determined in EQP: Minimum Indoor Air Quality Performance, whichever is greater. During each day of the flush-out period, ventilation shall start at least three hours before occupancy and continue during occupancy. These conditions shall be maintained until a total of 14,000 cubic feet per square foot of outdoor air (4 270 cubic meters of outdoor air per square meter) has been delivered to the space.

OR
Choice 1. Air Testing (2 points)
After completion of construction and before occupancy, but under ventilation conditions typical for occupancy, conduct baseline IAQ testing using protocols consistent with the methods listed in Table 1 for all occupied spaces. Use current versions of EPA compendium methods, ASTM standard methods, or ISO methods, as indicated. Laboratories that conduct the tests for chemical analysis of volatile organic compounds (VOCs) and formaldehyde must be accredited under ISO/IEC 17025 for the test methods they use. Retail projects may conduct the testing within 14 days of occupancy.

Show that contaminants do not surpass the concentration levels in Table 1.

Table 1. Maximum concentration levels, by contaminant and testing method				
Contaminant	**Maximum concentration**	**Maximum concentration (Healthcare only)**	**ASTM and U.S. EPA methods**	**ISO method**
Formaldehyde	27 ppb	16.3 ppb	ASTM D5197; EPA TO-11 or EPA Compendium Method IP-6	ISO 16000-3
Particulates (PM10 for all buildings; PM2.5 for buildings in EPA nonattainment areas; or local equivalent)	PM10: 50 micrograms per cubic meter PM2.5: 15 micrograms per cubic meter	20 micrograms per cubic meter	EPA Compendium Method IP-10	ISO 7708
Ozone (for buildings in EPA nonattainment areas)	0.075 ppm	0.075 ppm	ASTM D5149 - 02	ISO 13964
Total volatile organic compounds (TVOC s)	500 micrograms per cubic meter	200 micrograms per cubic meter	EPA TO-1, TO-15, TO-17, or EPA Compendium Method IP-1	ISO 16000-6
Target chemicals listed in CDPH Standard Method v1.1, Table 4-1, except formaldehyde	CDPH Standard Method v1.1–2010, Allowable Concentrations, Table 4-1	CDPH Standard Method v1.1–2010, Allowable Concentrations, Table 4-1	ASTM D5197; EPA TO-1, TO-15, TO-17	ISO 16000-3, 16000-6
Carbon monoxide (CO)	9 ppm; no more than 2 ppm above outdoor levels	9 ppm; no more than 2 ppm above outdoor levels	EPA Compendium Method IP-3	ISO 4224

ppb = parts per billion; ppm = parts per million; μg/cm = micrograms per cubic meter

Perform all measurements during normal occupied hours but before occupancy, with the building ventilation system started at the typical daily start time and operated at the lowest outdoor airflow rate for the occupied mode during the test.

For every sampling point where the concentration surpasses the limit, take remedial action and retest for the noncompliant contaminants at the location. Repeat until all criteria are met.

Note:
A building flush-out is an alternative to testing indoor air quality and is an effective way to diffuse pollutants left behind from construction, such as off-gassed compounds. A typical mechanical ventilation system is used as a base to set the threshold for duration of the building flush-out. Its typical supply airflow rate is 0.7 cubic feet per minute per square foot. For this reason, if a system operates at 100% outdoor air continuously for two weeks, the cubic feet of outdoor air per square foot of floor area is as follows:

14,112 cu ft of outdoor air / ft^2 of floor area =
{0.7 × (cfm/ ft^2) x 14 days × (24 hours/day) x (60 mins/hr)}

In SI units,
4,294,080 lps of outdoor air / sq meter of floor area =
{3.55 × (lps/m^2) × 14 days × (24 hours/day) x (60 mins/hr) × (60 sec/ min)}

This equation shows that two weeks of flush-out is sufficient time for removing pollutants from the construction phase.

Campus
Group Approach
Separate submittal for each building.

Campus Approach
Unqualified. Separate submittal for each building.

Submittals:

Submittals	Choice 1, Path 1	Choice 1, Path 2	Choice 2
Flush-out report	x	x	
IAQ testing report			x

Synergies
- EQP: Minimum Indoor Air Quality Performance
- EQC: Enhanced Indoor Air Quality Strategies
- EQC: Low-Emitting Materials
- EQC: Construction Indoor Air Quality Management

Extra Credit (Exemplary Performance):
None

Project Phase:
Construction Administration and Occupation/Operation

<u>LEED Submittal</u> Phase:
Construction

Related Code or Standard:

- **ASTM D5197–09e1 Standard Test Method for Determination of Formaldehyde and Other Carbonyl Compounds in Air (Active Sampler Methodology)**: astm.org/Standards/D5197.htm
- **ASTM D5149–02 (2008) Standard Test Method for Ozone in the Atmosphere: Continuous Measurement by Ethylene Chemiluminescence**: astm.org/Standards/D5149
- **ISO 16000-3, Indoor air–Part 3: Determination of formaldehyde and other carbonyl compounds in indoor air and test chamber air—Active sampling method**: iso.org/iso/home/store/catalogue_tc/catalogue_detail.htm?csnumber=51812
- **ISO 16000-6, Indoor air–Part 6: Determination of volatile organic compounds in indoor and test chamber air by active sampling on Tenax TA sorbent, thermal desorption and gas chromatography using MS or MS-FID**: iso.org/iso/home/store/catalogue_tc/catalogue_detail.htm?csnumber=52213
- **ISO 4224 Ambient air—Determination of carbon monoxide—Nondispersive infrared spectrometric method**: iso.org/iso/home/store/catalogue_tc/catalogue_detail.htm?csnumber=32229
- **ISO 7708 Air quality—Particle size fraction definitions for health-related sampling**: iso.org/iso/home/store/catalogue_tc/catalogue_detail.htm?csnumber=14534
- **ISO 13964 Air quality—Determination of ozone in ambient air—Ultraviolet photometric method**: iso.org/iso/home/store/catalogue_tc/catalogue_detail.htm?csnumber=23528
- **U.S. EPA Compendium of Methods for the Determination of Air Pollutants in Indoor Air, IP-1: Volatile Organic Compounds, IP-3: Carbon Monoxide and Carbon Dioxide, IP-6: Formaldehyde and other aldehydes/ketones, IP-10 Volatile Organic Compounds**: nepis.epa.gov
- **U.S. EPA Compendium of Methods for the Determination of Inorganic Compounds in Ambient Air, TO-1:Volatile Organic Compounds, TO-11: Formaldehyde, TO-15: Volatile Organic Compounds, TO-17:Volatile Organic Compounds**: epa.gov/ttnamti1/airtox.html
- **California Department of Public Health, Standard Method for the Testing and Evaluation of Volatile Organic Chemical Emissions from Indoor Sources using Environmental Chambers, v1.1–2010**: cal-iaq.org/separator/voc/standard-method

Responsible Party:

Contractor

EQC: **Thermal Comfort**

Applicable to

New Construction (1 point)
Schools (1 point)
Retail (1 point)
Data Centers (1 point)
Warehouses and Distribution Centers (1 point)
Hospitality (1 point)
Healthcare (1 point)

Purpose

Provides good thermal comfort, and improves occupant comfort, well-being, and productivity.

Credit Path:

New Construction, Schools, Retail, Data Centers, Hospitality, Healthcare
Choice 1. ASHRAE Standard 55-2010

Design HVAC systems and the building envelope per ASHRAE Standard 55–2010, Thermal Comfort Conditions for Human Occupancy, with errata or a local equivalent.

For natatoria, show compliance with ASHRAE HVAC Applications Handbook, 2011 edition, Chapter 5, Places of Assembly, Typical Natatorium Design Conditions, with errata.

***Note:** A **natatorium** (plural: natatoria) is a building containing a swimming pool*

OR

Choice2. ISO and CEN Standards

Design HVAC systems and the building envelope per the applicable standards:

- ISO 7730:2005, Ergonomics of the Thermal Environment, analytical determination and interpretation of thermal comfort, using calculation of the **PMV** and **PPD** indices and local thermal comfort criteria; and
- CEN Standard EN 15251:2007, Indoor Environmental Input Parameters for Design and Assessment of Energy Performance of Buildings, addressing indoor air quality, thermal environment, lighting, and acoustics, Section A2.

Note:
***Predicted percentage of dissatisfied (PPD)** and **predicted mean vote (PMV)** are two indices used as the referenced standards for this credit.*

Data Centers only

Meet the above criteria for regularly occupied spaces.

Warehouses and Distribution Centers

Meet the above requirements for office portions of the building.

In regularly occupied areas of the building's sorting, bulk storage, and distribution areas, include at least one of the following design alternatives:

- circulating fans;
- radiant flooring;
- passive systems, such as wind flow or nighttime air, heat venting;
- localized active cooling (refrigerant or evaporative-based systems) or heating systems; and
- localized, hard-wired fans that provide air movement for occupants' comfort

- other equivalent thermal comfort strategy.

Thermal Comfort Control
New Construction, Schools, Retail, Data Centers, Warehouses And Distribution Centers, Hospitality
Offer group thermal comfort controls for all shared multi-occupant spaces. Offer individual thermal comfort controls for 50% or more of individual occupant spaces.

Thermal comfort controls allow occupants, whether in shared multi-occupant spaces or individual spaces, to adjust one or more of the following in their local environment: air speed, air temperature, radiant temperature, and humidity.

Hospitality only
Guest rooms are not included in the credit calculations because they should be designed to provide adequate thermal comfort controls.

Retail only
Meet the above criteria for 50% or more of the individual occupant spaces in administrative and office areas.

Healthcare
Offer group thermal comfort controls for all shared multi-occupant spaces. Offer individual thermal comfort controls for every patient room and 50% or more of the remaining individual occupant spaces.

Thermal comfort controls allow occupants, whether in shared multi-occupant spaces or individual spaces, to adjust one or more of the following in their local environment: air speed, air temperature, radiant temperature, and humidity.

Note:
While frequently correlated with air temperature only, thermal comfort is a complex amalgam of ***six primary factors*** *including* ***surface temperature, air temperature, air movement, humidity, metabolic rate, and clothing****.*

Campus
Group Approach
Separate submittal for each building.

Campus Approach
Unqualified. Separate submittal for each building.

Submittals:

Submittals	Thermal comfort design		Thermal comfort controls	Warehouses &distribution centers only
	Choice 1	Choice 2		
Description of weather data used to determine operative temperatures, relative humidity, outdoor temperatures	x			
Plots or calculation results verifying that design parameters meet ASHRAE Standard 55–2010 for 80% acceptability (e.g., psychometric chart; PMV or PPD calculations; ASHRAE Thermal Comfort Tool results; copy of ASHRAE 55–2010, Figure 5.2.4.1, Figure 5.2.4.3, or Figure 5.2.4.4; or predicted worst-case indoor conditions for each month on copy of Figure 5.3)	x			
Documentation to verify thermally conditioned spaces meet ISO7730 or EN 15251, as applicable (e.g., for ISO, calculations based on Sections 4.1 and 6 or Annex H, computer program results based on Annex D, tables based on Annex E, or copy of Figures 2, 3, 4, A.1, A.2; for EN, documentation of worst-case indoor conditions for each month on copy of Figure A1)		x		
List of spaces by type, quantity, and controls			x	
List of regularly occupied bulk storage, sorting, and distribution areas				x
Narrative describing design strategy used in each space				x

Synergies

- EAP: Minimum Energy Performance
- EQP: Minimum Indoor Air Quality Performance
- EQC: Enhanced Indoor Air Quality Strategies
- EQC: Interior Lighting

Extra Credit (Exemplary Performance):

None

Project Phase:

Construction Documents

LEED Submittal Phase:
Design

Related Code or Standard:

- **ASHRAE Standard 55–2010, Thermal Environmental Conditions for Human Occupancy**: ashrae.org
- **ASHRAE HVAC Applications Handbook, 2011 edition, Chapter 5, Places of Assembly, Typical Natatorium Design Conditions**: ashrae.org
- **ISO 7730–2005 Ergonomics of the thermal environment, Analytical determination and interpretation of thermal comfort using calculation of the PMV and PPD indices and local thermal comfort criteria**: iso.org
- **European Standard EN 15251: 2007, Indoor environmental input parameters for design and assessment of energy performance of buildings addressing indoor air quality, thermal environment, lighting and acoustics**:
  cen.eu

Responsible Party:
Mechanical Engineer

EQC: **Interior Lighting**

Applicable to

New Construction (1–2 points)
Schools (1–2 points)
Retail (2 points)
Data Centers (1–2 points)
Warehouses and Distribution Centers (1–2 points)
Hospitality (1–2 points)
Healthcare (1 point)

Purpose

Provides high-quality lighting, and improves occupant comfort, well-being, and productivity.

Credit Path:

New Construction, Schools, Data Centers, Warehouses and Distribution Centers, Hospitality
Select one or both of the following two choices.

Choice 1. Lighting Control (1 point)
For 90% or more of individual occupant spaces, offer individual lighting controls that allow users to adjust the lighting to suit their individual tasks and preferences, with at least three lighting levels or scenes (on, off, midlevel). Midlevel is 30% to 70% of the maximum illumination level (excluding daylight contributions).

For all shared multi-occupant spaces, meet all of the following criteria.

- Offer multi-zone control systems that allow occupants to adjust the lighting to meet group needs and preferences, with at least three lighting levels or scenes (on, off, midlevel).
- Lighting for any projection or presentation wall must be separately controlled.
- A person operating the controls shall have a direct line of sight to the controlled lights. Manual controls or switches shall be located in the same space as the controlled lights.

Hospitality only
Guest rooms are not included in the credit calculations because they should be designed to provide adequate lighting controls.

AND/OR
Choice2. Lighting Quality (1 point)
Choose four of the following strategies.

- **Strategy A** minimizes light fixture luminance to help reduce discomfort glare and disability. It uses 2,500 candela per square meter as the threshold, because glare becomes objectionable above that level according to research by the Light Right Consortium.

  For all regularly occupied spaces, use light fixtures with a luminance of less than 2,500 cd/m^2 between 45 and 90 degrees from nadir.

  Exceptions include indirect uplighting fixtures, if there is no view down into these uplights from a regularly occupied space above; wall wash fixtures properly aimed at walls, as noted by the manufacturer's data; and any other specific applications (i.e., adjustable fixtures).

- **Strategy B** selects light sources with a color rendering index (CRI) over 80 to help simulate natural light.

  Exceptions include site lighting, lamps or fixtures specifically designed to provide colored lighting for effect or other special use.

- **Strategy C** uses light sources with a long lamp life to help preserve the integrity of the lighting design over a long period; it also reduces resource and material inputs and lowers maintenance costs. A lamp life of 24,000 hours encourages the use of longer-life fluorescents.

  For 75% or more of the total connected lighting load, use light sources that have a rated life (or L70 for LED sources) of at least 24,000 hours (at 3-hour per start, if applicable).

- **Strategy D** designs spaces with less direct-only overhead lighting to help minimize glare, reduces the perceived brightness of the direct luminaires, and reduces contrast between ceiling and luminaires.

  Use direct-only overhead lighting for not more than 25% of the total connected lighting load for all regularly occupied spaces.

- **Strategy E** specifies surfaces with high reflectance to use reflection to help make the space brighter and minimize the difficulty of viewing light documents on dark surfaces. The specific surface reflectance values for floors, walls, and ceilings are above the standard industry assumptions of 20, 50, and 80, respectively, according to in the latest edition of the Illuminating Engineering Society (IES) Lighting Handbook.

  For 90% or more of the regularly occupied floor area, meet or surpass the following thresholds for area weighted average surface reflectance: 25% for floors, 60% for walls, and 85% for ceilings.

- **Strategy F** is similar to Strategy E.
  If furniture is included in the scope of work, select furniture finishes to meet or surpass the following thresholds for area-weighted average surface reflectance: 45% for work surfaces, and 50% for movable partitions.

- **Strategy G** designs for an illuminance ratio less than 1:10 to minimize the amount of contrast that building users experience between their work surface or wall surfaces around them and the ceiling. The 1:10 illuminance ratio represents one log scale difference in lighting levels (illuminance is linear, but human eyes are logarithmic).

  For 75% or more of the regularly occupied floor area, meet a ratio of average wall surface illuminance (excluding fenestration) to average work plane (or surface, if defined) illuminance that does not exceed 1:10 must also meet strategy E, strategy F, or establish area-weighted surface reflectance of at least 60% for walls.

- **Strategy H** is similar to Strategy G.
  For 75% or more of the regularly occupied floor area, meet a ratio of average ceiling illuminance (excluding fenestration) to work surface illuminance that does not exceed 1:10. Must also meet

option E, option F, or establish area-weighted surface reflectance of at least 85% for ceilings.

Retail
For 90% or more of the individual occupant spaces in administrative and office areas, provide individual lighting controls.

In sales areas, provide controls that can reduce the ambient light levels to a midlevel (30% to 70% of the maximum illumination level, not including daylight contributions).

Healthcare
Offer individual lighting controls for 90% or more of individual occupant spaces in staff areas.

For 90% or more of patient positions, offer lighting controls that are readily accessible from the patient's bed. In multi-occupant patient spaces, the controls must be individual lighting controls. In private rooms, also provide exterior window shades, blinds, or curtain controls that are readily accessible from the patient's bed. Exceptions include pediatric, in-patient critical care, and psychiatric patient rooms.

For all shared multi-occupant spaces, provide multi-zone control systems that allow occupants to adjust the lighting to meet group needs and preferences, with at least three lighting levels or scenes (on, off, midlevel). Midlevel is 30% to 70% of the maximum illumination level (not including daylight contributions).

Campus
Group Approach
All buildings in the group may be submitted as one.

Campus Approach
Unqualified. Separate submittal for each building.

Submittals:

Submittals	Choice 1	Choice 2							
		A	B	C	D	E	F	G	H
Table of multi-occupant and individual occupant spaces and lighting controls in each space	X								
Table of regularly occupied spaces and related lighting details		X			X				
Calculations of total connected lighting load				X	X				
Lighting details, including results of estimations, manufacturer and model, or in situ or laboratory photometric tests		X	X	X	X				
List of floor, wall, and ceiling surfaces and their related surface reflectance values						X			
List of movable partitions and work surfaces and their related surface reflectance values							X		
Average surface reflectance calculations						X	X		
List of work surfaces and illuminance values (lux)								X	
List of wall or ceiling surfaces with illuminance values (lux)									X
Illuminance ratio calculations								X	X

Synergies

- EQC: Thermal Comfort
- EAP: Fundamental Commissioning and Verification
- EAC: Enhanced Commissioning

Extra Credit (Exemplary Performance):

None

Project Phase:

Construction Documents

LEED Submittal Phase:

Design

Related Code or Standard:

The Lighting Handbook, 10th edition, Illuminating Engineering Society of North America: ies.org

Responsible Party:

Electrical Engineer

EQC: **Daylight**

Applicable to

New Construction (1–3 points)
Core and Shell (1–3 points)
Schools (1–3 points)
Retail (1–3 points)
Data Centers (1–3 points)
Warehouses and Distribution Centers (1–3 points)
Hospitality (1–3 points)
Healthcare (1–2 points)

Purpose

Introduces daylight into the space, reduces the use of electrical lighting, and reinforces circadian rhythms by connecting building occupants with the outdoors.

Credit Path:

Provide automatic (with manual override) or manual glare-control devices for every regularly occupied space.

Select one of the following three choices.

Choice 1. Simulation: Spatial Daylight Autonomy and Annual Sunlight Exposure (2–3 points, 1–2 points Healthcare)

Show through annual computer simulations that spatial daylight autonomy$_{300/50\%}$ (sDA$_{300/50\%}$) of at least 55%, 75%, or 90% is reached. Use regularly occupied floor area. Healthcare projects should use the perimeter area determined under EQC: Quality Views. Points are awarded according to Table 1.

Table 1. Points for daylit floor area: Spatial daylight autonomy			
New Construction, Core and Shell, Schools, Retail, Data Centers, Warehouses and Distribution Centers, Hospitality		**Healthcare**	
sDA (for regularly occupied floor area)	**Points**	**sDA (for perimeter floor area)**	**Points**
55%	2	75%	1
75%	3	90%	2

AND

Show through annual computer simulations that annual sunlight exposure 1000,250 (ASE1000,250) of no more than 10% is reached. Use the regularly occupied floor area that is daylit per the sDA$_{300/50\%}$ simulations.

The sDA and ASE calculation grids should be 2 feet (600 millimeters) square or less and laid out across the regularly occupied area at a work plane height of 30 inches (76 millimeters) above finished floor (unless otherwise defined). Utilize an hourly time-step analysis based on typical meteorological year data, or an equivalent, for the nearest available weather station. Incorporate any permanent interior obstacles. Moveable partitions and furniture can be excluded.

***Note: sDA** refers to Spatial Daylight Autonomy. **ASE** refers to Annual Sunlight Exposure.*

Core and Shell only
If the finishes in the space will not be completed, use the following default surface reflectances: 20% for floors, 50% for walls, and 80% for ceilings. Assume that the total floor plate, except 50% for the core, will be regularly occupied space.

OR
Choice 2. Simulation: Illuminance Calculations (1–2 points)
Show through computer modeling that illuminance levels will be between 300 lux and 3,000 lux for 9 a.m. and 3 p.m., both on a clear-sky day at the equinox, for the floor area listed in Table 2. Use regularly occupied floor area. Healthcare projects should use the perimeter area defined under EQC: Quality Views.

Table 2. Points for daylit floor area: Illuminance calculation			
New Construction, Core and Shell, Schools, Retail, Data Centers, Warehouses and Distribution Centers, Hospitality		Healthcare	
Percentage of regularly occupied floor area	Points	Percentage of perimeter floor area	Points
75%	1	75%	1
90%	2	90%	2

Calculate illuminance intensity for sky (diffuse component) and sun (direct component) for clear-sky conditions as follows:

- Use typical meteorological year data, or an equivalent, for the nearest available weather station.
- Select one day within 15 days of March 21 and one day within 15 days of September 21 that represent the clearest sky conditions.
- Use the average of the hourly value for the two selected days.

Exclude shades or blinds from the model. Include any permanent interior obstacles. Moveable partitions and furniture can be excluded.

Core and Shell only
Assume the following default surface reflectances if the finishes in the space will not be completed: 20% for floors, 50% for walls, and 80% for ceilings. Assume that the total floor plate, except for the core, will be regularly occupied space.

OR
Choice 3. Measurement (2-3 points, 1-2 points Healthcare)
Achieve illuminance levels between 300 lux and 3,000 lux for the floor area indicated in Table 3.

Table 3. Points for daylit floor area: Measurement			
New Construction, Core and Shell, Schools, Retail, Data Centers, Warehouses and Distribution Centers, Hospitality		Healthcare	
Percentage of regularly occupied floor area	Points	Percentage of perimeter floor area	Points
75%	2	75%	1
90%	3	90%	2

With furniture, fixtures, and equipment in place, measure illuminance levels as follows:

- Measure at proper work plane height during any hour between 9 a.m. and 3 p.m.
- Take one measurement in any regularly occupied month and take a second per Table 4.
- For spaces larger than 150 square feet (14 square meters), take measurements on a 10 foot (3 meter) or less square grid.
- For spaces 150 square feet (14 square meters) or smaller, take measurements on a 3 foot or less (900 millimeters) square grid.

Table 4. Timing of measurements for illuminance

If first measurement is taken in...	take second measurement in...
January	May-September
February	June-October
March	June-July, November-December
April	August-December
May	September-January
June	October-February
July	November-March
August	December-April
September	December-January, May-June
October	February-June
November	March-July
December	April-August

Campus
Group Approach
Separate submittal for each building.

Campus Approach
Unqualified. Separate submittal for each building.

Submittals:

Submittals	All projects	Choice 1	Choice 2	Choice 3
Floor plans highlighting regularly occupied spaces (for Healthcare, regularly occupied perimeter area)	x	x	x	x
List of glare-control devices for all windows with their control mechanism	x	x	x	x
List of compliant spaces with their annual summary values for sDA and ASE		x		
Geometric plots from simulations.		x	x	
Narrative or output file describing daylight simulation program, simulation inputs, and weather file		x	x	
List of compliant spaces with their calculated illuminance values			x	
Floor plans or list of compliant spaces with measured illuminance values for each node				x
Calculations demonstrating percentage of compliant space between 300 lux and 3,000 lux				x

Synergies

- EAP: Minimum Energy Performance
- EAC: Optimize Energy Performance
- EQC: Quality Views
- EQC: Interior Lighting

Extra Credit (Exemplary Performance):

None

Project Phase:

Construction Documents and Occupation/Operation.

LEED Submittal Phase:

Construction

Related Code or Standard:

- **IES Lighting Measurements (LM) 83-12, Approved Method: IES Spatial Daylight Autonomy (sDA) and Annual Sunlight Exposure (ASE)**: webstore.ansi.org
- ***The Lighting Handbook, 10th edition,* Illuminating Engineering Society**: ies.org

Responsible Party:

MEP Engineers& Architect

EQC: **Quality Views**

Applicable to

New Construction (1 point)
Core and Shell (1 point)
Schools (1 point)
Retail (1 point)
Data Centers (1 point)
Warehouses and Distribution Centers (1 point)
Hospitality (1 point)
Healthcare (1-2 points)

Purpose

Provides quality views and gives building users a connection to the outdoor natural environment.

Credit Path:

New Construction, Core and Shell, Schools, Retail, Data Centers, Hospitality

Provide a direct line of sight to the outdoors via vision glazing for 75% of all regularly occupied floor area.

View glazing in the contributing area should provide a clear image of the exterior, not obstructed by fibers, frits, patterned glazing, or added tints that distort color balance.

In addition, 75% of all regularly occupied floor area shall have two or more of the following four kinds of views:

- multiple lines of sight to vision glazing in different directions 90 degrees or more apart;
- views that include two or more of the following: (1) fauna, flora, or sky; (2) movement; and (3) objects at least 25 feet (7.5 meters) from the exterior of the glazing;
- unobstructed views located within the distance of three times the head height of the vision glazing; and
- views with a view factor of 3 or greater per the definition in "Windows and Offices; A Study of Office Worker Performance and the Indoor Environment."

Include any permanent interior obstructions in the calculations. Movable partitions and furniture can be excluded.

Views into interior atria can be used to 30% maximum of the required area.

Warehouses and Distribution Centers

For the office portion of the building, meet the criteria above.

For the sorting, bulk storage, and distribution portions of the building, meet the criteria above for 25% of the regularly occupied floor area.

Healthcare

For inpatient units (IPUs), meet the criteria above (1 point).

For other areas, configure the building floor plates such that the floor area within 15 feet (4.5 meters) of the perimeter exceeds the perimeter area criteria (Table 1), and meet the criteria above for the perimeter area (1 point).

Table 1. Minimum compliant perimeter area, by floor plate area			
Floor plate area		Perimeter area	
(square feet)	(square meters)	(square feet)	(square meters)
Up to 15,000	Up to 1 400	7,348	682
20,000	1 800	8,785	816
25,000	2 300	10,087	937
30,000	2 800	11,292	1 049
35,000	3 300	12,425	1 154
40,000	3 700	13,500	1 254
45,000	4 200	14,528	1 349
50,000 and larger	4 600 and larger	15,516	1 441

Campus
Group Approach
Separate submittal for each building.

Campus Approach
Unqualified. Separate submittal for each building.

Submittals:

Submittals	All projects	View type			
		1: multiple lines of sight	2: exterior features	3: unobstructed views within 3H	4: view factor
List of all regularly occupied spaces, qualifying floor area in each space, and view features	x				
Sections, elevations, diagrams, renderings, or photos indicating sight lines to glazing do not encounter permanent interior obstructions.	x				
Floor plans or diagrams identifying regularly occupied spaces and the following:	x				
Multiple sight lines for each regularly occupied space		x			
Sight lines and exterior features labeled; provide multiple floor plans if view features change at varying building heights			x		
Sight lines and area indicating three times head height				x	

Area with view factor of 3 or greater					x
Sections, interior elevations, or other documentation that demonstrates the view factor assessment for the areas with a view factor of three or greater.					x
Method for determining view factor for each typical occupant location					x

Synergies

- EQC: Daylight
- EAP: Minimum Energy Performance

Extra Credit (Exemplary Performance):

New Construction, Core and Shell, Schools, Retail, Data Centers, Hospitality

- Meet the criteria for 90% of all regularly occupied area.

Warehouses and Distribution Centers

- Meet the criteria for 90% of the regularly occupied floor area in the office portion of the building, and for
- 50% of the regularly occupied floor area in the sorting, bulk storage, and distribution portions of the building.

Healthcare

- For inpatient areas, meet the criteria for 90% of the regularly occupied floor area.
- For non-inpatient areas, exceed the area criteria in Table 1 by 10% or more.

Project Phase:

Construction Documents

LEED Submittal Phase:

Design

Related Code or Standard:

Windows and Offices: A Study of Office Worker Performance and the Indoor Environment: h-m-g.com

Responsible Party:

Architect

EQC: **Acoustic Performance**

Applicable to

New Construction (1 point)
Schools (1 point)
Data Centers (1 point)
Warehouses and Distribution Centers (1 point)
Hospitality (1 point)
Healthcare (1-2 points)

Purpose

Creates effective acoustic design, and provides classrooms and workspaces that promote occupant communication, productivity, and well-being.

Credit Path:

New Construction, Data Centers, Warehouses and Distribution Centers, Hospitality

For all occupied spaces, comply with the following criteria, as applicable, for sound isolation, HVAC background noise, reverberation time, and sound reinforcement and masking.

HVAC Background Noise

Achieve maximum background noise levels from HVAC systems per 2011 ASHRAE Handbook, HVAC Applications, Chapter 48, Table 1; AHRI Standard 885-2008, Table 15; or a local equivalent. Measure or calculate sound levels.

For measurements, use a sound level meter per ANSI S1.4 for type 1 (precision) or type 2 (general purpose) sound measurement instrumentation, or a local equivalent.

Meet design criteria for HVAC noise levels resulting from the sound transmission paths listed in ASHRAE 2011 Applications Handbook, Table 6, or a local equivalent.

Sound Transmission

Comply with the composite sound transmission class (STCC) ratings listed in Table 1 or local building code, whichever is more restrictive.

Table 1. Maximum composite sound transmission class ratings for adjacent spaces

Adjacency combinations		STC_C
Residence (within a multifamily residence), hotel or motel room	Residence, hotel or motel room	55
Residence, hotel or motel room	Common hallway, stairway	50
Residence, hotel or motel room	Retail	60
Retail	Retail	50
Standard office	Standard office	45
Executive office	Executive office	50
Conference room	Conference room	50
Office, conference room	Hallway, stairway	50
Mechanical equipment room	Occupied area	60

Reverberation Time

Comply with the reverberation time criteria in Table 2 (adapted from Table 9.1 in the Performance Measurement Protocols for Commercial Buildings).

Table 2. Reverberation time requirements		
Room type	Application	T60 (sec), at 500 Hz, 1000 Hz, and 2000 Hz
Apartment and condominium	—	< 0.6
Hotel/motel	Individual room or suite	< 0.6
	Meeting or banquet room	< 0.8
Office building	Executive or private office	< 0.6
	Conference room	< 0.6
	Teleconference room	< 0.6
	Open-plan office without sound masking	< 0.8
	Open-plan office with sound masking	0.8
Courtroom	Unamplified speech	< 0.7
	Amplified speech	< 1.0
Performing arts space	Drama theaters, concert and recital halls	Varies by application
Laboratories	Testing or research with minimal speech communication	< 1.0
	Extensive phone use and speech communication	< 0.6
Church, mosque, synagogue	General assembly with critical music program	Varies by application
Library		< 1.0
Indoor stadium, gymnasium	Gymnasium and natatorium	< 2.0
	Large-capacity space with speech amplification	< 1.5
Classroom	—	< 0.6

Sound Reinforcement and Masking Systems

Sound Reinforcement

For all auditoriums and large conference rooms seating more than 50 persons, evaluate whether AV playback and sound reinforcement capabilities are necessary.

If needed, the sound reinforcement systems shall comply with the following requirements:

- Achieve a common intelligibility scale (CIS) rating of at least 0.77 or speech transmission index (STI) of at least 0.60 at representative points within the area of coverage to provide acceptable intelligibility.
- Have a minimum sound level of 70 dBA.
- Maintain sound-level coverage within +/–3 dB at the 2000 Hz octave band throughout the space.

Masking Systems

For projects that use masking systems, the design levels shall be 48 dBA or less. Ensure that speech spectra are effectively masked and that loudspeaker coverage provides uniformity of +/–2 dBA.

SCHOOLS

HVAC Background noise

Achieve a background noise level of not more than 35 dBA from HVAC systems in core learning spaces including classrooms. Follow the best practices and recommended methodologies for mechanical system noise control in ANSI Standard S12.60–2010, Part 1, Annex A.1; AHRI Standard 885–2008; the 2011 HVAC Applications ASHRAE Handbook, Chapter 48, Sound and Vibration Control, with errata; or a local equivalent.

Sound Transmission

Design core-learning spaces, including classrooms per the sound transmission class (STC) criteria of ANSI S12.60–2010 Part 1, or a local equivalent. Exterior windows must have an STC rating of 35 or more, unless outdoor and indoor noise levels can be verified to justify a lower rating.

Healthcare

Design the facility to exceed or meet the sound and vibration requirements outlined below, which are adapted from the 2010 FGI Guidelines for Design and Construction of Health Care Facilities ("2010 FGI Guidelines") and the reference document on which it is based, Sound and Vibration Design Guidelines for Health Care Facilities ("2010 SV Guidelines").

Choice 1. Speech Privacy, Sound Isolation, and Background Noise (1 point)

Speech Privacy and Sound Isolation

Design sound isolation to achieve acoustical comfort, speech privacy, and minimal annoyance from noise-producing sources. Consider sound levels at both receiver locations and source, the occupants' acoustical privacy, and the background sound at receiver locations and acoustical comfort needs. Speech privacy is defined as "techniques…to render speech unintelligible to casual listeners" (ANSI T1.523-2001, Telecom Glossary 2007).

Design the facility to comply with the requirements outlined in the sections of Table 1.2-3, Design Criteria for Minimum Sound Isolation Performance between Enclosed Rooms, and Table 1.2-4 Speech Privacy for Enclosed Room and Open-Plan Spaces (in the 2010 FGI Guidelines and 2010 SV Guidelines).

Measure or calculate sound isolation and speech privacy descriptors achieved for representative adjacencies as necessary to verify compliance with the criteria in the 2010 FGI Guidelines, Sections1.2-6.1.5 and 1.2-6.1.6, and the 2010 SV Guidelines (including the appendix).

Background Noise

Consider background noise levels generated by all air distribution systems, building mechanical-electrical-plumbing systems and other facility noise sources under the purview of the project building design-construction team.

Design the facility to comply with the 2010 FGI Guidelines, Table 1.2-2 Minimum-Maximum Design Criteria for Noise in representative interior rooms and spaces.

Measure or calculate sound levels in representative rooms and spaces of each type to confirm compliance with criteria in the afore-mentioned table using a sound level meter that conforms to ANSI S1.4 for type 1 (precision) or type 2 (general purpose) sound measurement instrumentation. For spaces not listed in Table 1.2-2, see ASHRAE 2011 Handbook, Chapter 48, Sound and Vibration Control, Table 1.

Choice 2. Acoustical Finishes and Site Exterior Noise (1 point)
Comply with the criteria for acoustical finishes and site exterior noise.
Acoustical Finishes
Require materials, products systems installation details, and other design features to comply with the 2010 FGI Guidelines, Table 1.2-1, Design Room Sound Absorption Coefficients (including associated sections of the appendix) and the 2010 SV Guidelines.

Measure or calculate the average sound absorption coefficients for representative unoccupied rooms of each type in the building to verify compliance with the criteria.

Site Exterior Noise
Minimize the effect on building users of site exterior noise produced by on-site heliports, aircraft flyovers, road traffic, railroads, emergency power generators during maintenance testing, outdoor facility MEP and building services equipment, etc. Also minimize effects on the surrounding community from all facility MEP equipment and activities as necessary to meet (1) local applicable codes or (2) Table 1.2-1 of the 2010 FGI Guidelines, Table 1.2-1, and the 2010 SV Guidelines, Table 1.3-1, whichever is more stringent.

Meet the 2010 FGI Guidelines for the following noise sources:
- building services, A2.2-5.3
- generators, 2.1-8.3.3.1;
- heliports, A1.3-3.6.2.2; and
- mechanical equipment, 2.1-8.2.1.1.

Determine the exterior noise classification (A, B, C, or D) of the facility site by measuring and analyzing data. Refer to the 2010 FGI Guidelines, Categorization of Health Care Facility Sites by Exterior Ambient Sound, Table A1.2a, and the 2010 SV Guidelines, Table 1.3-1.

Design the building envelope composite STC rating per the 2010 FGI Guidelines, Categorization of HealthCare Facility Sites by Exterior Ambient Sound, and show conformance with requirements.

For exterior site exposure categories B, C, or D, measure or calculate the sound isolation performance of representative elements of the exterior building envelope to determine the composite sound transmission class (STCc) rating for typical façade sections. Measurements should generally conform to ASTM E966, Standard Guide for Field Measurements of Airborne Sound Insulation of Building Façades and Façade Elements, current edition.

Campus
Group Approach
Separate submittal for each building.

Campus Approach
Unqualified. Separate submittal for each building.

Submittals:

New Construction, Data Centers, Warehouses and Distribution Centers, Hospitality		All projects
HVAC background noise	Occupied spaces' sound level values	x
	Calculation, measurement description, or manufacturers' data	x
	Noise reduction description	x
Sound isolation	STC ratings for space adjacencies	x
	Calculation, measurement description, or manufacturers' data	x
Reverberation time	Reverberation time criteria for each room	x
	Calculation, measurement description, or manufacturers' data	x
Sound reinforcement and masking systems	List of all large conference rooms and auditoriums	x
	Explanation of sound reinforcement methodology (if installed)	x
	Explanation of sound reinforcement system components and specifications (if installed)	x
	Explanation of masking system components and specifications description (if installed)	x

Schools		All projects
Background noise	**See EQP: Minimum Acoustic Performance**	x
Sound isolation	STC calculation or measurement method	x
	List of STC ratings	x
	STC rating assembly source data	**x**

Healthcare		Choice 1	Choice 2
Speech privacy and sound isolation	List of spaces, adjacencies, STC ratings	x	
	List of spaces, privacy index values	x	
	Calculation or simulation results, or report of field measurements	x	
Room noise levels	List of spaces, design criteria, values	x	
	Lab test reports and simulation results, or report of field measurements	x	
Acoustical finishes	Documentation of wall, ceiling, and floor finishes with associated NRC values		x
	Calculated average sound absorption coefficients for representative room types		x
Site exterior noise	Exterior building envelope STC rating		x
	Site noise exposure category description		x
	Mitigation description for each 2010 FGI guideline		x
	Special neighborhood considerations description		x

Synergies

- For Schools, EQP: Minimum Acoustic Performance

Extra Credit (Exemplary Performance):

None

Project Phase:
Occupation/Operation

LEED Submittal Phase:
Construction

Related Code or Standard:
ASHRAE 2011, HVAC Applications Handbook, Chapter 48, Noise and Vibration Control: ashrae.org
AHRI Standard 885–2008: ahrinet.org
ANSI S1.4, Performance Measurement Protocols for Commercial Buildings: ashrae.org
2010 Noise and Vibration Guidelines for Health Care Facilities: http://speechprivacy.org/joomla//index.php?option=com_content&task=view&id=33&Itemid=43
ANSI/ASA S12.60–2010 American National Standard Acoustical Performance Criteria, Design Requirements,
and Guidelines for Schools, Part 1, Permanent Schools: asastore.aip.org
FGI Guidelines for Design and Construction of Health Care Facilities, 2010 edition: www.fgiguidelines.org
ANSI T1.523–2001, Telecom Glossary 2007: ansi.org
E966, Standard Guide for Field Measurements of Airborne Sound Insulation of Building Facades and Facade
Elements: astm.org

Responsible Party:
Acoustical Engineer, Mechanical Engineer, and Architect

Chapter 12

Innovation (IN)

Overall Purpose

Sustainable design measures and strategies are continuously improving and evolving. Contemporary scientific research affects building design strategies, and new technologies constantly emerge in the marketplace. This LEED credit category is to acknowledge projects for innovation in sustainable building practices, strategies, and features.

Sometimes, a strategy can help a building perform much better than the existing LEED credit requirements. Other strategies should be considered for their sustainable benefits, but they may not be covered by any LEED prerequisite or credit. This category also addresses the role of a LEED Accredited Professional as part of a cohesive team in implementing the cohesive process.

Innovation Credit (INC): **Innovation**

Applicable to

New Construction (1-5 points)
Core and Shell (1-5 points)
Schools (1-5 points)
Retail (1-5 points)
Data Centers (1-5 points)
Warehouses and Distribution Centers (1-5 points)
Hospitality (1-5 points)
Healthcare (1-5 points)

Purpose

Encourages projects to achieve innovative or exceptional performance.

Credit Path:

Sustainable design originates from innovative thinking and strategies. This credit and other institutional measures reward innovative thinking, and benefit our environment. Acknowledgment of exceptional performance will stimulate more innovation.

When project teams go above and beyond LEED requirements and innovate, they achieve measurable environmental benefits exceeding LEED rating system criteria, and have the chance to help the development of future LEED credits and explore the latest pilot credits. When they can show that the project exceeds the standard level of performance related to one or more LEED credits, their innovations can be implemented by other teams in the future.

For this credit, project teams can attempt the following points:

- Innovation (4 points maximum)
- Pilot credits (4 points maximum)
- Exemplary Performance (2 points maximum)

Projects may earn up to 5 points in total through any combination of three afore-mentioned strategies.

Choice 1. Innovation (1 point)

Accomplish measurable, significant environmental performance using a strategy not addressed in the LEED green building rating system.

Identify the following:

- the *intent* of the proposed innovation credit;
- proposed *criteria* for compliance;
- proposed *submittals* to demonstrate compliance; and
- the *strategies or design approach* used to meet the criteria.

AND/OR

Choice 2. Pilot (1 point)

Attain one pilot credit from USGBC's LEED Pilot Credit Library

AND/OR

Choice3. Additional Strategies

Innovation (1-3 points)

- Defined in afore-mentioned Choice 1.

Pilot (1–3 points)
- Meet the criteria of Choice 2.

Exemplary Performance (1–2 points)
- Accomplish exemplary performance in an existing LEED v4 prerequisite or credit that allows exemplary performance per the LEED Reference Guide, v4 edition. An exemplary performance point is typically earned for achieving double the credit criteria or the next incremental percentage threshold.

Campus
Group Approach
All buildings in the group may be submitted as one.

Campus Approach
Qualified. All buildings in the group may be submitted as one.

Submittals:

Submittals	Innovation	Pilot credit	Exemplary performance
Innovation description	x		
Supporting documentation	x	x	x
Pilot credit registration		x	
Pilot credit survey		x	
Pilot credit specific submittals		x	
Exemplary performance credit and level			x

Synergies:
None

Extra Credit (Exemplary Performance):
This entire credit is about Extra Credit (Exemplary Performance).

Project Phase:
It can be at any of the project phases: Pre-Design, Schematic Design, Design Development, Construction Documents, Construction Administration, and Occupation/Operation.

LEED Submittal Phase:
Design or Construction Submittals phase

Related Code or Standard:
None

Responsible Party:
Varies

INC: **LEED Accredited Professional**

Applicable to

New Construction (1 point)
Core and Shell (1 point)
Schools (1 point)
Retail (1 point)
Data Centers (1 point)
Warehouses and Distribution Centers (1 point)
Hospitality (1 point)
Healthcare (1 point)

Purpose

Encourages the team assimilation to meet a LEED project requirements, and streamlines the application and certification process.

Credit Path:

A minimum of one *principal* participant of the project team must be a LEED Accredited Professional (AP) with a specialty *suitable* for the project.

A LEED AP with specialty is a valuable resource in the LEED certification process. She or he helps the project team members understand the LEED application process, the rating system, and the importance of synergies (i.e., the interactions among the prerequisites and credits).

Campus
Group Approach
Separate submittal for each building.

Campus Approach
Unqualified. Separate submittal for each building.

Submittals:

- Full name and specialty credential of LEED AP

Synergies

None

Extra Credit (Exemplary Performance):

None

Project Phase:

Pre-design

LEED Submittal Phase:

Design

Related Code or Standard:

None

Responsible Party:

LEED Accredited Professional (AP) with a specialty *suitable* for the project

Chapter 13

Regional Priority (RP)

Overall Purpose

Since every locale has some unique environmental issues, volunteers from the LEED International Roundtable and USGBC chapters have pinpointed specific environmental priorities within their areas and the credits that address them. These RP credits encourage project teams to concentrate on their local environmental priorities.

USGBC set up a procedure that pinpointed six RP credits for every rating system and every location within country boundaries or chapter. USGBC asked participants to decide which environmental issues were most significant in their country or chapter area. The issues could be man-made, such as polluted watersheds, or naturally occurring, such as water shortages, and could reflect environmental assets, such as abundant sunlight, or environmental concerns, such as water shortages. The zones, or areas, were identified by a mixture of priority issues, such as an urban area with an intact watershed versus an urban area with an impaired watershed. USGBC then asked the participants to prioritize credits to tackle the critical issues of certain locations. Because each LEED project type, such as a data center, may be related to distinctive environmental impacts, each rating system has its own RP credits.

The ultimate goal of RP credits is to improve the ability of LEED project teams to tackle essential environmental issues around the world and across the country.

Regional Priority Credit (RPC): **Regional Priority**

Applicable to

New Construction (1-4 points)
Core and Shell (1-4 points)
Schools (1-4 points)
Retail (1-4 points)
Data Centers (1-4 points)
Warehouses and Distribution Centers (1-4 points)
Hospitality (1-4 points)
Healthcare (1-4 points)

Purpose

Offers an incentive to achieve credits that cover geographically specific public health, social equity, and environmental priorities.

Credit Path:

Project teams design, build, and operate LEED buildings in many different circumstances. Local regulations, population density, and climate can vary drastically from one site to another, making some environmental issues more significant than others. Rainwater management in wet climates versus water conservation in arid climates is one example.

If project teams identify their location's priority environmental issues and tackle them in design, construction, and operation, LEED projects can be more transformative. LEED uses RP credits to promote a focus on regional issues. The current RP LEED credits are those that USGBC volunteers have decided to be especially important in a certain area. For every location in the United States, volunteers prioritize six credits. The ultimate goal is to encourage project teams to earn the credits that tackle an area's priority issues.

See the RP credit database at the following link:
http://www.usgbc.org

You can obtain one to four credits out of the six potential RP points. You can choose which four credits you want to pursue for your project.

The USGBC has prioritized the projects located in the United States, the US Virgin Islands, Guam, and Puerto Rico. Project teams for other international projects can check the database above for eligible RP points.

Campus
Group Approach
Not applicable

Campus Approach
Not applicable

Submittals:

- No additional documentation is necessary. Document compliance for the chosen credits, and the associated RP bonus points will be awarded automatically.

Synergies

None

Project Phase:
Varies

LEED Submittal Phase:
Design or Construction Submittals

Related Code or Standard:
None

Responsible Party:
LEED Accredited Professional (AP) with a specialty *suitable* for the project

Chapter 14

LEED v4 AP BD+C Exam Sample Questions, Answers and Exam Registration (Including Both Section One and Section Two)

I. LEED AP BD+C Exam sample questions

Use these sample questions to prepare for the mock exam and the real exam. They will give you an idea what the USGBC is looking for on the LEED AP BD+C Exam, and how the questions will be asked. These sample questions are quite easy. If you can answer 90% of the sample questions correctly, you are ready to take the mock exam in my other book, *LEED v4 BD&C Mock Exam*. The 90% passing score is based on feedback from previous readers. You need to read the study material the in previous chapters one or more times to become familiar with it and then take the mock exam. You really need to read this book several times and MEMORIZE the important information before you do the sample questions. Just like on the real exam, sometimes a question may ask you to pick two or three correct answers out of four, or four correct answers out of five (some LEED exam questions have five choices). This means that if you do not know any one of the correct answers, you will probably get the overall answer wrong. You need to know the LEED system very well to get the correct answer.

Exam Part One sample questions:

1. With regard to the Optimize Energy Performance credit, which of the following statements is correct?
   a. Compare your building performance to the baseline building performance.
   b. Compare your baseline building performance to ASHRAE Standard 90.1-2010 (with errata but without addenda).
   c. Compare your baseline building performance to ASHRAE Standard 90.1-2007.
   d. Compare your baseline building performance to ASHRAE Standard 90.1-2003.

2. Which of the following factors does not improve human comfort?
   a. air temperature
   b. ventilation
   c. radiation exchange
   d. none of the above

3. The standard used for Measurement and Verification is
   a. ASHRAE Standard 90.1-2010 (with errata but without addenda)
   b. the Department of Energy Verification Protocol
   c. a signed statement from the designer
   d. International Performance Measurement and Verification Protocol

4. Optimal IAQ performance can do which of the following?
   a. Create savings in electrical bills.
   b. Improve the productivity and health of building occupants.
   c. Cause higher operation cost.
   d. Create higher rents.

5. What is the best way to control Environmental Tobacco Smoke (ETS)?
   a. Ban smoking inside the building.
   b. Place exterior smoking areas at least 25 feet away from operable windows, entrances and air intakes.
   c. Give all interior spaces a negative pressure.
   d. both a and b

6. With regard to the Construction IAQ Management Plan, if your project uses permanently installed air handlers during construction, you should use
   a. filtration media with a minimum Efficiency Reporting Value (MERV) of 6 at each return air grille
   b. filtration media with a minimum Efficiency Reporting Value (MERV) of 7 at each return air grille
   c. filtration media with a minimum Efficiency Reporting Value (MERV) of 8 at each return air grille
   d. filtration media with a minimum Efficiency Reporting Value (MERV) of 9 at each return air grille

7. For EQC: Enhanced Indoor Air Quality Strategies, which of the following are not design strategies? **(Choose two)**
   a. Increase ventilation.
   b. Submit drawings and cutsheets for the plumbing systems in chemical mixing areas.
   c. Prevent occupants from bringing contaminants inside the building by installation of entryway systems.
   d. Design the exterior sidewalk and pavement to drain away from the building at 2% minimum slope.

8. Placing a lighting control in a hallway does not help you with Controllability of Systems because
   a. You need to make sure the hallway does not have a dead end corridor that is over 20 feet in length.
   b. You also need to add temperature control.
   c. You also need to make sure the hallway has a view to the outside.
   d. none of the above.

9. Which of the following standard(s) is mentioned with regard to EQC: Construction Indoor Air Quality Management Plan?
   a. ASHRAE Standard 52.2-1999
   b. ASHRAE Standard 62.1-2010
   c. ASHRAE Standard 90.1-2010 (with errata but without addenda)
   d. SMACNA
   e. SCAQMD Rule 1168

10. Which of the following standard(s) is (are) mentioned in SSC: Light Pollution Reduction?
    a. ASHRAE/IESNA Standard 90.1-2010 (with errata but without addenda)
    b. IESNA RP-33
    c. International Dark Sky Association Outdoor Lighting Standard
    d. BUG
    e. both a and b

11. California Title 24-2013 is considered to be equal to ASHRAE/IESNA Standard 90.1-2010 (with errata but without addenda) for the following LEED BD+C rating systems credit(s)
    a. EAP: Minimum Energy Performance
    b. EAC: Optimize Energy Performance
    c. EAC: Green Power and Carbon Offsets
    d. all of the above

12. Which of the following is not a consideration for MRC: Building Product Disclosure and Optimization—Sourcing of Raw Materials?
    a. the harvest cycle of the raw materials
    b. the Sustainable Agriculture Standard
    c. corporate sustainability reports (CSRs)
    d. USGBC-approved program

13. What does "Xeriscape" mean?
    a. Drip irrigation to save water.
    b. "Dry Landscape" design by using plants that use little or no water.
    c. Recycle existing plants on the project site.
    d. Reuse graywater for landscape irrigation.

14. Which of the following is a responsibility for the contractor to support the LEED documentation process?
    a. Document and provide calculations for waste diverted from landfill.
    b. Maintain a submittal log.
    c. Maintain a RFI log.
    d. Provide written documentation to justify a change order for rough grading.

15. Materials that qualify for MRC: Building Product Disclosure and Optimization—Sourcing of Raw Materials may also qualify for which of the following credit(s)?
    a. MRC: Building Life Cycle Impact Reduction
    b. MRC: Building Product Disclosure and Optimization—Environmental Product Declarations
    c. MRC: Building Product Disclosure and Optimization—Material Ingredients
    d. all of the above

16. Which of the following three statements is incorrect?
    a. For non-residential projects, water closet uses per day per FTE female is three.
    b. For residential projects, water closet uses per day per female is five.
    c. The flow rate for a conventional water closet is 1.8 gpf.
    d. The flow rate for a low-flow water closet is 1.1 gpf.

17. Which of the following is the standard for paints and coatings wet-applied on site? **(Choose two)**
    a. The California Air Resources Board (CARB) 2007, Suggested Control Measure (SCM) for Architectural Coatings
    b. The South Coast Air Quality Management District (SCAQMD) Rule 1113, effective June 3, 2011
    c. Green Seal Standard for Commercial Adhesives GS-36 requirements
    d. Green Label Plus
    e. Green Guard

18. Why should a developer locate a green building in a previously developed urban area?
    a. to be close to public transportation
    b. to use existing community services
    c. to be close to existing utilities
    d. a and b
    e. a, b, and c

19. Blackwater is water drained from a
    a. kitchen sink
    b. toilet
    c. both a and b
    d. none of the above

20. With regard to ozone depletion potential (ODP), the order from high ODP to low ODP is
    a. CFC> HFC>HCFC
    b. CFC>HCFC>HFC
    c. HCFC>HFC>CFC
    d. HCFC> CFC>HFC

Exam Part Two sample questions:

21. A developer is building a new shopping center on a landfill site with a large amount of underground methane gas. Which three of the following statements are correct?
    a. The contractor can use perforated pipe under the building to collect the methane gas, and then vent it to a certain height above the roof.
    b. The contractor can use the "pump and treat" method to treat the methane gas.
    c. The contractor can use the "pump and treat" method to treat the groundwater.
    d. The contractor can use in-situ remediation.
    e. The contractor cannot vent the methane gas, and has to burn it at the site per EPA regulation.
    f. The contractor can use the solar detoxification strategy.

22. An elementary school is built on a large site and a bicycle storage is within a 200-yard (180-meter) walking distance or bicycling distance from a bicycle network. What other attributes can help you to qualify for one point under LTC: Bicycle Facilities? (Choose 2)
    a. The bicycle network connects to a minimum of 10 diverse uses
    b. Separating bike lanes and pedestrian paths from vehicular traffic.
    c. Providing a school bus for handicap students.
    d. Extending a bike lane or pedestrian path to the school's property line in two directions

without fences or other barriers.

c. Shower and changing facilities for 0.5% of the FTE within 200 yards of the building.
e. The bicycle network connects a light or heavy rail station, commuter rail station, bus rapid transit stop, or ferry terminal.

23. A developer is building an office building. He is concerned about the cost related to offering individual lighting controls per the criteria of EQC: Interior Lighting. How can the design team convince him about potential synergy and saving in first cost?
    a. The reduction in related heat load will reduce the size and amount of HVAC equipment.
    b. The lighting system will reduce tenants' electrical costs.
    c. This will increase occupant comfort and in turn increase production.
    d. A lighting system qualifying for the credit can be integrated with sensors and natural light to reduce energy costs.

24. A supermarket project has south-facing clear glazing. The design team is considering installing a tint film on the glazing to reduce HVAC heat load. Which of the followings will achieve point(s) for both EQC: Daylight and EQC: Daylight Quality Views?
    a. Using the tint film on the glazing as proposed, with 65% of the space having a view, and spatial daylight autonomy of 35%
    b. Using the proposed film, with 85% of the space having a view, and spatial daylight autonomy of 65%
    c. Using a shading device instead of the film, with 65% of the space having a view, and spatial daylight autonomy of 50%
    d. Using a shading device instead of the film, with 75% of the space having a view, and spatial daylight autonomy of 55%

25. A contractor salvages windows from an existing building for a CS project. Which LEED prerequisites or credits may he achieve? (Choose 2)
    a. MR Prerequisite (MRP): Storage and Collection of Recyclables
    b. MRC: Building Life-Cycle Impact Reduction
    c. MRC: Construction and Demolition Waste Management
    d. MRC: Building Product Disclosure and Optimization—Sourcing of Raw Materials

26. A new office building has 200 occupants. What is the baseline potable water usage for sewage conveyance for WEP: Indoor Water Use Reduction?
    a. 192,800 gallons (729,826 liters)
    b. 200,000 gallons (757,082 liters)
    c. 218,400 gallons (826,732 liters)
    d. 280,600 gallons (1,062,186 liters)

27. For the same office building as described in Question 26 above, how much water can the design team save if they use waterless urinals and single flush, pressure assist HETs?
    a. 104,400 gallons (395,197 liters)
    b. 114,400 gallons (433,051 liters)
    c. 124,400 gallons (470,905 liters)
    d. 134,400 gallons (508,759 liters)

28. A school district is planning to spend 25 million dollars to build a new modern-style school building on a 12-acre landfill site. The buildings in the neighborhood are all Spanish style buildings. Which of the following statements is true regarding this building's LEED certification?
    a. The design team needs to perform a Phase I Environmental Assessment (per ASTM E1527-05) to find out if the site is contaminated.
    b. The school district needs to perform a Phase II Environmental Assessment (per ASTM E1903-97, 2002) if the project team suspects the site is contaminated.
    c. This project is not eligible for LEED certification.
    d. The remediation process can earn 2 points for LTC: High-Priority Site if this is a core and shell project, and project team provides successful documentation for the remediation of the site.
    e. The remediation process can earn 2 points for LTC: High-Priority Site if the project team provides successful documentation for the remediation of the site.
    f. This project is not eligible for LEED certification because it is not compatible with the neighborhood building style.

29. The term "off-gassing" is related to:
    a. SSP: Construction Activity Pollution Prevention
    b. SSP: Environmental Site Assessment
    c. MRP: Storage and Collection of Recyclables.
    d. EQC: Low-Emitting Materials

30. CEE stands for:
    a. Consortium for Energy Efficiency.
    b. Consortium for Energy Evaluation.
    c. Committee for Energy Efficiency.
    d. Consumer Energy Efficiency.

31. NRC stands for:
    a. National Resource Center.
    b. Noise Reduction Coefficient.
    c. National Resource Consumption.
    d. Noise Reduction Coefficiency.

32. ETV stands for:
    a. Environmental Test Verification.
    b. Environmental Test Value.
    c. Environmental Technology Verification.
    d. Environmental Technology Value.

33. The typical background-sound level for classrooms is about 30 dBA, and a noisy cafeteria has an <u>80 dBA</u> sound level. This means: (Choose One)
    a. The sound level for the cafeteria is about twice the volume of the background noise level of the classroom.
    b. The sound level for the cafeteria is about thirty-two times the volume of the background noise level of the classroom.
    c. The sound level for the cafeteria cannot be compared with the volume of the background noise level of the classroom.
    d. None of the above

34. Select three of the following standards or codes that are related to the most LEED prerequisites and credits:
    a. ASHRAE
    b. ANSI
    c. DOE
    d. EPA
    e. ASTM
    f. DHS

35. Select three of the following project phases that are related to the most LEED prerequisites and credits:
    a. Pre-Design
    b. Schematic Design
    c. Design Development
    d. Construction Documents
    e. Construction Administration
    f. Occupation/Operation

36. When was LEED v4 released?
    a. April, 2013
    b. June, 2013
    c. November, 2013
    d. December, 2013

37. With regard to synergies, SSP: Construction Activity Pollution Prevention, is related to which of the following credits? (Choose 2)
    a. SSC: Site Assessment
    b. SSC: Site Development—Protect or Restore Habitat
    c. SSC: Rainwater Management
    d. SSC: Heat Island Reduction

38. With regard to synergies, SSC: Heat Island Reduction, is related to which of the following credits? (Choose 3)
    a. SS SSC: Site Assessment
    b. SSC: Site Development—Protect or Restore Habitat
    c. SSC: Light Pollution Reduction
    d. EAP: Minimum Energy Performance
    e. EAC: Optimize Energy Performance

39. With regard to submittals, what does the project team need to submit for MRP: Storage and Collection of Recyclables? (Choose 2)
    a. A tenant guideline
    b. Manufacturer's data sheets if available
    c. Floor plans, site plans, etc. if needed
    d. Verification of recycled material types

40. With regard to project team coordination, who is responsible for submitting MRP: Storage and Collection of Recyclables?
    a. The architect
    b. The developer
    c. The tenant
    d. Any of the above team members

II. Answers for the LEED AP BD+C Exam sample questions

Part One:

1. Answer: a. Compare your building performance to the baseline building performance.
   For Optimize Energy Performance credit, there are two ways to gain the credit, through a prescriptive approach or performance approach. Performance approach uses **whole building energy simulation** to compare your building performance to the baseline building and awards points based on percentage improvement in energy performance.

   See "EAC: Optimize Energy Performance" for more information.

   The following are distracters to confuse you:
   - Compare your baseline building performance to ASHRAE Standard 90.1-2010 (with errata but without addenda).
   - Compare your baseline building performance to ASHRAE Standard 90.1-2007.
   - Compare your baseline building performance to ASHRAE Standard 90.1-2004.

2. Answer: d. none of the above
   Pay attention to the word "not."

   While frequently correlated with air temperature only, thermal comfort is a complex amalgam of **six primary factors** including **surface temperature, air temperature, air movement, humidity, metabolic rate, and clothing**. See EQC: Thermal Comfort for more information.

   All of the following factors do improve human comfort, and therefore are the incorrect answers.
   - air temperature
   - ventilation (air movement)
   - radiation exchange

3. Answer: d. International Performance Measurement and Verification Protocol

   This information is pretty obscure, and not covered by our previous discussion. You will probably run into a very small number of questions that you have no clue on the correct answer for in the real test. We intentionally include this hard question with obscure information at the beginning of the sample questions to test your ability to manage your time. You need to be able to manage your time, pick a guess answer for a very hard question, move on to the other questions, and come back to review it later if you have time.

   The following are distracters to confuse you:
   - ASHRAE Standard 90.1-2010 (with errata but without addenda)
   - the Department of Energy Verification Protocol
   - a signed statement from the designer

4. Answer: b. Improve the productivity and health of building occupants.

   Optimal Indoor Air Quality (IAQ) performance will not create savings in electrical bills, and does not necessary cause higher operation cost, or create higher rents.

5. Answer: d. both a and b
   See EQP: Environmental Tobacco Smoke Control

   Giving all interior spaces a negative pressure is not the best way to control Environmental Tobacco Smoke (ETS).

6. Answer: c. filtration media with a minimum Efficiency Reporting Value (MERV) of 8 at each return air grille

   See EQC: Construction Indoor Air Quality Management Plan.

7. Answer: b and d
   Pay attention to the word "not."

   For EQC: Enhanced Indoor Air Quality Strategies, both of the following are not design strategies, and therefore the correct answers:
   - Submit drawings and cut sheets for the plumbing systems in chemical mixing areas.
   - Design the exterior sidewalk and pavement to drain away from the building at 2% minimum slope.

   The following are correct design strategies but incorrect answers:
   - Increase ventilation.
   - Prevent occupants from bringing contaminants inside the building by installation of entryway systems.

8. Answer: d. none of the above
   See EQC: Thermal Comfort.

   Placing a lighting control in a hallway does not help you with Controllability of Systems because a hallway is a common transportation space, and does not give occupants a sense of control over their own space.

   The following are distracters to confuse you:
   - You need to make sure the hallway does not have a dead end corridor that is over 20 feet in length.
   - You also need to add temperature control.
   - You also need to make sure the hallway has a view to the outside.

9. Answer: d. SMACNA
   See EQC: Construction Indoor Air Quality Management Plan. One of the requirements for this credit is to develop and implement a construction IAQ management plan per the **Sheet Metal and Air Conditioning National Contractors' Association (SMACNA)** IAQ guidelines.

   The following are distracters to confuse you:
   - ASHRAE Standard 52.2-1999
   - ASHRAE Standard 62.1-2010
   - ASHRAE Standard 90.1-2010 (with errata but without addenda)
   - SCAQMD Rule 1168

10. Answer: d. BUG

    See SSC: Light Pollution Reduction. This credit offers two choices to give designers flexibility: **a new backlight, uplight, and glare (BUG) rating method;** and **a calculation method** (as in LEED 2009).

    The following are distracters to confuse you:
    - ASHRAE/IESNA Standard 90.1-2010 (with errata but without addenda)
    - IESNA RP-33
    - International Dark Sky Association Outdoor Lighting Standard ("Outdoor Lighting Standard" is an invented term that does not exist at all. The correct term is Illuminating Engineering Society and International Dark Sky Association (IES/IDA) Model Lighting Ordinance (MLO) User Guide and IES TM-15-11, Addendum A. For further info see ies.org.)

11. Answer: d. all of the above

    California Title 24-2013 is considered to be equal to ASHRAE/IESNA Standard 90.1-2010 (with errata but without addenda) for all the following LEED BD+C rating systems credit(s):
    - EAP: Minimum Energy Performance
    - EAC: Optimize Energy Performance
    - EAC: Green Power and Carbon Offsets

12. Answer: a. the harvest cycle of the raw materials

    Pay attention to the word "not."

    See MRC: Building Product Disclosure and Optimization—Sourcing of Raw Materials.

    This is a change from LEED 2009. Bio-based materials are *not* defined by the harvest cycle of the raw materials anymore; instead, products must meet the Sustainable Agriculture Standard to count toward this credit.

    The following are considerations for MRC: Building Product Disclosure and Optimization—Sourcing of Raw Materials, and therefore *not* the correct answers:
    - the Sustainable Agriculture Standard
    - corporate sustainability reports (CSRs)
    - USGBC-approved program

13. Answer: b. "Dry Landscape" design by using plants that use little or no water.

    "Xeriscape" is a very common term used in sustainable landscape practice, and you need to know about it.

    The following arc distracters to confuse you:
    - Drip Irrigation to save water.
    - Recycle existing plants on the project site.
    - Reuse graywater for landscape irrigation.

14. Answer: a. Document and provide calculations for waste diverted from landfill.
    The following are typical responsibilities for the contractor in a standard construction practice but are not a responsibility for the contractor to support the LEED documentation process.
    - Maintain a submittal log.
    - Maintain a RFI log.
    - Provide written documentation to justify a change order for rough grading.

15. Answer: d. all of the above
    See synergies for MRC: Building Product Disclosure and Optimization—Sourcing of Raw Materials.

    Materials that qualify for MRC: Building Product Disclosure and Optimization—Sourcing of Raw Materials may also qualify for all of the following credit(s):
    - MRC: Building Life Cycle Impact Reduction
    - MRC: Building Product Disclosure and Optimization—Environmental Product Declarations
    - MRC: Building Product Disclosure and Optimization—Material Ingredients

16. Answer: c
    See "Some use information for WE Category" at the end of WE Category.
    The flow rate for a conventional water closet is actually 1.6 gpf, instead of 1.8 gpf.

    The following three statements are correct:
    - For non-residential projects, water closet uses per day per FTE female is three.
    - For residential projects, water closet uses per day per female is five.
    - The flow rate for a low-flow water closet is 1.1 gpf.

17. Answer: a and b
    See EQC: Low-Emitting Materials.

    The following are standards for paints and coatings wet-applied on site:
    - The California Air Resources Board (CARB) 2007, Suggested Control Measure (SCM) for Architectural Coatings
    - The South Coast Air Quality Management District (SCAQMD) Rule 1113, effective June 3, 2011

    The following are distracters to confuse you:
    - **Green Seal Standard for Commercial Adhesives GS-36 requirements** (Green Seal certification is for identifying metal-free paints or an equivalent source of lead- and cadmium-free documentation)
    - **Green Label Plus (**This is a Carpet and Rug Institute (CRI) standard for carpet and adhesives.)
    - **Green Guard** ("GREENGUARD Certification is part of UL Environment, a business unit of UL (Underwriters Laboratories). GREENGUARD Certification helps manufacturers create and helps buyers identify interior products and materials that have low chemical emissions, improving the quality of the air in which the products are used." See http://www.greenguard.org for more information.)

18. Answer: e
    All of the following are reasons why a developer should locate a green building in a previously developed urban area:
    - to be close to public transportation
    - to use existing community services
    - to be close to existing utilities

19. Answer: c
    Water drained from a kitchen sink or toilet is considered blackwater because it is contaminated by human waste or grease.

20. Answer: b
    With regard to ozone depletion potential (ODP), the order from high ODP to low ODP is CFC>HCFC>HFC.

    See the FREE PDF entitled "The Treatment by LEED® of the Environmental Impact of HVAC Refrigerants (LEED Technical and Scientific Advisory Committee, 2004)." This is one of the documents listed in the latest LEED Green Associate Exam Candidate Handbook. You should read all the documents listed by the handbook a few times and become familiar with them.

Part Two:

21. Answer: a, c, and d
    Choice f is NOT correct and is dangerous for the project because of the large amount of underground methane gas at the site.
22. Answer: a and e
    To gain one point for LTC: Bicycle Facilities, school projects must meet the following criteria: Place or design the project so that a bicycle storage or functional entrance is within a 200-yard (180-meter) walking distance or bicycling distance from a bicycle network that connects to a minimum of one of the following:
    - a minimum of 10 diverse uses (see Appendix 1);
    - a light or heavy rail station, commuter rail station, bus rapid transit stop, or ferry terminal.

    All destinations must be within a 3-mile (4800-meter) bicycling distance of the project boundary.

    Provide dedicated bicycle lanes that extend at least to the end of the school property with no fences or other barriers on school property.

    The project team can count planned bicycle trails or lanes that are fully funded by the date of the C of O and are scheduled to complete within one year of that date.

23. Answer: a
    The key in this question is first cost. While other answers may be reasonable and can reduce long-term cost, they cannot reduce first cost. The GBCI loves to use words like this to trick you. So read the questions carefully, and do not get tricked by the GBCI.

24. Answer: d
    Using the tint film on the glazing as proposed will NOT allow the project to achieve EQC: Daylight Quality Views because per the USGBC:
    "View glazing in the contributing area must provide a clear image of the exterior, not obstructed by frits, fibers, patterned glazing, or added *tints* that distort color balance."

    To gain point(s) for EQC: Daylight, spatial daylight autonomy has to be 55% or higher.

25. Answer: c and d

    To achieve MR Prerequisite (MRP): Storage and Collection of Recyclables, the project team need to offer dedicated areas accessible to building occupants and waste haulers for the collection and storage of recyclable materials for the entire building.

    Choice 3 of MRC: Building Life-Cycle Impact Reduction excludes window assemblies and any hazardous materials that are remediated as a part of the project in the calculation.

    To achieve MRC: Construction and Demolition Waste Management, the project team needs to recycle and/or salvage nonhazardous demolition and construction materials. Calculations can be by volume or weight but need to be consistent throughout. A contractor who salvages windows from an existing building for a CS project may achieve this credit.

    Choice 2 of MRC: Building Product Disclosure and Optimization—Sourcing of Raw Materials include the following:
    Materials reuse. Reuse includes refurbished, salvaged, or reused products. Products meeting materials reuse criteria are counted at 100% of their cost for credit achievement calculation.

    A contractor who salvages windows from an existing building for a CS project may achieve this credit.

26. Answer: c
    Assuming 50% male and 50% female
    5 work days per week x 52 weeks = 260 work days per year
    See Tables 1 and 6 on WEP: Indoor Water Use Reduction, and refer to the following detailed calculation:

Fixture Type	Daily Use	Flow rate (gpf)	Occupants	Sewage Generation (gal)
WC (Male)	1	1.6	100	160
WC (Female)	3	1.6	100	480
Urinal (Male)	2	1.0	100	200
Urinal (Female)	0	1.0	100	0
Total Daily Volume (gal)				840
Annual Work Days				260
Total Annual Volume (gal)				218,400

27. Answer: a
Refer to the following detailed calculation:

Fixture Type	Daily Use	Flow rate (gpf)	Occupants	Sewage Generation (gal)
Single flush, pressure assist HET (Male)	1	1.0	100	100
Single flush, pressure assist HET (Female)	3	1.0	100	300
Waterless Urinal (Male)	2	0	100	0
Urinal (Female)	0	1.0	100	0
Total Daily Volume (gal)				400
Annual Work Days				260
Total Annual Volume (gal)				104,000
Total Annual Volume of Water Saved (gal)	2164,00-104,000 = 114,400 Or 52.38%			

28. Answer: c
A school project can NOT earn any point for LTC: High-Priority Site even if the project team provides successful documentation for the remediation of the site.

The remediation process can earn 2 points for LTC: High-Priority Site *if* this is a Core and Shell project and the project team provides successful documentation for the remediation of the site. This is Choice 3 for this credit.

Phase I Environmental Assessment (per ASTM E1527-05) & Phase II Environmental Assessment (per ASTM E1903-97, 2002), modern-style school building, and Spanish style buildings are all distracters to confuse you.

29. Answer: d
The term "off-gassing" is related to EQC: Low-Emitting Materials. It refers to the emission of especially noxious gases (as from a building material) or volatile organic compound (VOC).

30. Answer: a
CEE stands for Consortium for Energy Efficiency. It is mentioned in WEP: Outdoor Water Use Reduction.

31. Answer: b
NRC stands for Noise Reduction Coefficient. Per Wikipedia: "The Noise Reduction Coefficient (commonly abbreviated NRC) is a scalar representation of the amount of sound energy absorbed upon striking a particular surfacc." It is mentioned in EQP: Minimum Acoustic Performance & EQC: Acoustic Performance.

32. Answer: c
ETV stands for Environmental Technology Verification. Per Wikipedia: "Environmental Technology Verification (ETV) consists in the verification of the performance of environmental technologies or in other words is the establishment or validation of environmental technology

performance by qualified third parties based on test data generated through testing using established protocols or specific requirements. There are several ETV programs running all over the world, organized through government initiatives, with the pioneer program being the one developed in the United States of America, followed by the Canadian ETV Program."

33. Answer: b
    One measurement used for acoustical performance is **A-weighted decibel (dBA) measurement** of noise level. It is a nonlinear scale: if you double the noise level, the measurement will increase 10 dBA instead of double. So, when the sound level increases from 30 dBA to 80 dBA, the volume of the sound increases 2 x 2 x 2 x 2 x 2 = 32 times.

34. Answer: a, b, and d
    The three standards or codes that are related to the most LEED prerequisites and credits are ASHRAE, ANSI, and EPA.

35. Answer: a, b, and d
    The three project phases that are related to the most LEED prerequisites and credits are Pre-Design, Schematic Design, and Construction Documents.

36. Answer: c
    The USGBC released LEED v4 in GreenBuild International Conference and Expo in November, 2013.

37. Answer: b and c
    With regard to synergies, SSP: Construction Activity Pollution Prevention is related to
    - SSC: Site Development—Protect or Restore Habitat
    - SSC: Rainwater Management

38. Answer: b, d, and e
    With regard to synergies, SSC: Heat Island Reduction, is related to:
    - SSC: Site Development—Protect or Restore Habitat
    - EAP: Minimum Energy Performance
    - EAC: Optimize Energy Performance

39. Answer: c and d
    With regard to submittals, the project team needs to submit:
    - Floor plans, site plans, etc. if needed
    - Verification of recycled material types

40. Answer: d
    With regard to project team coordination, any of the following can be responsible for submitting MRP: Storage and Collection of Recyclables:
    - The architect
    - The developer
    - The tenant

III. How were the LEED AP BD+C sample questions created?

The actual LEED AP BD+C Exam has 200 questions (100 questions for each section) and you must finish it within four hours. The raw exam score is converted to a scaled score ranging from 125 to 200. The passing score is 170 or higher.

I tried to be scientific when selecting the sample questions, so I based the number of questions for each credit category roughly on the number of points that you can get for that category. The level difficulty for each question was designed to match the official sample questions that can be downloaded from the official GBCI website. Feedback from our readers has indicated that these sample questions are relatively easy when compared to the actual LEED AP BD+C Exam.

IV. Where can I find the latest and official sample questions for the LEED AP BD+C Exam?

Answer: You can find them, as well as the exam content, from the candidate handbook, at:
http://www.gbci.org/credentialing
http://www.usgbc.org/resources/leed-v4-ap-bdc-candidate-handbook

V. Latest trend for LEED exams

Recently, some readers have encountered versions of the LEED exams that contain many questions on refrigerants (CFC, HCFC, and HFC). The following advice will help you answer these questions correctly:

For more information, download the free PDF file called "The Treatment by LEED of the Environmental Impact of HVAC Refrigerants" at the following link:
http://www.usgbc.org/resources/treatment-leed-environmental-impact-hvac-refrigerants

This is a VERY important document that you need to become familiar with. Many real LEED exam questions (CFC, HCFC, HFC, etc.) come from this document. Be familiar with this material.

Pay special attention to the table on ODP and GWP on page 3. You do not have to remember the exact value of all ODPs and GWPs, but you do need to know the rough numbers for various groups of refrigerants.

This latest trend regarding refrigerants (CFC, HCFC, and HFC) for LEED Exams has much to do with LEED v4 Credit Weighting. EA (including refrigerants) is the biggest winner in LEED v4, meaning the category has MORE questions than any other areas for ALL the LEED exams.

VI. LEED AP BD&C Exam registration

1. **How to register for the LEED AP BD+C Exam?**
   Answer: Per the USGBC:
   a. "Log in to your Credentials account using your existing USGBC® site user account or creating a new account if you do not have one.
   b. Verify that the name you enter in matches the name on the ID you will present at the test center. If it does not match, please update your name in your site user account "settings". Contact GBCI if you experience issues updating your name.*
   c. Select the credential exam you wish to apply for and follow the instructions on the screen to complete the application.
   d. You will be redirected to prometric.com/gbci to schedule your exam date and location."
   e. You can reschedule or cancel the LEED AP BD+C Exam at www.prometric.com/gbci with your Prometric-issued confirmation number for the exam. You need to bring two forms of ID to the exam site. See www.prometric.com/gbci for a list of exam sites. Call 1-800-795-1747 (within the US) or 202-742-3792 (Outside of the US) or e-mail exam@gbci.org if you have any questions.

2. **Important Note:** You can download the "LEED AP BD+C Candidate Handbook" from the GBCI website and get all the latest details and procedures. Ideally you should download it and read it carefully at least three weeks before your exam. Refer to the following links:
   http://www.gbci.org/credentialing
   http://www.usgbc.org/resources/leed-v4-ap-bdc-candidate-handbook

Chapter 15

Frequently Asked Questions (FAQ) and Other Useful Resources

The following are tips on how to pass the LEED exam on the first try with only one week of preparation. I also include my responses to several readers' questions. Hopefully they may help you.

1. I found the reference guide way too tedious. Can I only read your books and just refer to the USGBC reference guide (if one is available for the exam I am taking) when needed?

Response: Yes. That is one way to study.

2. Is one week really enough for me to prepare for the exam while I am working?

Response: Yes, if you can put in 40 to 60 hours during the week, study hard and you can pass the exam. This exam is similar to a history or political science exam; you need to MEMORIZE the information. If you take too long, you will probably forget the information by the time you take the test.

In my book, I give you tips on how to MEMORIZE the information, and I have already highlighted/underlined the most important information that you definitely have to MEMORIZE to pass the exam. It is my goal to use this book to help you to pass the LEED exam with the minimum time and effort. I want to make your life easier.

3. Would you say that if I buy your LEED Exam Guide Series books, I could pass the exam using no other study materials? The books sold on the USGBC website run in the hundreds of dollars, so I would be quite happy if I could buy your book and just use that.

Response: First of all, there are readers who have passed the LEED Exam by reading only my books in the LEED Exam Guides Series (www.**GreenExamEducation**.com). My goal is to write at least one book for each of the LEED exams, and my books stand alone to prepare people for one specific LEED exam.

Secondly, people learn in many different ways. That is why I have added some new advice below for people who learn better by doing practice tests.

If you do the following things, you have a very good chance of passing the LEED exam (NOT a guarantee, nobody can guarantee you will pass):

If you study, understand and MEMORIZE all of the information in my books, *LEED v4 BD &C Exam Guide* and *LEED v4 BD&C Mock Exam*, and do NOT panic when you run into problems you are not familiar with, and use the guess strategy in my books, then you have a very good chance of passing the exam.

You need to UNDERSTAND and MEMORIZE the information in the books and score almost a perfect score on the mock exam in my book. This book will give you the BULK of the most CURRENT information that you need for the specific LEED exam you are taking. You HAVE to know the information in my book in order to pass the exam.

If you have not done any LEED projects before, I suggest you also go to the USGBC website and download the latest LEED credit templates for the LEED rating system related to the LEED exam you are taking. Read the templates and become familiar with them. This is important.
See the following link:
http://www.usgbc.org/leed#rating

The LEED exam is NOT an easy exam, but anyone with a 7th grade education should be able to study and pass the LEED exam if he prepares correctly.

If you have extra time and money, the other books I would recommend are *LEED v4 GA Mock Exams* and the USGBC reference guide, the official book for the LEED exam. I know some people who did not even read the reference guide from cover to cover when they took the exam. They just studied the information in my books, and only referred to the reference guide to look up a few things, and they passed on the first try. Some of my readers have even passed WITHOUT reading the USGBC reference guide AT ALL.

4. I am preparing for the LEED exam. Do I need to read the 2" thick reference?

Response: See answer above.

5. For LEED v4, will the total number of points be more than 110 in total if a project gets all of the extra credits and all of the standard credits?

Response: No. For LEED v4, there are 100 base points and 10 possible bonus points. There are many different ways to achieve bonus points (extra credits or exemplary performance), but you can have a maximum number of 6 Innovation (IN) bonus points and 4 Regional Priority (RP) bonus points. So, the maximum points for ANY project will be 110.

6. For the exam, do I need to know the project phase in which a specific prerequisite/credit takes place? (i.e., pre-design, schematic design, etc.)

Response: The information on the project phase (NOT LEED submittal phase) for each prerequisite/credit is NOT mentioned in the USGBC reference guide, but it is covered in the USGBC workshops. If it is important enough for the USGBC workshops to cover, then it may show up on the actual LEED exam.

Most, if not all, other third party books completely miss this important information. I cover it for each prerequisite/credit in my book for the LEED exam because I think it is very important.

Some people THINK that the LEED exam ONLY tests information covered by the USGBC reference guide. They are wrong.

The LEED exam does test information NOT covered by the USGBC reference guide at all. This may include the process of LEED submittal and project team coordination, etc.

I would MEMORIZE this information if I were you, because it may show up on the LEED exam. Besides, this information is not hard to memorize once you understand it, and you need to know it to do actual LEED submittal work anyway.

7. Are you writing new versions of books for the new LEED exams? What new books are you writing?

Response: Yes, I am working on other books in the LEED Exam Guide series. I will be writing one book for each of the LEED AP specialty exams. See GreenExamEducation.com or GeeForum.com for more information.

8. Important documents that you need to download for free, become familiar with and memorize:

Note: GBCI and USGBC changes the links to their documents every now and then, so, by the time you read this book, they may have changed some of those listed in this book. You can simply go to their main website, search for the document or subject by name, or Google it, and should be able to find the most current link. You can use the same technique to search for documents by other organizations.

The main website for the GBCI is at the following link:
http://www.gbci.org/

The main website for the USGBC is at the following link:
http://www.usgbc.org/

a. Every LEED exam **always tests** Credit Interpretation Request (CIR). Download "Credit Interpretation Request and Innovation and Design Request Procedures for LEED for Homes Providers," read, and memorize.
See https://www.usgbc.org/ShowFile.aspx?DocumentID=2941

b. Every LEED exam **always tests** project team coordination. Download *Sustainable Building Technical Manual: Part II,* by Anthony Bernheim and William Reed (1996), read, and memorize.
See http://www.usgbc.org/resources/sustainable-building-technical-manual-part-ii-pre-design-issues

c. Project registration application and LEED certification process can be found at the following link:
http://www.usgbc.org/leed/certification#tools

9. Important documents that you need to download for free, and become familiar with:

a. *LEED for Operations and Maintenance Reference Guide-Introduction* (v4)
http://www.usgbc.org/sites/all/assets/section/files/v4-guide-excerpts/Excerpt_v4_OM.pdf

b. *LEED for Operations and Maintenance Reference Guide-Glossary* (US Green Building Council, 2008)
https://www.dropbox.com/sh/3wjtitz1s50bljn/AAC82m00P-tg61SRUTHclkDJa?dl=0

c. *LEED for Homes Rating System* (US Green Building Council, 2008)
http://www.usgbc.org/LEED/

d. *Cost of Green Revisited,* by Davis Langdon (2007)
http://www.usgbc.org/resources/cost-green-revisited

e. *The Treatment by LEED® of the Environmental Impact of HVAC Refrigerants (*LEED Technical and Scientific Advisory Committee, 2004)
http://www.usgbc.org/resources/treatment-leed-environmental-impact-hvac-refrigerants

f. *Guidance on Innovation and Design (ID) Credits* (US Green Building Council, 2004)
http:*//www.usgbc.org/Docs/LEEDdocs/IDcredit_guidance_final.pdf*

10. Do I need to take many practice questions to prepare for a LEED exam?

Response: There is NO absolutely correct answer to this question. People learn in many different ways. Personally, I am NOT crazy about doing many practice questions. Consider if you do 700 practice questions, not only must you read them all, but each question has at least 4 choices. That totals to at least 2,800 choices, which is a great deal of reading. I have seen some third-party materials that have 1,200 practice questions. That will require even MORE time to go over the materials.

I prefer to spend most of my time reading, digesting, and really understanding the fundamental materials, and MEMORIZE them naturally by rereading the materials multiple times. This is because the fundamental materials for ANY exam will NOT change, and the scope of the exam will NOT change for the same main version of the test (until the exam moves to the next advanced version). However, there are many ways to ask you questions.

If you have a limited amount of time for preparation, it is more efficient for you to focus on the fundamental materials and actually master the knowledge that GBCI wants you to learn. If you can do that, then no matter how GBCI changes the exam format or how GBCI asks the questions, you will do fine in the exam.

Strategy 101 for the LEED AP BD+C Exam is that you must recognize that you have only a limited amount of time to prepare for the exam. Therefore, you must concentrate on the most important contents of the LEED AP BD+C Exam.

The key to passing the LEED AP BD+C Exam, or any other exam, is to know the scope of the exam, and not to read too many books. Select one or two helpful books and focus on them. You must understand the content and memorize it. For your convenience, I have underlined the fundamental information that I think is very important. You definitely need to memorize all the information that I have underlined. You should try to understand the content first, and then memorize the content of the book by rereading it. This is a much better way than "mechanical" memory without understanding.

Most people fail the exam NOT because they are unable to answer the few "advanced" questions on the exam, but because they have read the information but can NOT recall it on the day of the exam. They spend too much time preparing for the exam, drag the preparation process on too long, seek too much information, go to too many Web sites, do too many practice questions and too many mock exams (one or two sets of mock exams are probably sufficient), and spread themselves too thin. They end up missing out on the most important information of the LEED exam, and they will fail.

To me, memorization and understanding work hand-in-hand. Understanding always comes first. If you really understand something, then memorization is easy.

For example, I'll read a book's first chapter very slowly but make sure I really understand everything in it, no matter how long it takes. I do NOT care if others are faster readers than I. Then, I reread the first chapter again. This time, the reading is so much easier, and I can read it much faster. Then I try to retell the contents, focusing on substance, not the format or any particular order of things. This is a very good way for me to understand and digest the material, while absorbing and memorizing the content.

I then repeat the same procedure for each chapter, and then reread the book until I take the exam. This achieves two purposes:

a. I keep reinforcing the important materials that I already have memorized and fight against the human brain's natural tendency to forget things.

b. I also understand the content of the book much better by reading it multiple times.

If I were to attempt to memorize something without understanding it first, it would be very difficult for me to do so. Even if I were to memorize it, I would likely forget it quickly.

Appendixes

1. Use Types and Categories

Category	Use Type
Food retail	Supermarket
	Grocery with produce section
Community-serving retail	Convenience store
	Farmers market
	Hardware store
	Pharmacy
	Other retail
Services	Bank
	Family entertainment venue (e.g., theater, sports)
	Gym, health club, exercise studio
	Hair care
	Laundry, dry cleaner
	Restaurant, café, diner (excluding those with only drive-thru service)
Civic and community facilities	Adult or senior care (licensed)
	Child care (licensed)
	Community or recreation center
	Cultural arts facility (museum, performing arts)
	Education facility (e.g., K—12 school, university, adult education center, vocational school, community college)
	Government office that serves public on-site
	Medical clinic or office that treats patients
	Place of worship
	Police or fire station
	Post office
	Public library
	Public park
	Social services center
Community anchor uses (BD+C and ID+C only)	Commercial office (100 or more full-time equivalent jobs)

Adapted from Criterion Planners, INDEX neighborhood completeness indicator, 2005.

2. Default occupancy factors

	Gross square feet per occupant		Gross square feet per occupant	
	Employees	**Transients**	**Employees**	**Transients**
General office	250	0	23	0
Retail, general	550	130	51	12
Retail or service (e.g., financial, auto)	600	130	56	12
Restaurant	435	95	40	9
Grocery store	550	115	51	11
Medical office	225	330	21	31
R&D or laboratory	400	0	37	0
Warehouse, distribution	2	500	0	232
Warehouse, storage	20,000	0	1,860	0
Hotel	1,500	700	139	65
Educational, daycare	630	105	59	10
Educational, K–12	1,300	140	121	13
Educational, postsecondary	2,100	150	195	14

Note: This table is for projects (like CS) where the final occupant count is not available. If your project's occupancy factors are not listed above, you can use a comparable building to show the average gross sf per occupant for your building's use.

3. Important resources and further study materials you can download for <u>free</u>

Energy Performance of LEED for New Construction, by Cathy Turner and Mark Frankel (2008):
http://www.usgbc.org/resources/energy-performance-leed-new-construction

Foundations of the Leadership in Energy and Environmental Design Environmental Rating System: A Tool for Market Transformation (LEED Steering Committee, 2006):
http://www.usgbc.org/Docs/Archive/General/Docs2040.pdf

AIA Integrated Project Delivery: A Guide (www.aia.org):
http://www.aia.org/contractdocs/AIAS077630

Review of ANSI/ASHRAE Standard 62.1-2007: Ventilation for Acceptable Indoor Air Quality, by Brian Kareis:
http://www.workplace-hygiene.com/articles/ANSI-ASHRAE-3.html

Bureau of Labor Statistics (www.bls.gov)

International Code Council (www.iccsafe.org)

Americans with Disabilities Act (ADA): Standards for Accessible Design (www.ada.gov):
http://www.ada.gov/stdspdf.htm

GSA 2015 Facilities Standards (General Services Administration, 2015):
http://www.gsa.gov/portal/content/104821

Guide to Purchasing Green Power (Environmental Protection Agency, 2010):
http://www.epa.gov/greenpower/documents/purchasing_guide_for_web.pdf

USGBC Definitions:
https://www.usgbc.org/ShowFile.aspx?DocumentID=5744

3. Annotated bibliography

Chen, Gang. ***LEED v4 Green Associate Exam Guide (LEED GA):*** *Comprehensive Study Materials, Sample Questions, Mock Exam, Green Building LEED Certification, and Sustainability*, Book 2, LEED Exam Guide series, ArchiteG.com, the latest edition. ArchiteG, Inc. Latest Edition. This is a very comprehensive and concise book on the LEED Green Associate Exam. Some readers have passed the LEED Green Associate Exam by studying this book for 10 hours.

Chen, Gang. ***LEED GA MOCK EXAMS (LEED v4):*** *Questions, Answers, and Explanations: A Must-Have for the LEED Green Associate Exam, Green Building LEED Certification, and Sustainability*. ArchiteG, Inc, the latest version. This is a companion to *LEED v4 Green Associate Exam Guide (LEED GA)*. It includes 200 questions, answers, and explanation, and is very close to the real LEED Green Associate Exam.

Chen, Gang. ***LEED v4 BD&C MOCK EXAMS:*** *Questions, Answers, and Explanations: A Must-Have for the LEED AP BD+C Exam, Green Building LEED Certification, and Sustainability*, LEED Exam Guide series, ArchiteG.com. Latest Edition. This is a companion to *LEED v4 BD&C Exam Guide*. It includes 200 questions, answers, and explanation, and is very close to the real LEED AP BD+C Exam.

4. Valuable Web sites and links

a. The Official Web sites for the U.S. Green Building Council (USGBC):
http://www.usgbc.org/
http://www.GreenBuild365.org
http://www. GreenBuildExpo.com/

Pay special attention to the purpose of LEED Online, LEED project registration, LEED certification content, LEED reference guide introductions, LEED rating systems, and checklists.

You can download or purchase the following useful documents from the USGBC or GBCI Web site:

Latest and official LEED exam candidate handbooks including an exam content outline and sample questions:
http://www.usgbc.org/resources/list/credentialing-resources

LEED Reference Guides, **LEED Rating System Selection Policy,** and various versions of LEED Green Building Rating Systems and Project Checklist:
http://www.usgbc.org/certification#tools

Read the **LEED Rating System Selection Policy** at least three times, because it is VERY important, and it tells you which LEED system to use.

USGBC issue LEED Addenda for various LEED Green Building Rating **Systems** and **reference guides** on a quarterly basis. **Make sure you download the latest LEED Addenda** related to your exam and read them at least three times. See link below for detailed information:
http://www.usgbc.org/resources/list/addenda

b. Natural Resources Defense Council:
http://www.nrdc.org/

c. Environmental Construction + Design - Green Book (Offers print magazine and online environmental products and services resources guide):
http://www.edcmag.com/greenbook

d. Cool Roof Rating Council Web site:
http://www.coolroofs.org

5. Important Items Covered by the Latest Edition of *Green Building and LEED Core Concepts Guide*

Starting on December 1, 2011, GBCI began drawing LEED Green Associate Exam questions from the latest edition of *Green Building and LEED Core Concepts Guide*. The following are some "new" and important items covered by this book:

adaptive reuse: Designing and constructing a building to accommodate a future use that is different from its original use.

biomimicry: Learning from nature and designing systems using principles that have been tested in nature for millions of years.

carbon overlay: LEED credit weighting based on each credit's impact on reducing carbon footprint.

charrettes: Intensive (design) workshops.

cradle to cradle: A method where materials are used in a closed system and generate no waste.

cradle to grave: A process that examines materials from their point of extraction to disposal.

closed system: There is no "away." Everything goes somewhere within the system; the waste generated by a process becomes the "food" of another process. Nature is a closed system.

embodied energy: The total energy consumed by extracting, harvesting, manufacturing, transporting, installing, and using a material through its entire life cycle.

ENERGY STAR's Portfolio Manager: An online management tool for tracking and evaluating water and energy use. An ENERGY STAR Portfolio Manager score of 50 means a building is at national average energy use level for its category. A score higher than 50 means a building is more energy efficient than the national average energy use level for its category. The higher the score, the better.

evapotranspiration: Loss of water due to evaporation.

externalities: Benefits or costs that are NOT part of a transaction.

feedback loop: Information flows within a system that allows the system to adjust itself. A thermostat or melting snow is an example of a negative feedback loop. Population growth, heat island effect, or climate change is a positive feedback loop. A positive feedback loop can create chaos in a system.

International Green Construction Code (IGCC): A national model green building code published by International Code Council (ICC).

integrated process: Emphasizes communications and interactions among stakeholders throughout the life of a project. Integrated process is a holistic decision making process based on systems thinking and life-cycle approach.

iterative process: A repetitive and circular process that helps a team to define goals and check ideas against these goals.

Integrated Pest Management (IPM): A sustainable approach to pest management.

LEED interpretations: Precedent-setting (project credit interpretation) rulings. A project team can opt into the LEED interpretation process when submitting an inquiry to GBCI.

leverage points: Places where a small intervention can generate big changes.

life cycle approach: Looking at a product or building through its entire life cycle.

life cycle assessment (LCA): Use life cycle thinking in environmental issues.

life cycle costing: Looking at the cost of purchasing and operating a building or product and the relative savings.

low impact development (LID): A land development approach mimicking natural systems and managing storm water as close to the source as possible.

Net-Zero: A project that doesn't use any more resources than what it can produce. Similar concepts include carbon neutrality and water balance.

negative feedback loop: A signal for the system to stop changes when a response is not needed anymore.

open system: Resources are brought from the outside, consumed, and then disposed of as waste to the outside.

permaculture: Designing human habitats and agriculture systems based on models and relationships found in nature.

positive feedback loop: A stimulus causes an effect and encourages the loop to produce more of this effect.

Prius effect: Provides real time feedback of energy use so that users can adjust behaviors to save energy.

project CIRs: LEED credit interpretation rulings for specific project circumstances.

retrocommissioning: A building tune-up that restores efficiency and improves performance.

regenerative: Regenerative buildings and communities evolve with living systems and help to renew resources and life. Regenerative projects generate electricity and sell the excess back to the grid, as well as return water to nature that is cleaner than it was before use.

systems thinking: In a system, each component affects many other components. They are all related to each other.

Wingspread Principles on the US Response to Global Warming: A set of principles signed by organizations and individuals to express their commitment to address global warming. It calls for 60% to 80% reduction of greenhouse gas emissions by midcentury (based on 1990 levels).

Back Page Promotion

You may be interested in some other books written by Gang Chen:

A. **ARE Mock Exam series. See the following link:**
http://www.GreenExamEducation.com

B. **LEED Exam Guides series. See the following link:**
http://www.GreenExamEducation.com

C. ***Building Construction:*** *Project Management, Construction Administration, Drawings, Specs, Detailing Tips, Schedules, Checklists, and Secrets Others Don't Tell You (Architectural Practice Simplified, 2nd edition)*
http://www.ArchiteG.com

D. ***Planting Design Illustrated***
http://outskirtspress.com/agent.php?key=11011&page=GangChen

ARE Mock Exam Series

Published ARE books (One Mock Exam book for each ARE division, plus California Supplemental Mock Exam):
Programming, Planning & Practice (PPP) ARE Mock Exam (Architect Registration Exam): ARE Overview, Exam Prep Tips, Multiple-Choice Questions and Graphic Vignettes, Solutions and Explanations. **ISBN-13:** 9781612650067

Site Planning & Design ARE Mock Exam (SPD of Architect Registration Exam): ARE Overview, Exam Prep Tips, Multiple-Choice Questions and Graphic Vignettes, Solutions and Explanations**. ISBN-13:** 9781612650111

Building Design and Construction Systems (BDCS) ARE Mock Exam (Architect Registration Exam): ARE Overview, Exam Prep Tips, Multiple-Choice Questions and Graphic Vignettes, Solutions and Explanations. **ISBN-13:** 9781612650029

Schematic Design (SD) ARE Mock Exam (Architect Registration Exam): ARE Overview, Exam Prep Tips, Graphic Vignettes, Solutions and Explanations
ISBN: 9781612650050

Structural Systems ARE Mock Exam (SS of Architect Registration Exam): ARE Overview, Exam Prep Tips, Multiple-Choice Questions and Graphic Vignettes, Solutions and Explanations. **ISBN**: 9781612650012

Building Systems (BS) ARE Mock Exam (Architect Registration Exam): ARE Overview, Exam Prep Tips, Multiple-Choice Questions and Graphic Vignettes, Solutions and Explanations**. ISBN-13**: 9781612650036

Construction Documents and Service (CDS) Are Mock Exam (Architect Registration Exam): ARE Overview, Exam Prep Tips, Multiple-Choice Questions and Graphic Vignettes, Solutions and Explanations. **ISBN-13:** 9781612650005

Mock California Supplemental Exam (CSE of Architect Registration Exam): CSE Overview, Exam Prep Tips, General Section and Project Scenario Section, Questions, Solutions and Explanations. **ISBN**: 9781612650159

Upcoming ARE books:
Other books in the ARE Mock Exam Series are being produced. Our goal is to produce one mock exam book PLUS one guidebook for each of the ARE exam divisions.

See the following link for the latest information:
http://www.GreenExamEducation.com

LEED Exam Guides series: Comprehensive Study Materials, Sample Questions, Mock Exam, Building LEED Certification and Going Green

LEED (Leadership in Energy and Environmental Design) is the most important trend of development, and it is revolutionizing the construction industry. It has gained tremendous momentum and has a profound impact on our environment.

From LEED Exam Guides series, you will learn how to

1. Pass the LEED Green Associate Exam and various LEED AP + exams (each book will help you with a specific LEED exam).

2. Register and certify a building for LEED certification.

3. Understand the intent for each LEED prerequisite and credit.

4. Calculate points for a LEED credit.

5. Identify the responsible party for each prerequisite and credit.

6. Earn extra credit (exemplary performance) for LEED.

7. Implement the local codes and building standards for prerequisites and credit.

8. Receive points for categories not yet clearly defined by USGBC.

There is currently NO official book on the LEED Green Associate Exam, and most of the existing books on LEED and LEED AP are too expensive and too complicated to be practical and helpful. The pocket guides in LEED Exam Guides series fill in the blanks, demystify LEED, and uncover the tips, codes, and jargon for LEED as well as the true meaning of "going green." They will set up a solid foundation and fundamental framework of LEED for you. Each book in the LEED Exam Guides series covers every aspect of one or more specific LEED rating system(s) in plain and concise language and makes this information understandable to all people.

These pocket guides are small and easy to carry around. You can read them whenever you have a few extra minutes. They are indispensable books for all people—administrators; developers; contractors; architects; landscape architects; civil, mechanical, electrical, and plumbing engineers; interns; drafters; designers; and other design professionals.

Why is the LEED Exam Guides series needed?

A number of books are available that you can use to prepare for the LEED exams:

1. *USGBC Reference Guides*. You need to select the correct version of the *Reference Guide* for your exam.

   The *USGBC Reference Guides* are comprehensive, but they give too much information. For example, *The LEED 2009 Reference Guide for Green Building Design and Construction (BD&C)* has about 700 oversized pages. Many of the calculations in the books are too detailed for the exam. They are also expensive (approximately $200 each, so most people may not buy them for their personal use, but instead, will seek to share an office copy).

   It is good to read a reference guide from cover to cover if you have the time. The problem is not too many people have time to read the whole reference guide. Even if you do read the whole guide, you may not remember the important issues to pass the LEED exam. You need to reread the material several times before you can remember much of it.

   Reading the reference guide from cover to cover without a guidebook is a difficult and inefficient way of preparing for the LEED AP Exam, because you do NOT know what USGBC and GBCI are looking for in the exam.

2. The USGBC workshops and related handouts are concise, but they do not cover extra credits (exemplary performance). The workshops are expensive, costing approximately $450 each.

3. Various books published by a third party are available on Amazon, bn.com and books.google.com. However, most of them are not very helpful.

   There are many books on LEED, but not all are useful.

   LEED Exam Guides series will fill in the blanks and become a valuable, reliable source:

a. They will give you more information for your money. Each of the books in the LEED Exam Guides series has more information than the related USGBC workshops.

b. They are exam-oriented and more effective than the USGBC reference guides.

c. They are better than most, if not all, of the other third-party books. They give you comprehensive study materials, sample questions and answers, mock exams and answers, and critical information on building LEED certification and going green. Other third-party books only give you a fraction of the information.

d. They are comprehensive yet concise. They are small and easy to carry around. You can read them whenever you have a few extra minutes.

e. They are great timesavers. I have highlighted the important information that you need to understand and MEMORIZE. I also make some acronyms and short sentences to help you easily remember the credit names.

It should take you about 1 or 2 weeks of full-time study to pass each of the LEED exams. I have met people who have spent 40 hours to study and passed the exams.

You can find sample texts and other information on the LEED Exam Guides series in customer discussion sections under each of my book's listing on Amazon, bn.com and books.google.com.

What others are saying about *LEED GA Mock Exams*...

"Great news, I passed!!! As an educator and business professional I would absolutely recommend this book to anyone looking to take and pass the LEED Green Associate exam on the first attempt."
—Luke Ferland

"Elite runners will examine a course, running it before they race it...This book is designed to concentrate on increasing the intensity of your study efforts, examine the course, and run it before you race it..."
—Howard Patrick (Pat) Barry, AIA NCARB

"Like many similar test prep guides, Mr. Chen cites the resources that will be useful to study. But he goes beyond this and differentiates which ones must memorize and those you must be at least familiar with. "
—NPacella

"Read *LEED GA Mock Exams* before you start studying other resource materials. It will serve to bring your attention to the information that you are most likely to be asked on the exam as you come across it in your studying. "
—Mike Kwon

"I found these exams to be quite tougher compared to the others I took a look at, which is good as it made me prepare for the worst I would definitely recommend using these mock exams. I ultimately passed with 181... "
—Swankysenor

Note: Other books in the **LEED Exam Guides series** are in the process of being produced. At least **one book will eventually be produced for each of the LEED exams.** The series include:

LEED v4 Green Associate Exam Guide (LEED GA): *Comprehensive Study Materials, Sample Questions, Mock Exam, Green Building LEED Certification, and Sustainability*, LEED Exam Guide series, ArchiteG.com. Latest Edition.

LEED GA MOCK EXAMS (LEED v4): *Questions, Answers, and Explanations: A Must-Have for the LEED Green Associate Exam, Green Building LEED Certification, and Sustainability*, LEED Exam Guide series, ArchiteG.com. Latest Edition

LEED v4 BD&C EXAM GUIDE: *A Must-Have for the LEED AP BD+C Exam: Comprehensive Study Materials, Sample Questions, Mock Exam, Green Building Design and Construction, LEED Certification, and Sustainability*, LEED Exam Guide series, ArchiteG.com. Latest Edition.

LEED v4 BD&C MOCK EXAMS: *Questions, Answers, and Explanations: A Must-Have for the LEED AP BD+C Exam, Green Building LEED Certification, and Sustainability*, LEED Exam Guide series, ArchiteG.com. Latest Edition.

LEED ID&C Exam Guide: *A Must-Have for the LEED AP ID+C Exam: Study Materials, Sample Questions, Green Interior Design and Construction, Green Building LEED Certification, and Sustainability,* LEED Exam Guide series, ArchiteG.com. Latest Edition.

LEED ID&C Mock Exam: *Questions, Answers, and Explanations: A Must-Have for the LEED AP ID+C Exam, Green Interior Design and Construction, Green Building LEED Certification, and Sustainability,* LEED Exam Guide series, ArchiteG.com. Latest Edition.

LEED O&M MOCK EXAMS: *Questions, Answers, and Explanations: A Must-Have for the LEED O&M Exam, Green Building LEED Certification, and Sustainability*, LEED Exam Guide series, ArchiteG.com. Latest Edition.

LEED O&M EXAM GUIDE: *A Must-Have for the LEED AP O+M Exam: Comprehensive Study Materials, Sample Questions, Mock Exam, Green Building Operations and Maintenance, LEED Certification, and Sustainability*, LEED Exam Guide series, ArchiteG.com. Latest Edition.

LEED HOMES EXAM GUIDE: *A Must-Have for the LEED AP Homes Exam: Comprehensive Study Materials, Sample Questions, Mock Exam, Green Building LEED Certification, and Sustainability*, LEED Exam Guide series, ArchiteG.com. Latest Edition.

LEED ND EXAM GUIDE: *A Must-Have for the LEED AP Neighborhood Development Exam: Comprehensive Study Materials, Sample Questions, Mock Exam, Green Building LEED Certification, and Sustainability*, LEED Exam Guide series, ArchiteG.com. Latest Edition.

How to order these books:
You can order the books listed above at:
http://www.GreenExamEducation.com

OR
http://www.ArchiteG.com

Building Construction

Project Management, Construction Administration, Drawings, Specs, Detailing Tips, Schedules, Checklists, and Secrets Others Don't Tell You (Architectural Practice Simplified, 2nd edition)

Learn the Tips, Become One of Those Who Know Building Construction and Architectural Practice, and Thrive!

For architectural practice and building design and construction industry, there are two kinds of people: those who know, and those who don't. The tips of building design and construction and project management have been undercover—until now.

Most of the existing books on building construction and architectural practice are too expensive, too complicated, and too long to be practical and helpful. This book simplifies the process to make it easier to understand and uncovers the tips of building design and construction and project management. It sets up a solid foundation and fundamental framework for this field. It covers every aspect of building construction and architectural practice in plain and concise language and introduces it to all people. Through practical case studies, it demonstrates the efficient and proper ways to handle various issues and problems in architectural practice and building design and construction industry.

It is for ordinary people and aspiring young architects as well as seasoned professionals in the construction industry. For ordinary people, it uncovers the tips of building construction; for aspiring architects, it works as a construction industry survival guide and a guidebook to shorten the process in mastering architectural practice and climbing up the professional ladder; for seasoned architects, it has many checklists to refresh their memory. It is an indispensable reference book for ordinary people, architectural students, interns, drafters, designers, seasoned architects, engineers, construction administrators, superintendents, construction managers, contractors, and developers.

You will learn:

1. How to develop your business and work with your client.
2. The entire process of building design and construction, including programming, entitlement, schematic design, design development, construction documents, bidding, and construction administration.
3. How to coordinate with governing agencies, including a county's health department and a city's planning, building, fire, public works departments, etc.
4. How to coordinate with your consultants, including soils, civil, structural, electrical, mechanical, plumbing engineers, landscape architects, etc.
5. How to create and use your own checklists to do quality control of your construction documents.
6. How to use various logs (i.e., RFI log, submittal log, field visit log, etc.) and lists (contact list, document control list, distribution list, etc.) to organize and simplify your work.
7. How to respond to RFI, issue CCDs, review change orders, submittals, etc.
8. How to make your architectural practice a profitable and successful business.

Planting Design Illustrated

A Must-Have for Landscape Architecture: A Holistic Garden Design Guide with Architectural and Horticultural Insight, and Ideas from Famous Gardens in Major Civilizations

One of the most significant books on landscaping!

This is one of the most comprehensive books on planting design. It fills in the blanks of the field and introduces poetry, painting, and symbolism into planting design. It covers in detail the two major systems of planting design: formal planting design and naturalistic planting design. It has numerous line drawings and photos to illustrate the planting design concepts and principles. Through in-depth discussions of historical precedents and practical case studies, it uncovers the fundamental design principles and concepts, as well as the underpinning philosophy for planting design. It is an indispensable reference book for landscape architecture students, designers, architects, urban planners, and ordinary garden lovers.

What Others Are Saying about *Planting Design Illustrated* …

"I found this book to be absolutely fascinating. You will need to concentrate while reading it, but the effort will be well worth your time."
—Bobbie Schwartz, former president of APLD (Association of Professional Landscape Designers) and author of *The Design Puzzle: Putting the Pieces Together*.

"This is a book that you have to read, and it is more than well worth your time. Gang Chen takes you well beyond what you will learn in other books about basic principles like color, texture, and mass."
—Jane Berger, editor & publisher of gardendesignonline

"As a longtime consumer of gardening books, I am impressed with Gang Chen's inclusion of new information on planting design theory for Chinese and Japanese gardens. Many gardening books discuss the beauty of Japanese gardens, and a few discuss the unique charms of Chinese gardens, but this one explains how Japanese and Chinese history, as well as geography and artistic traditions, bear on the development of each country's style. The material on traditional Western garden planting is thorough and inspiring, too. *Planting Design Illustrated* definitely rewards repeated reading and study. Any garden designer will read it with profit."
—Jan Whitner, editor of the *Washington Park Arboretum Bulletin*

"Enhanced with an annotated bibliography and informative appendices, *Planting Design Illustrated* offers an especially "reader friendly" and practical guide that makes it a very strongly recommended addition to personal, professional, academic, and community library gardening & landscaping reference collection and supplemental reading list."
—Midwest Book Review

"Where to start? *Planting Design Illustrated* is, above all, fascinating and refreshing! Not something the lay reader encounters every day, the book presents an unlikely topic in an easily digestible, easy-to-follow way. It is superbly organized with a comprehensive table of contents, bibliography, and appendices. The writing, though expertly informative, maintains its accessibility throughout and is a joy to read. The detailed and beautiful illustrations expanding on the concepts presented were my favorite portion. One of the finest books I've encountered in this contest in the past 5 years."
—Writer's Digest 16th Annual International Self-Published Book Awards Judge's Commentary

"The work in my view has incredible application to planting design generally and a system approach to what is a very difficult subject to teach, at least in my experience. Also featured is a very beautiful philosophy of garden design principles bordering poetry. It's my strong conviction that this work needs to see the light of day by being published for the use of professionals, students & garden enthusiasts."
—Donald C. Brinkerhoff, FASLA, chairman and CEO of Lifescapes International, Inc.

Index

52628025R00182

Made in the USA
Charleston, SC
22 February 2016